STATISTICS

This volume forms part of a series of text-books published under the authority of the Institute of Actuaries and the Faculty of Actuaries and is designed to meet the needs of students preparing for the actuarial examinations.

STATISTICS

AN INTERMEDIATE TEXT BOOK

BY

N. L. JOHNSON
M.Sc., Ph.D., F.I.A.

AND

H. TETLEY
M.A., F.I.A.

VOLUME I

CAMBRIDGE
Published for the Institute of Actuaries and the Faculty of Actuaries
AT THE UNIVERSITY PRESS
1951

PUBLISHED BY
THE SYNDICS OF THE CAMBRIDGE UNIVERSITY PRESS
London Office: Bentley House, N.W. 1

First printed 1949
Reprinted 1951

Printed in Great Britain at the University Press, Cambridge
(*Brooke Crutchley, University Printer*)

CONTENTS

PREFACE

Although this book is intended primarily for those studying for the statistical sections of the actuarial examinations, it is hoped that it will be found useful in a considerably wider field.

The word 'Intermediate' has been introduced into the title to indicate that the level of treatment is between that of elementary text-books requiring little or no mathematics beyond matriculation stage, and that of advanced text-books and original papers employing, where necessary, the resources of modern analysis.

The standard of mathematics assumed is approximately that of the more advanced papers of the Higher School Certificate examination or of the *Advanced* or *Scholarship* papers in the new school examinations. Certain further special results which are required are developed in Appendices. It is the object of the book to take advantage of the mathematical standard assumed, and to concentrate more particularly on the especially *statistical*, as opposed to the *mathematical*, aspects of the problems encountered.

The book has been published for convenience in two volumes, corresponding to the requirements of Parts I and II respectively of the examinations of the Institute of Actuaries. It has, however, been written as a continuous whole, the chapters being numbered consecutively throughout. There are frequent references to results proved elsewhere in the book, even when they do not appear in the same volume.

A number of approximations, which give useful results when the sample size is not too small, have been used in Chapter 10. The more exact theory, sometimes called 'small sample theory' (although it applies equally to large samples), is developed in the second volume. Nevertheless, a number of fundamental ideas, important in more advanced statistical theory, are introduced at an early stage in Volume I. This may make the first volume somewhat more difficult to master than would otherwise have been the case, but should ease the path of the student in reading Volume II.

The authors are glad of this opportunity of expressing their sincere thanks to several friends and colleagues who wish to remain anonymous but who have greatly assisted in the preparation of the book in all its stages by detailed criticism and helpful suggestions.

The typescript of a book such as this with numerous tables and diagrams must always cause great difficulty to the printers, and the pages which follow bear ample testimony to the skill and patience of the staff of the Cambridge University Press. There must inevitably be a number of errors, however, and the authors will be grateful to anyone who draws their attention to them.

We are indebted to the Controller of H.M. Stationery Office for permission to reproduce the extracts from Government publications.

N.L.J.
July 1949 H.T.

INTRODUCTION TO VOLUME I

It is inevitable that differences of opinion will exist about the most suitable form of development for a text-book on statistics. The authors of any text-book will no doubt have their own views on this matter, but they will also have clearly in mind the needs of the readers to whom the book is addressed. Furthermore, they will appreciate the fact that in any group of students there will be some who take naturally to a generalized development of the basic theory and others who require to proceed largely by way of a succession of examples which indicate the form of generalized theory needed. There are also those who prefer a strictly analytical development and those who are greatly helped by geometrical illustration.

In writing this book we have addressed ourselves mainly to the needs of actuarial students studying for the examinations of the new Syllabus of the Institute of Actuaries, in which the subject of statistics is approached in two successive sections corresponding to the two volumes of this book. The first section is studied side by side with finite differences and the theory of probability of the algebraic type traditionally associated with urns, dice and other games of chance, including problems in geometrical probability requiring the use of the calculus. Accordingly, in chapters 6 to 8, where the probability basis of statistical theory is introduced, it has been sufficient to confine attention to fundamental questions and basic theorems. An outline of the main theories is given to encourage a liberal outlook, but it has been necessary to adopt one theory (the choice is a frequency theory on the lines of Kerrich's introduction) as the basis for subsequent developments. Reference is made to standard works on other theories to which interested students may refer.

The second section is studied side by side with the subject of life contingencies and with the particular problems involved in the compilation, analysis and graduation of mortality and other actuarial statistics. These subjects are associated with the particular theoretical distribution and frequency functions typified by the Life Table on the basis of which a special mathematical and arithmetical technique is developed for dealing with practical problems.

Accordingly, the division of the subject that we have made between Volume I and Volume II has been largely dictated by the division of the subject in the actuarial examinations, and the general development has naturally taken account of the previous and concurrent training of actuarial students. The two parts do, however, provide a systematic development and are practically confined to the general subject of statistics. Thus the statistical principles underlying actuarial work are systematically dealt with in the wider setting of general statistics, without straying into the special fields of actuarial science, and it is hoped that the work may be found to be useful for other students of statistics.

From what has been said, it is clear that the development required is a suitable blend of theory and practice. Moreover, the actuarial student in his particular actuarial studies and office work is trained to apply the test of arithmetic, largely in monetary terms, at all stages of his work. He not only learns the theory but also engages in quite extensive computation of all kinds, thus avoiding the common pitfalls of the student who concentrates on the theoretical side and is therefore often in danger of missing the arithmetical wood for the algebraic trees. The actuarial student thus takes quite naturally to the processes of descriptive statistics.

With all these considerations in mind, we have adopted a form of development which has been found to be effective in many other fields of applied science

Briefly this is:

(i) practical acquaintance with the problems to be attacked,
(ii) theoretical studies, and
(iii) application of theory to practical problems.

Such a system of development is, indeed, natural. Suppose, for instance, that a boy wished to learn surveying. He might, in the first place, do some practical work such as measuring fields and trying to draw plans of them, marking out tennis courts, circular ponds with the aid of a post and a length of rope, or even marking out ellipses. At this stage we may assume that he has had no theoretical training, so that he does not appreciate why a triangle with sides 3 units, 4 units and 5 units *must* have a right angle at one corner, or why the practical devices he has been taught to use will always give him a good circle, ellipse, etc. Before he has done much practical work he will, however, realize that the various tasks he has carried out are all interrelated and form part of a single logical system. At this stage he might well begin the study of Euclidean geometry and trigonometry. He would then abandon for a time his measuring tape, his chalk and such practical tools, and deal entirely with a world of abstractions in which points have no size and straight lines no thickness, and will become acquainted with a vast logical framework built up from a few fundamental ideas and axioms.

As a third stage of training he might return to his practical work equipped with a sound theoretical background which he must use intelligently if he is to solve the problems he will meet. He will, for instance, know that the construction of a triangle with sides 3 units, 4 units and 5 units is only one of many ways of producing a right angle, and if he is wise he will be prepared to adopt whatever method is most suited to the particular problem with which he is dealing, always bearing in mind that the points, lines, curves, etc., with which he is concerned correspond only approximately to their counterparts in the theoretical model of pure geometry or trigonometry.

In this book the first four chapters deal with observed data and describe the various devices which are used to reduce a mass of information to manageable proportions and to summarize the salient points by means of a few calculated values.

In the next four chapters probability theory is developed, and the reader is introduced to concepts such as expected values, random variables, and probability distributions which flow from the definition of probability and are not based on actual observations.

Finally, in the last two chapters, the emphasis shifts back again to experimental data, and the theoretical results previously obtained are applied to solve practical problems. The reader should always bear in mind, however, that in setting up a 'theoretical model' in this way, it is essential that he should choose a model which is appropriate to the problem with which he is dealing. Thus, for example, if his data have a marked degree of skewness he may obtain quite misleading results if he applies to them tests which were derived from the study of Normal populations.

Each reader will have his own method of study which he has found by experience to be most appropriate to his own capabilities, but few will find that the subject of statistics can be fully grasped at a first reading. The student is advised, therefore, to read each chapter, or, in appropriate cases, each section of a chapter twice; first to obtain a general grasp of the ground covered and later in detail. Sections marked with an asterisk should be omitted from the first reading and studied only when the reader feels reasonably confident that he has mastered the remainder of the book. Only after a second reading and allowing ample time for reflexion on the fundamental issues involved should any attempt be made to answer a few of the exercises given at the ends of the chapters, the remainder being left for revision. To try to answer too many formal questions at an early stage merely focuses attention on details of the analytical work.

It will be noticed that in some cases the number of an exercise is printed in heavy type. This indicates that the exercise involves methods or leads to results which are of considerable importance, although it has not been found possible to include them in the text. Special attention, therefore, should be given to such exercises.

CHAPTER I

ESSENTIAL FEATURES OF STATISTICAL DATA

1·1. Essential features of statistical data.

An extract from an edition of a standard Dictionary published about a century ago reads:

STATISTICS. 1. A collection of facts respecting the condition of the people in a nation or country, their health, longevity, domestic economy....
2. The science which treats of these subjects.

According to this definition the science of statistics is concerned with information about a number of persons belonging to a certain broadly defined group, e.g. a nation. The information provides a more detailed description of the persons concerned. The simplest form of this information is the total number of persons, which may be regarded as the result of counting one for each person in the group. Further information may be obtained in the form of answers to questions addressed to each person as to (1) sex, (2) whether the person in question has had measles in the previous twelve months, (3) age, and so on. The accumulation of answers to these questions enables tables to be made showing the numbers of males and females, the number having measles in the previous year, and the numbers aged 0–1, 1–2, 2–3, ... at the time the questions were asked. By combining the answers to the various questions many further tables may be constructed showing, for example, the proportion of girls now aged 5 last birthday who have had measles in the last year, or the ratio of males to females in various age-groups.

Now let us consider the essential points of the preceding paragraph. We have a group consisting of a number of persons. We recognize these persons as distinct one from the other, but sufficiently alike for them to be classified together in a group defined in a broad manner. In technical language we have a number of *individuals* forming a *population*. In respect of each person (*individual*) we obtain answers to a number of questions. It should be noted that each individual provides just one answer to each question; this is an example of the position of the individual as the fundamental unit in the population. Now consider the nature of the answers. In reply to each of questions (1) and (2) only two answers are possible—in the first case 'male' or 'female'—in the second case 'yes' or 'no'. In reply to the third question the answer is numerical, and depends upon the accuracy asked for (or possible). Despite the difference between the types of answer required the accumulated answers to each question form 'statistics'. What, then, have the answers in common? They each tell us something about the individual. Each answer tells us about some *characteristic* or *character* of the individual. Age may be expressed numerically and by asking the question and having it answered we may be said to have measured the character—'age'. Age is said to be a *quantitative character*. Sex is not measured numerically, but it is still a character and is called a *qualitative character*. There is a certain overlap between quantitative and qualitative characters. For example 'having measles in the last year' is on the face of it a qualitative character and yet the answer 'yes' may be represented by '1' and 'no' by '0'.

To sum up now in more technical language, the science of statistics deals with the measurements of characters (quantitative or qualitative) of a number of individuals forming a population. This statement, however, in its general sense does not limit the 'individuals' to be human beings or indeed any particular entities.

All that is necessary is that we should be able to describe the individuals in a general way and define the population to which they belong. Thus, our individuals may be villages and the population may consist of all villages in a given geographical area, e.g. a county. Examples of characters of such individuals are 'number of inhabitants', 'number of dwelling houses' or 'superficial area'. Equally we might take penny coins as our individuals and all the penny coins in a savings box as our population. Examples of possible characters in this case are 'weight', 'date', 'thickness'.

The student will doubtless be able to construct for himself many other suitable combinations of individuals, populations and characters. It is evident therefore that these concepts are man-made and may be altered according to circumstances. The general notions involved will be discussed later in Chapter 9.

The point to be noticed at present is that a wide variety of cases are reducible to the same fundamental elements—individuals, population, characters—to which we were led by a consideration of the original subject-matter of statistics. It is therefore no cause for surprise that the methods of statistics have been found applicable in a wide variety of problems.

This extension of the scope of the science is illustrated by another dictionary definition, this time from a 1919 edition:

> In early use, that branch of political science dealing with the collection, classification, and discussion of facts (especially of a numerical kind) bearing on the condition of a state or community. In recent use, the department of study that has for its object the collection and arrangement of numerical facts or data whether relating to human affairs or to natural phenomena.

1·2. Statistical data.

The 'raw material' of any statistical investigation is a set or collection of individual observations or measurements or of characteristics classified in some way. A mere collection of facts is not suitable for statistical work until it is ordered or sorted. Generally speaking we are interested in *measurements* and the more completely the characteristic or characteristics with which we are dealing can be represented by measurements the more likely are they to be amenable to statistical treatment.

Suppose, for instance, that we were trying to investigate 'musical aptitude'. Our first step would be to classify the data we proposed to deal with into such groups as (*a*) elementary school children aged 10–12, (*b*) secondary school children aged 14–16, (*c*) university students, and (*d*) professional men.

The next step would be to obtain some measure of 'musical aptitude' and although marks allotted in a suitably devised examination might be appropriate for children they would be far less satisfactory for adults. 'Musical aptitude', like 'beauty' and 'intelligence', is not a very fitting subject for statistical analysis because of the difficulty of assigning a suitable measure. As we shall see in Vol. II, one way out of the difficulty which is sometimes appropriate is to assign 'ranks' to the individuals concerned. Thus a judge at a beauty contest would probably be puzzled to allot a 'measure' to the degree of beauty of each contestant but he could arrange them in an order of merit without great difficulty. The winner is then regarded as holding 'rank' 1, the second 'rank' 2, and so on.

As another example let us consider the state of the heart, arteries and veins of men proposing for life assurance. This seems a most unsuitable subject for statistical analysis and if we restricted attention to such features as the hardness or softness of the arteries we should probably be able to do little more than group according to such descriptions as 'very hard', 'hard' and 'normal' or 'soft'—categories which relate to a crude type of measurement but which would be unlikely to yield useful results, partly because of the difficulty of dealing with borderline cases and partly because of the different standards likely to be used. By using readings of the blood-pressure, however, we have a measurable characteristic to which a wide range of statistical technique can be applied.

1·3. Homogeneity.

A dictionary definition of this word is 'having parts or elements of the same kind throughout' but this is not sufficiently explicit for our purpose and we must consider the problem in some detail because much statistical technique can be applied only to homogeneous data.

Suppose that a miller, buying wheat, were concentrating his attention on a large 'sample' bin. He would probably wish to be satisfied that the contents were homogeneous and to do this he might take handfuls from various parts of the bin and at various levels. He would not expect these handfuls to be uniform, i.e. he would be prepared to find considerable variation in the size and weight of the grains in each handful, but he would be suspicious if he found, for instance, that the grains taken from the top of the bin were *persistently* bigger and heavier than those taken from near the bottom. This idea of persistent 'bias' in samples is the fundamental feature of heterogeneous material.

Even in homogeneous data the individual elements may differ widely and if samples or small groups are taken from various parts of the whole, the samples may differ one from the other as shown by, say, the average of the values in the sample. What indicates that the data are not homogeneous is a *persistent* tendency for samples taken from one part to differ in a constant direction from those taken from another part.

The usual way of dealing with heterogeneity when it is present is to subdivide the data into sections, each of which is homogeneous or appreciably so.

When the late Sir Alfred Watson carried out his classical investigation into the mortality and sickness experience of the Manchester Unity of Oddfellows he was particularly concerned with three possible sources of heterogeneity: (*a*) age, (*b*) geographical area of the individual 'lodge', and (*c*) the occupation of the individual member.

As is almost invariably the case in actuarial work, the data were subdivided according to age thus dealing effectively with (*a*). On investigating the mortality of the members Watson found that there were persistent and systematic differences between geographical areas but no such marked differences between the different occupations. He therefore published separate mortality tables for different districts but for all occupations combined. On investigating the sickness experience, however, he found the data reasonably homogeneous as regards district, but markedly heterogeneous with regard to occupation and accordingly produced different tables of sickness rates for different occupational groups, but ignored for this purpose any differences in geographical position. (It will be observed that data which are homogeneous with regard to one characteristic may be heterogeneous with regard to another.)

There is always a danger that in the desire to achieve absolute homogeneity the data may be split into groups so small that no useful results can be obtained. This applies especially to data based on human life as the following example will show.

The following sources of heterogeneity had to be considered in the data on which the A 1924–29 Mortality Tables are based.

(1) Age.

(2) Calendar Year of Observation.

(3) Time elapsed since the policy was effected.

(4) Class of policy:

(*a*) Whether Whole Life or Endowment Assurance.

(*b*) Whether with or without Profits.

(*c*) Whether with or without Medical Examination.

(For more precise definitions see the Report of the Committee.)

(5) Company which issued the policy.

Female lives and any accepted on special terms were excluded As regards (1) the data for each age or small group of ages were examined separately, (2) was allowed for by examining data for each calendar year separately, (3) was allowed for by investigating separately the experience relating to each of the first 5 years from the date the policy was issued. The subdivision into years in this way is of course arbitrary but shorter intervals would have led to some very small groups of data. The effect of (5) was found to be much more important than (4). To allow for the effect of all factors the data would have had to be split into so many small elements that no useful tables would have been constructed. Eventually the effects of (2), (4) and (5) were ignored and the main published table was based on the combined experience, making allowance for the effects of (1) and (3) only. This is a good example of how theoretical niceties have to give way to practical necessity and shows how, by striving after homogeneity, we might be led to subdivide the data too far.

1·4. Descriptive and analytical statistics.

A question which naturally arises is 'What do we hope to achieve by a scientific study of accumulations of data in numerical form?'

A mass of data is in itself a mere collection of certain details of the individuals in a population. If the number of individuals be large the simple perusal of figures for each successive individual leads to a state of mental chaos. Imagine for instance reading through

5,000 sets of results each giving the height, age and nationality of a man. Some vague general impression say, of variation of height with age, might be obtained, but even this is doubtful and many other points, such as variability of height between men in the same age-group, or change in this variability with change in age-groups would not be noted owing to the difficulty of absorbing so many facts at once.

The division of statistics called *descriptive statistics* attempts to meet this difficulty by providing methods of summarizing data into compact form so as to present the more important results of the data in an easily appreciated way. Geometrical diagrams are often of great use in this connexion. The other methods of descriptive statistics are the classification of data and the use of indices to measure the over-all nature of the data.

Beyond the pure description of the data there is the problem of finding what meaning we can ascribe to our results in the sense of making statements about the individuals concerned and the population to which they belong. This problem gives rise to *analytical statistics*, which, as its name suggests, is concerned with analysing data. The methods of analytical statistics are of particular importance if measurements of some individuals in the population are not available and we wish to draw conclusions from our data about the whole population. This is the problem of sampling and will be dealt with in later chapters. As will be seen later, however, even when measurements are available in respect of every member of the population the methods of analytical statistics are still of value.

1·5. Early work in demography and vital statistics.

We shall close this preliminary chapter with brief references to the work of some pioneers in the realm of statistics, partly because a historical background is useful in itself and partly to show how the modern theory has sprung from two distinct roots, the work of the early demographers on 'political arithmetic', and the mathematical theory of probability which was originally inspired by games of chance.

It should, of course, be borne in mind that although the particular writers mentioned have been chosen to illustrate the main lines of development there are doubtless many others whose claims to inclusion are at least as strong. Considerations of space made it undesirable to extend the list. The standard works referred to in the Bibliography give a much more complete history of the development of statistics.

It is of interest to note that the word 'statistics' began to be used in its modern sense only in the middle of the eighteenth century. The first important worker to use the word regularly was J. P. Süssmilch (1707–67), a German writer on demography.

(The actual 'coining' of the word 'Statistik' is attributed to H. Conring (1606–81), a professor at Hellmstadt University, Brunswick).

1·6. John Graunt (1620–1674).

John Graunt, the son of a City tradesman, achieved the distinction of being elected F.R.S. (in 1663). In his early thirties he came in contact with a young Oxford professor of anatomy, Dr William Petty, and they worked so closely together thereafter on 'political arithmetic' that there is still doubt as to how much of the results ascribed to Graunt are really Petty's. The literary critics working on internal evidence as to style are inclined to favour Petty but statisticians with one or two exceptions take the opposite view. (See Bibliography.)

The results published under Petty's name are not of great interest to actuaries but Graunt can claim to have been the first to introduce the important idea of an arbitrary 'radix' representing the number of births associated with the numbers who would survive to certain ages. His material consisted of statements, covering the 20 years 1629–36 and 1647–58, of christenings and burials with causes of death under some sixty headings. These causes of death were reported by sworn searchers appointed in each parish who were required to view the corpse before burial but whose diagnosis was unlikely to be reliable.

That he succeeded in evolving any sort of life table without any information about the population, or even the ages at death, is remarkable. He first scrutinized the causes of death and allotted to the first 4 or 5 years of life deaths due to such causes as thrush, convulsions, rickets, etc., while at the other end of life he allotted deaths of people described as 'aged'.

He thus obtained three 'pivotal values' $l_0 = 100$, $l_6 = 64$ and $l_{76} = 1$. The intermediate points $l_{16} = 40$, $l_{26} = 25$, $l_{36} = 16$, $l_{46} = 10$, $l_{56} = 6$ and $l_{66} = 3$ were inserted by some more or less arbitrary method of which we have no record. No other values were given. The table is chiefly of importance because of its influence on other workers in England and on the Continent.

Graunt was a careful worker who examined his data critically particularly with regard to the cause of death recorded, as he suspected—no doubt with good reason—that many of the changes in numbers from year to year were probably due to changes in the method of classification.

1·7. Johan de Witt (1625–1672).

de Witt was a Dutch politician whose statistical work was concerned with annuities. He had particulars concerning several thousand annuitants and from these he evolved a law of mortality. In doing so he seems to have treated the observations somewhat freely but he did not give particulars of his method. He assumed that

(i) of 128 persons in the 4th year of life one will die every half-year for 50 years leaving 28 alive in the 54th year;

(ii) of these one would die every 9 months in the next 10 years leaving $14\frac{2}{3}$ survivors in the 64th year;

(iii) of these one-half would die every 6 months in the next 10 years leaving $4\frac{2}{3}$ survivors in the 74th year;

and (iv) that these survivors would die off at the rate of one-third every half-year until they had disappeared after a further 7 years.

This table was, of course, much more complete than Graunt's but de Witt's chief claim to the attention of actuaries is his correct calculation of annuity values. His methods were laborious by modern standards but he avoided the mistake of his predecessors who had based their values on the 'expectation of life'. They had, in effect, assumed in calculating the annuity values for a given age, that each annuitant would live for the average number of years corresponding to that entry age; this would be correct only if the effect of those who lived longer than the average was exactly counterbalanced by the effect of those who died younger than the average. The introduction of compound interest in valuing the payments made this assumption erroneous.

1·8. Dr Richard Price (1723–1791).

Dr Richard Price had a considerable effect on the financial history of his time; his views on the Sinking Fund profoundly influenced William Pitt the younger, while the Northampton Table which he constructed was for many years used for the sale of annuities and cost the country a large sum of money. He was not blind to the dangers of constructing a mortality table from the deaths alone but he believed that the population of the parish of All Saints in Northampton was nearly stationary during the years 1735–80 and, in effect, he took the average number of deaths per annum as the d_x column of a life table. In fairness to Price it should be pointed out that he intended his table for use in dealing with assurances and it was in fact used for this purpose very successfully for many years.

He also put forward what was, in effect, the first 'social security' project although it never reached the statute book and he wrote a book on life contingencies which ran into several editions.

Unfortunately, he allowed political prejudice to cloud his judgement, or at least to bias his writings, on the subject of demography. Although he did not go to such extremes as Farr he believed that the wealth of a country was its people and that the policy of the Government then in power was bad for the country. He therefore set out, in defiance of the facts, as we now know them, to prove that the population was diminishing and no evidence to the contrary would shake his belief.

1·9. Adolphe Quetelet (1796–1874).

Quetelet first published his great work under the title *Sur l'homme et le développement de ses facultés*, but it is the second and subsequent editions which are most important. The title was changed for the second edition to *Physique sociale ou essai sur le développement des facultés de l'homme* and a preface by the astronomer Herschel was introduced setting out a detailed theory of probability (Quetelet was himself Director of the Royal Observatory at Brussels). We thus have in the same book a 'marriage' of probability theory and statistical methods and theories. The subjects dealt with range over a wide field including biology and, to some extent, medicine. The concept of the 'average man' was introduced and attention was drawn to the remarkable consistency of social phenomena. It had been argued that free-will was so important in human behaviour that it was futile to seek for any general law in relation to it. Quetelet showed conclusively, however, that such factors as the proportion of crime in different countries and social classes showed quite surprising consistency and his work helped to set on foot those investigations into social conditions and behaviour which have played such an important part in the history of the last 50 years. Quetelet's work was of great importance to widening the field of application of statistical method.

1·10. William Farr (1807–1883).

In his youth William Farr studied medicine in Paris and London, qualifying in 1832. After practising a few years with indifferent success he took a position in the Registrar-General's Office in 1837. He was consulted on the 1841 Census and acted as an assistant commissioner for the 1851 and 1861 Censuses and as commissioner for the 1871 Census. In 1879 the office of Registrar-General became vacant but Farr was not selected for the post. Soon after he resigned his post and retired. In the censuses with which he was concerned Farr introduced systematic methods of treatment which were embodied in the Reports which he wrote. These methods formed the basis for subsequent work and are of interest as being the first recorded introduction of scientific method in official statistics.

1·11. Early work in analytical statistics.

The persons so far named in this section were concerned mainly with the original aspect of statistics as the science dealing with collections of facts relating to human society. We have seen how there were on this side widening influences exemplified especially by Quetelet. At the same time there were workers in the field of the natural sciences who were dealing with what were essentially statistical problems.

The questions arising in connexion with games of chance were brought to the notice of a number of mathematicians, notably Pascal (1623–62) and Fermat (1601–65) in France, and James Bernoulli (1654–1705) in Switzerland. As a result of their researches the foundations of a theory of probability were constructed. In England De Moivre (1667–1754) who was of French birth, but lived in England from childhood, published his book *The Doctrine of Chances* in 1718. This book gives a coherent account of the theory of probability as then existing and applies the theory to the calculation of annuity values. In later editions of this work an appendix was added, giving a derivation of the Normal curve of which the reader will learn much later.

The scientists, mentioned in §§ 1·12–1·15, to whom important developments in theory are due, were all concerned, in some way or other, with practical problems in agriculture, astronomy, biology, economics, or geodesy which drew their attention to the necessity of developing appropriate theory. Astronomy, in particular, was a science in which it was necessary to deal with accumulations of many observations. It is not surprising, therefore, that many of the important early developments in the methods of analysis of observations came from scientists who were deeply interested in astronomy.

1·12. Pierre Simon Laplace (1749–1827) and Karl Friedrich Gauss (1777–1855).

P. S. Laplace was born of humble parents. His abilities procured him influential friends and in 1771 he obtained a position at a military school in Paris. For 16 years from this date Laplace engaged in research, mainly in astronomy. From 1787 to 1805 he was writing two great works *Exposition du système du monde* and *Mécanique céleste*. In 1812 he published his *Théorie Analytique des Probabilités*. This large work includes a theoretical development of the method of least squares, which had been put forward by Gauss and Legendre (1752–1833). This method has since proved of great value in dealing with observational material. Gauss was also born in poor circumstances and like Laplace gained influential friends by his abilities. While studying at Göttingen in 1797 he considered the method of least squares. Returning to his home in Brunswick in 1798 he made a meagre living by private tuition and pursued his researches in mathematics and astronomy. In 1807 he was appointed Director of the Observatory at Göttingen and Professor of Astronomy there. He retained these posts till his death, producing much valuable work in many branches of natural science. In 1809 he published his work on the analysis of observations *Theoria Combinationis Observatorium Erroribus Minimis Obnoxia*. This theory was intended to apply to observations in any branch of natural science and is an indication of the trend towards a wider field of application of statistical methods.

1·13. Antoine Augustin Cournot (1801–1877).

A. A. Cournot was a professor of mathematics holding posts at Lyons and Grenoble and finally becoming Rector of Dijon in 1854. In early life he turned his attention to the application of mathematics to economics. In 1838 he published the results of his studies in a book entitled *Recherches sur les principes mathématiques de la théorie des richesses*. Cournot realized the importance of probability theory in the analysis of statistical data and put his views forward in his *Exposition de la théorie des chances et des probabilités* published in 1843.

1·14. Later developments.

In the latter half of the nineteenth century a number of workers obtained isolated results which have since proved of great value in the systematic development of the science of statistics. Notable among them were P. L. Tchebyshev* (1821–94) in Russia, F. R. Helmert (1843–1917) and W. Lexis (1837–1914) in Germany, T. N. Thiele (1838–1910) in Denmark and F. Y. Edgeworth (1845–1926) in Great Britain. Many of the results obtained by these scientists were premature in the sense that their value was not apparent until after the lapse of a quarter of a century or more.

* Many other varieties of spelling of this name are current.

Their work is most interesting as an indication of the way in which the current of thought was moving towards the creation of a separate science of statistics.

1·15. Karl Pearson (1857–1936).

Karl Pearson was born in London in 1857. His father was a leading barrister. Pearson was a student at Cambridge and was Third Wrangler in the Mathematical Tripos of 1879. During the next 5 years he studied law in London and a wide variety of subjects from physics and biology to history and philosophy while travelling in Germany. In 1884 he became Professor of Applied Mathematics at University College, London. Between 1890 and 1900 Pearson developed a science of dealing with observational data, the stimulus for this work coming largely from his association with Weldon, who was then Professor of Zoology at the same college. Weldon, continuing the work of Galton (1822–1911), was developing the new science of 'Biometry' which involved the analysis of accumulations of measurements on biological material. Pearson continued to broaden the scope of his work and finally in 1911 succeeded in forming an independent department of Applied Statistics at University College. In the course of his life he published a large amount of original work including *The Grammar of Science* (1892), a book setting out his ideas on scientific method.

1·16. Conclusion.

With the work of Karl Pearson statistics achieved recognition as an independent discipline. Until Pearson's time methods of analysis of observations had been developed as the need arose in that branch of science with which the data were concerned. Since Pearson's time statistics has been studied to an increasing extent as a science in itself and many important developments in statistical technique have resulted. It should not be forgotten, however, that statistics arose from the practical requirements of problems in various spheres and it is from its use in treating such problems that the theory of statistics derives its importance.

The majority of the readers of this book will be concerned,

ultimately, with the application of statistics in actuarial work. This chapter should have made it clear, however, that the science of statistics is much wider in scope and it is this more general aspect of statistical theory and methods which we shall now develop.

EXERCISES 1

1·1 What are the 'characteristics', 'individuals' and 'populations' concerned in the following types of statistical data?

(i) Weekly records of births and deaths for a certain town.
(ii) Total births and deaths in a year for each of a number of towns.
(iii) Age distribution of lives assured by endowment assurances with a certain company.

1·2 Suggest possible sources of heterogeneity in each of the above three cases.

1·3 Tabulate the statistical information contained in Chapters 1–4 of the Book of Numbers in the Old Testament.

Note. The following two problems should be solved with the help of a suitable method of *tabulation* of the information given.

1·4 All the persons present at a certain meeting voted either for or against each of two proposals, A and B. The ratio of the number of persons voting for A to the number voting against it was 50% greater than the corresponding ratio in the case of B. Of those who voted in favour of A there was a majority of 33 in favour of B, and of those who voted against A there was a majority of 27 in favour of B. If 22 of those who voted in favour both of A and B had joined those who voted against both proposals, the numbers of the former would have been twice the number of the latter.

Find the number of persons attending the meeting, and the number voting for each proposal.

(Institute of Actuaries Examinations, Jan. 1940.)

1·5 (See note before question 1·4.)

An attacking force of 50 bombers and fighters is met by a defending force also consisting of 50 planes. The number of planes lost by the attackers is five times the number lost by the defenders, who lose 20% of their bombers and 10% of their fighters. Before the battle the number of the defending fighters is to the number of attacking bombers as 2 : 1, but after the battle this ratio is 3 : 1. If each side had lost two more planes, the attackers would have lost four times as many planes as the defenders.

Find the number of bombers and fighters left in each force after the battle.

(Institute of Actuaries Examinations, Jan. 1941.)

1·6 Indicate, with as much detail as possible, what aspects of the following organizations are more, and what are less, susceptible of statistical treatment:

(*a*) a large lending library,
(*b*) a railway station,
(*c*) a holiday resort.

BIBLIOGRAPHY

MAJOR GREENWOOD. Medical Statistics from Graunt to Farr. *Biometrika*, vols. 32 (1941), 33 (1943). (Reprinted in book form: Cambridge University Press, 1948.)

W. W. ROUSE BALL. *A Short History of Mathematics*. Macmillan and Co., 1927.

E. S. PEARSON. *Karl Pearson*. Cambridge University Press, 1938.

HARALD WESTERGAARD. *Contributions to the History of Statistics*. P. S. King and Son. 1932.

E. C. RHODES. *Elementary Statistical Methods* (chapters 1–3). Geo. Routledge and Sons Ltd., London, 1933.

YULE AND KENDALL. *An Introduction to the Theory of Statistics* (Chapter 1). Griffin and Co., London, 14th ed., 1948.

L. H. C. TIPPETT. *Statistics* (Home University Library). Oxford, Clarendon Press. 3rd ed. 1943.

CHAPTER 2

DESCRIPTIVE STATISTICS. FIRST STEPS

2·1. Continuous and discontinuous variables.

The use of the terms continuous and discontinuous in pure mathematics will be familiar to readers but whereas mathematical functions usually have either no discontinuities or a limited number of discontinuities and are continuous elsewhere, in statistics we are often concerned with variables which can take only a finite set of discrete values. These variables are called *discontinuous* (*or discrete*) *variables*.

In investigations into housing conditions, for instance, the number of rooms occupied must be a positive integer unless some more or less arbitrary convention is introduced whereby fractions may arise.

Similarly, examination marks are usually restricted to positive integers, and the same applies to all characters which are measured by 'counting heads', e.g. the number of children in a family.

Many measurable characters, however, are represented by a continuous variable which in practice, if not necessarily in theory, has a limited range. Height of man, for instance, is represented by a continuous variable which has a lower limit of zero and for practical purposes an upper limit of, say, 8 ft.

2·2. Graphic representation. Dot diagrams.

As was pointed out in Chapter 1 the human mind is limited in the extent to which it can grasp the significance of a mass of detailed information and a graphic or pictorial representation is of use to many people in assisting comprehension. We shall consider several such representations in the next few paragraphs, and the reader will find it instructive to consider for each method whether it is suitable for discontinuous or for continuous variables.

One of the simplest graphical methods, if the data are not too numerous, is the dot diagram (Fig. 2·1). Each observation is represented by a dot and it is desirable to have these dots evenly spaced, above points representing the values observed.

The data of Fig. 2·1 were the marks obtained by 105 candidates in a certain examination for which the maximum mark was 100. Along a horizontal straight line points were marked off to represent

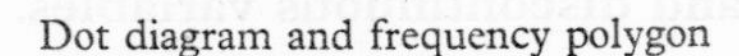

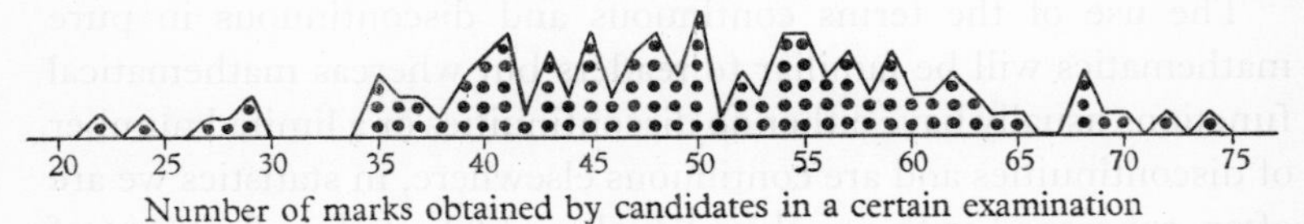

Fig. 2·1

all integral values, although in the figure only the points representing 20, 25, ..., 70 and 75 marks are indicated. A dot was then placed for each candidate above the point representing the marks he gained, e.g. six candidates obtained 50 marks but no candidate obtained 34 or 66. The figure gives a clear indication of the way in which marks were 'bunched' in the range 35–65 and draws attention to some special features such as the hollow between 50 and 55.

A set of values such as the above is said to form a *distribution*.

2·3. Frequency and frequency polygons.

For our present purposes it is sufficient to define the *frequency* of a value x as the number of times it occurs although we shall find it convenient in later work to adopt a somewhat wider conception which does not limit us to integral values and enables us in fact to treat frequency as a continuous variable.

The assembly of dots in Fig. 2·1 gives us an impression of 'shape' and if the dots are evenly spaced vertically it shows how the frequency varies over the range of values. It is often more convenient, however, to use a *frequency polygon*. In drawing this each frequency is first represented by a point, the ordinate of which gives the frequency on an assigned scale. These points are then joined by a series of straight lines as shown in Fig. 2·1. Thus the frequency 5 for marks 54 and 55 is represented by a point five units from the x axis above each of the points representing 54 and 55. Zero frequencies are, of course, represented by points on the x axis.

For purposes of illustration the dot diagram and the frequency polygon are both shown on the same diagram but this is neither necessary nor customary and the scale used for the ordinates need not correspond to the spacing of the dots, e.g. if the dots are $\frac{1}{4}$ cm. apart vertically there is nothing to prevent us from using 1 cm. as the unit of y in plotting frequencies.

2·4. Grouping.

In the last two paragraphs we have implicitly assumed that the variable was discontinuous and that the number of different values which it could assume was not very great. Even in such circumstances it is often convenient to group the data in order to reduce them to manageable proportions and this is almost essential if the number of possible values of the variable is very great. It should, however, be borne in mind that some of the information is lost in the process of grouping, the extent of the loss varying with the range of the groups adopted. Experience is therefore necessary before the most appropriate grouping can be decided in any particular instance; if the groups are too narrow the data may not be reduced to a form in which they can be readily grasped or manipulated whereas, if the groups are too wide or 'coarse', valuable information may be lost.

If the variable is continuous the data are necessarily grouped because even the most exact measurement is correct only to a certain degree of accuracy. Thus, it may be possible, by delicate instruments, to measure a given length as 3·4172 cm. We should presume, in the absence of further information, that this was to the nearest ten-thousandth of a centimetre so that for statistical purposes we should regard such data as grouped, the range of each group being that very small (but essentially non-zero) interval. We often speak of 'exact age' in mortality investigations but inevitably our data must be grouped and the phrase is misleading; we may mean 'age x measured to the nearest day' or 'age x measured to the nearest hour' but however we subdivide the interval of measurement, it still is a non-zero interval. In a strict sense, therefore, we should speak of the frequency with which values *between* x_1 and x_2 (say) occur when we are dealing with continuous variables.

Data arranged in this way are said to form a *grouped frequency distribution.*

2·5. Histograms and frequency polygons for grouped data.

Suppose we group the observations represented by Fig. 2·1 in groups of five marks as shown in Table 2·1.

TABLE 2·1

Number of marks obtained by 105 *candidates in a certain examination*

Marks	Frequency	Cumulative frequency	
		(*a*)	(*b*)
20–24	2	2	105
25–29	4	6	103
30–34	—	6	99
35–39	11	17	99
40–44	16	33	88
45–49	19	52	72
50–54	17	69	53
55–59	18	87	36
60–64	10	97	18
65–69	5	102	8
70–74	3	105	3
Total	105	—	—

In attempting to represent this information graphically we are immediately faced with the problem of the value of the variable corresponding to each grouped frequency. A dot diagram could be constructed by spacing the dots at equal intervals horizontally as well as vertically, although the horizontal interval need not be equal to the vertical, but care is needed if the groups do not all cover the same range of values. Thus, if the first three ranges were 20–23, 24–29 and 30–31 a misleading impression of the 'shape' of the distribution is given unless the corresponding dots are distributed horizontally over distances in the ratio 4:6:2.

In drawing a frequency polygon it is usual to regard the frequency of each group as concentrated at the mid-point of the group and the plotting and drawing of the polygon then proceeds as before. Thus, in dealing with Table 2·1 the frequencies 2, 4 and 11 at the top of the table would be plotted as corresponding to 'marks' 22·5, 27·5 and 37·5 even though these marks could not possibly arise. In Fig. 2·2 the frequency polygon is represented by the dotted line.

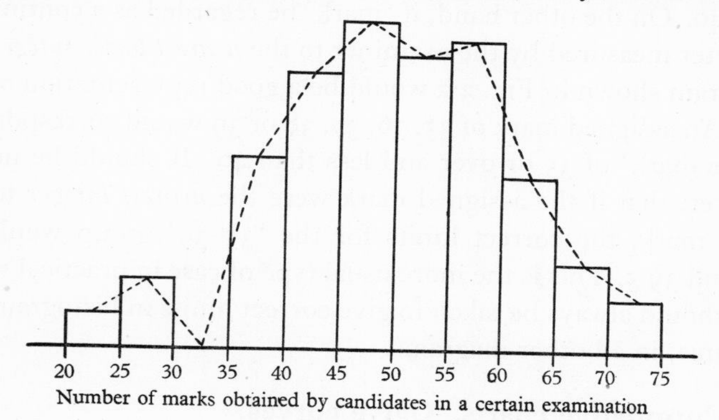

Fig. 2·2

In many ways, the most satisfactory representation of grouped data is the *histogram*. This consists of a set of rectangles, one for each group, the base being proportionate to the range of the group and the *area* to the group frequency. If the groups all have the same range as in Table 2·1 the heights of the rectangles are also proportionate to the group frequencies but this does not apply in the more general case.

The data of Table 2·1 are represented in Fig. 2·2 by a histogram as well as by a frequency polygon which is based on the usual arbitrary assumption that the group frequency is concentrated at the mid-point.

With the exception of the dip to zero in the group 30–34 the shape of the histogram and frequency polygon are typical of many which arise in statistical investigations and which are often described as belonging to the 'single humped' or 'cocked-hat' type of distribution.

The histogram is the natural form of diagram to employ when the character observed is continuous. It may also be used to represent grouped observations of a discontinuous character. In such cases, however, there is some difficulty in deciding the limits of the blocks in the histogram.

In Fig. 2·2 for example, consider the group of marks 35–39. If 'mark' be regarded as a discontinuous character, taking only integral values there is no real justification for continuing the block up to 40. On the other hand, if 'mark' be regarded as a continuous character measured by the examiner to the *nearest lower integer* the histogram shown in Fig. 2·2 would be a good representation of the data. An assigned mark of 35, 36, 37, 38 or 39 would correspond to a 'true mark' of 35 or over and less than 40. It should be noted, however, that if the assigned mark were the *nearest integer* to the 'true' mark, the correct limits for the '35–39' group would be 34·5 and 39·5. This is the more usual type of case in practical work. Care should always be taken to give correct limits in histograms as, of course, in all other diagrams.

2·6. Cumulative charts. Ogive curves.

So far we have considered only the frequencies corresponding to given values (discontinuous variable) or values within given ranges (continuous variable or other grouped data). It is often convenient to consider the frequencies with which values *below* certain fixed values, and sometimes the frequencies with which values *above* certain fixed values, occur. The point mentioned in the previous section with regard to the limits of ranges is important in this connexion. If the group 'a–b' includes all values equal to, or greater than a, but less than b it seems logical to use a curve giving the total frequency less than a given value whereas if the group includes all values greater than the lower limit but less than or equal to the upper limit another form of curve is more satisfactory.

The columns (a) and (b) of Table 2·1 giving certain cumulative frequencies are obtained from the second column by adding continuously (a) from the top and (b) from the bottom. Thus, there were 6 candidates who obtained 34 marks or less, 52 who obtained 49 or less and 102 who obtained 69 or less. From column (b) we find similarly that there were 88 who obtained 40 or over and 36 who obtained 55 or over.

The cumulative frequencies obtained in this way are a type of 'step-function', i.e. they are discontinuous at every value for which one or more observations are recorded and constant between every successive pair of such values. When the variable is continuous these 'steps' may occur at any point and although, in the absence of some convention about fractions, the cumulative frequency must in fact increase by one or more at each 'step', it is convenient to assume that it increases continuously. We assume, therefore, if the variable is continuous that the cumulative frequencies tabulated are specimen values of a function which may be approximately represented by a smooth curve. The error involved is small if the frequencies are large.

Such a method of tabulation applies whether the data are grouped or not and avoids the difficulty which sometimes arises if the upper limit of the last group is not given. We may, for instance, be given particulars of the deaths occurring in quinquennial age-groups 20–25, 25–30, etc., with a final group '80 and over'. By recasting

TABLE 2·2

Estimated population of Great Britain at the beginning of 1948. (*Figures in thousands*)

(From the Report of the Government Actuary on the National Insurance Bill, 1946)

Age-group	Population (men)	Total population over age x (men)	Value of x
0–15	5,161	23,195	0
15–20	1,647	18,034	15
20–25	1,752	16,387	20
25–30	1,834	14,635	25
30–35	1,714	12,801	30
35–40	1,879	11,087	35
40–45	1,822	9,208	40
45–50	1,621	7,386	45
50–55	1,350	5,765	50
55–60	1,217	4,415	55
60–65	1,060	3,198	60
65–70	869	2,138	65
Over 70	1,269	1,269	70

the data in the form '20 and over', '25 and over' and so on, we avoid the difficulty of estimating the range of the final group.

In this form the data are best represented by a series of points which may then be joined by a set of straight lines or (on the assumption mentioned above) by a continuous curve.

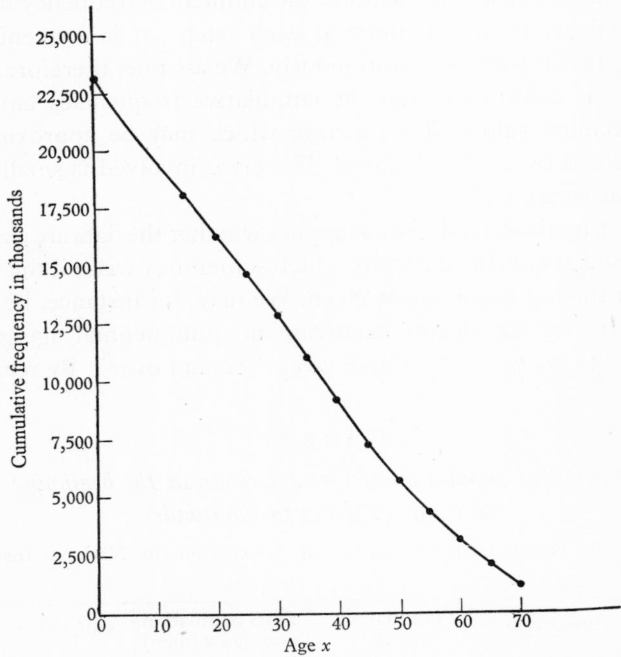

Fig. 2·3. Estimated population of Great Britain (men) aged x or over at the beginning of 1948. (From the Report of the Government Actuary on the National Insurance Bill, 1946.)

Table 2·2 is an example involving a continuous variable 'age', a wide initial group and a final group 'over 70'. The third column shows the total frequency for ages greater than the corresponding ages in the final column, and in Fig. 2·3 the data in this form are represented by a series of points. The smooth curve joining them is of a type often described as an 'Ogive curve'. It will be noticed that the figures involved are very large so that an ogive curve may be rather insensitive because of the scale needed to bring the values to reasonable dimensions for plotting.

The curve shown in Fig. 2·3 is appropriate in this case because of the last group 'Over 70' but the more usual type of ogive curve shows the total frequency *below* given values of the variable and therefore starts near the origin and has a positive slope at all points. Whichever form is used it will be seen that the total frequency between two values x_1 and x_2 is given by the difference between the ordinates at the points representing x_1 and x_2.

2·7. 'Pie' charts.

The methods already described are those most commonly used but others have been developed to deal with special problems and in this section and the next we shall consider two of them.

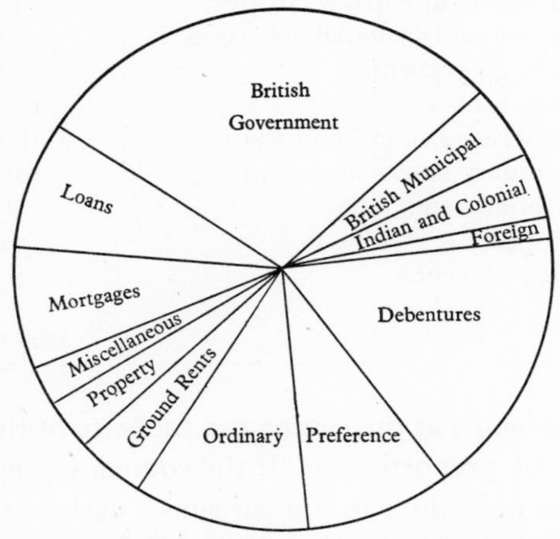

Fig. 2·4. Distribution of assets of a Life Assurance Company. (Data of Table 2·3.)

In the so-called 'pie' charts a circle is divided into segments like slices of a pie. The data are usually prepared in the form of percentages and the diagram shows what proportion of the whole is represented by each of the subdivisions considered. The value of this pictorial representation is increased if the segments are shown in contrasting colours and if the same colours and approximately the same positions are retained for other charts which are to be compared with the first. The following example will help to make this clear. In Table 2·3 the assets of a Life Assurance Company are subdivided into certain broad categories, the appropriate balance-sheet totals being shown in the form of percentages. These percentages are the basis of the chart shown in Fig. 2·4; it will be noticed that in drawing such a chart it is immaterial whether we use (i) the arc, (ii) the

TABLE 2·3

Distribution of assets of a Life Assurance Company

Description	Percentage of total assets
Mortgages on property	7·9
Loans on rates, policies, etc.	7·5
British Government securities	28·7
British Municipal securities	4·5
Indian and Colonial securities	4·6
Foreign securities	·7
Debentures	17·5
Preference stocks and shares	8·6
Ordinary stocks and shares	10·3
Ground rents, etc.	3·5
Property	3·9
Miscellaneous	2·3
	100·0

area, or (iii) the angle at the centre as a measure of the percentage since all three are proportionate. If the company prepared similar charts each year it would help comparisons if each section occupied roughly the same position each year and if the same colours were used.

This method of graphic representation is useful for qualitative variables and in this respect it differs from most of the other methods.

2·8. 'Z' charts.

Most industrial concerns like to keep a careful watch on such items as total output, total expenses, or total profit from the date of the last account up to the date considered. Similarly a government is interested in the total exports to date or the total imports to date in various categories.

An obvious way of representing this information is to plot the totals and join them by a set of lines starting with the first period's figure and finishing with the year's total. The chart is made more

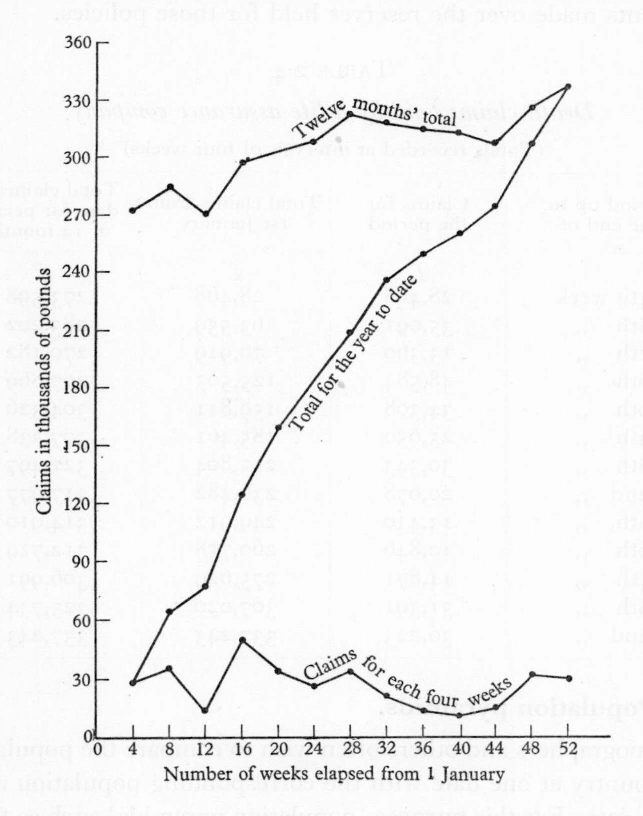

Fig. 2·5. Death claims paid by a life assurance company.

informative by plotting at the same time points representing the total for the 12 months ending on the date considered and the figures for the last period under review. Thus we should record at the same time the total from 1st January to 31st March, the total from 1st April of the previous year to the same 31st March and the figures for the last period since the previous recording. The lines joining the three sets of points produce the shape of a crude 'Z'. In Fig. 2·5 the data of Table 2·4 are represented in this way. The totals are rather irregular and the shape is less clear-cut than usual. The data relate to amounts paid on claims by death although it will be appreciated that the more useful measure is the 'strain', i.e. the excess of the payments made over the reserves held for those policies.

TABLE 2·4

Death claims paid by a life assurance company

(Totals recorded at intervals of four weeks)

Period up to the end of	Claims for the period	Total claims from 1st January	Total claims to date for period of 12 months
	£	£	£
4th week	28,468	28,468	273,598
8th ,,	35,091	63,559	285,202
12th ,,	13,360	76,919	270,182
16th ,,	48,584	125,503	297,869
20th ,,	34,308	159,811	304,326
24th ,,	25,650	185,461	307,338
28th ,,	30,343	215,804	321,497
32nd ,,	20,678	236,482	317,977
36th ,,	13,430	249,912	314,910
40th ,,	10,846	260,758	312,729
44th ,,	14,871	275,629	306,991
48th ,,	31,391	307,020	325,734
52nd ,,	30,223	337,243	337,243

2·9. Population pyramids.

Demographers and others often wish to compare the population of a country at one date with the corresponding population at an earlier date. For this purpose 'population pyramids' such as those of Figs. 2·6 and 2·7 are often used. Both sexes are represented on the same diagram and each horizontal 'block' can be made to represent the population at a given age or for a given group of ages. In Figs. 2·6 and 2·7 the populations are represented for quinquennial age-groups and it will be noticed that each diagram consists, in effect, of a pair of histograms with the axis of the variable vertical instead of horizontal.

The lessons to be learnt from a study of such pyramids are discussed in text-books on demography. One important feature in the present case is immediately apparent from a comparison of the two figures. Owing to the fall in the birth rate the population at

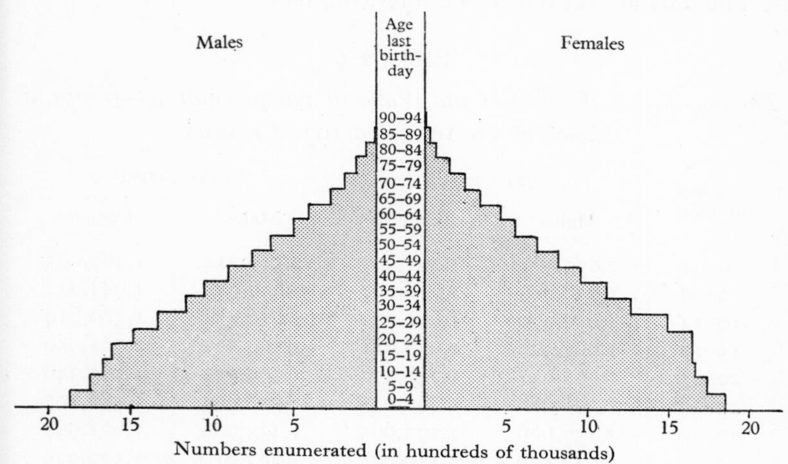

Fig. 2·6. Population pyramid. England and Wales 1901 Census.

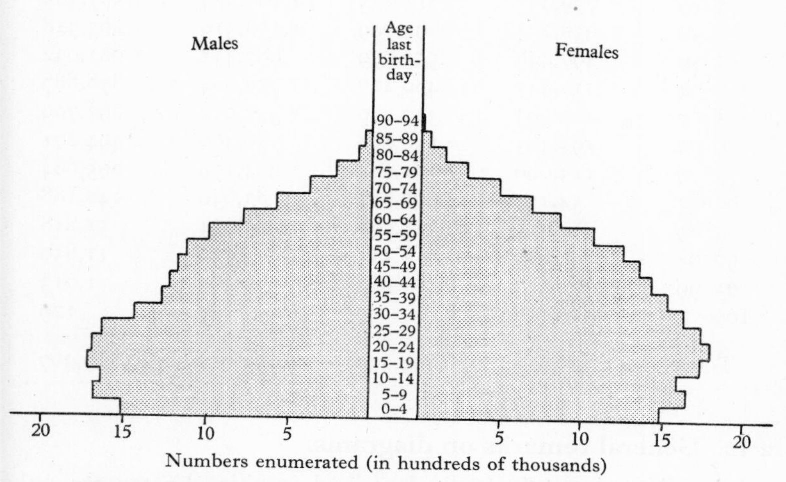

Fig. 2·7. Population pyramid. England and Wales 1931 Census.

ages 0–4 has fallen by nearly 20% over the years 1901–31, while the improvement in mortality has caused a considerable increase in the numbers at the middle and older ages. The problems of the ageing population and of the 'erosion' (as it is sometimes called) at the base of the pyramid are clearly illustrated in this way.

The data are set out in the following table:

TABLE 2·5

The population of England and Wales in quinquennial age-groups, as shown by the 1901 *and* 1931 *Censuses*

Age last birthday	1901 Census		1931 Census	
	Males	Females	Males	Females
0– 4	1,855,361	1,861,347	1,510,214	1,480,083
5– 9	1,738,993	1,748,298	1,677,845	1,644,811
10–14	1,670,970	1,670,770	1,620,431	1,586,814
15–19	1,607,522	1,638,621	1,709,512	1,724,989
20–24	1,472,644	1,648,278	1,699,141	1,795,346
25–29	1,328,288	1,496,221	1,628,993	1,728,107
30–34	1,157,666	1,273,665	1,433,289	1,621,997
35–39	1,034,459	1,110,924	1,283,010	1,520,029
40–44	897,484	953,138	1,229,346	1,434,207
45–49	759,955	813,233	1,186,554	1,367,385
50–54	636,254	692,749	1,116,319	1,265,318
55–59	497,498	555,079	987,445	1,081,032
60–64	410,447	480,226	778,064	878,887
65–69	282,403	347,270	577,970	692,700
70–74	195,465	250,868	376,480	494,271
75–79	113,096	151,384	204,179	295,684
80–84	52,137	76,631	83,640	142,188
85–89	14,915	24,046	25,254	51,818
90–94	2,687	5,515	4,732	11,859
95–99	322	868	565	1,713
100–	47	99	27	129
Total	15,728,613	16,799,230	19,133,010	20,819,367

2·10. General remarks on diagrams.

The diagrams and charts described in this chapter are only a few of those which are used but they illustrate the varied ways in which statistical data may be represented 'pictorially'.

The 'pie' charts and 'Z' charts are chiefly of value in comparing one year with another and are used for the most part where people have not the necessary statistical technique to apply numerical methods.

All statistical diagrams should be clearly labelled with descriptions of the data on which they are based. Generally the description should be sufficient to enable the diagram to be understood without recourse to the data or to any detailed reading matter. To this end all relevant facts should be included in the description.

Diagrams such as those described are a valuable method of conveying statistical information to the general public and, in fact, to anyone who has little knowledge of the science of statistics.

2·11. Index numbers.

Another useful method is the use of index numbers which enable *comparisons* to be made between one year and another or between one set of data and another. A particular set of observations are taken as a 'base' and all other similar sets are referred to the 'base' usually in the form of a percentage. We may, for instance, be told that the cost of living index is 145 (1914 = 100) implying that 1914 is the base-year and that the present index is 145 % of the corresponding value in 1914. Clearly any attempt to summarize a set of data by a single index is unlikely to be wholly satisfactory and before using any particular index the reader is strongly advised to find out exactly how it has been constructed.

2·12. The cost of living index.

In 1904 an investigation was made into working-class 'budgets' and a representative 'basket' of goods was constructed showing the amounts of various staple commodities consumed. The cost of purchasing this 1904 'basket' of goods in July 1914 was taken as the base and the increase in the cost of purchasing the same quantities at a later date was expressed as a percentage of the base figure.

In symbols—if Q_r is the amount of a certain commodity in the standard (1904) basket and the prices per unit amount were P_r in July 1914 and P'_r at the subsequent date under review, the index would be of the form

$$100\left\{\frac{\Sigma P'_r Q_r}{\Sigma P_r Q_r} - 1\right\}.$$

It is usually published in this form, i.e. as a percentage increase in the weighted average of prices, as compared with the base date, though the form mentioned in § 2·11 is sometimes used.

The obvious weakness of the index was that it took no account of the changes which had taken place since 1904 in the amount of the various commodities and services entering into a typical budget. Entertainment, for instance, and the cost of travelling (particularly in the London area) represented much more important items in 1947 than they did at the beginning of the century. In an endeavour to remedy this an attempt was made in 1937–38 to construct a new index based on the 'consumption patterns' at that time. Four weeks were selected, one in each quarter of the period, and elaborate questionnaires were filled up by trained canvassers who were given detailed instructions about the houses to be visited. The new index was not issued owing to the imminence and eventual outbreak of war.

In March 1947 the report of a cost of living advisory committee was published (Cmd. 7077). This recommended that as an interim measure a new index should be constructed based on the 1937–38 inquiry as regards quantities consumed and on 'current prices'. The prices ruling at the date the new index was introduced were to be taken as a 'base line' so that the first value published would be 100. It was, of course, realized that the 1937–38 household 'budgets' gave no very reliable indication of 1947 spending and it was the unanimous opinion of the committee that the permanent index should be of a different type, allowing for changes in the relative weights of the various commodities from time to time as well as changes in price.

*2·13. The C.M.F. and the S.M.R.

In comparing the mortality of one occupation with another or of one district with another or with the country as a whole it is convenient to have a single index which will eliminate certain systematic errors.

The so-called 'crude death-rate' obtained by dividing the number of deaths by the number in the population considered and usually expressed in some such phrase as '26 per thousand' is open to the serious objection that it takes no account of the age (and sex) distribution. Thus a residential suburb with a high proportion of retired men and their wives would probably have a high crude death rate whereas a new housing estate of young married couples would have a very low one. The 'Standardized Mortality Ratio' (S.M.R.) seeks to overcome this objection in the following way. We first calculate the number of deaths which would have occurred if the particular population considered had experienced, age-group by age-group, the rates of mortality experienced by the country as a whole. Call these the total 'expected' deaths. The ratio of the deaths actually observed to the 'expected' deaths is expressed as a percentage to give the S.M.R. In symbols:

Let P_x^a = the number in the age-group x in the population considered.

m_x^a = the central death-rate for the age-group x in the population considered.

m_x^s = the central death-rate for the age-group x in the country as a whole.

Then the S.M.R. $= 100 \dfrac{\Sigma P_x^a m_x^a}{\Sigma P_x^a m_x^s} = 100 \dfrac{\Sigma P_x^a m_x^s \dfrac{m_x^a}{m_x^s}}{\Sigma P_x^a m_x^s}.$

The 'Comparative Mortality Figure' (C.M.F.) used in the Registrar-General's Report on the 1921 Census was based on a different approach. First a 'standard' population was constructed based on the number of occupied and retired civilian males between the ages of 20 and 65 enumerated at the 1921 Census. The actual numbers enumerated were multiplied by a constant factor so as to ensure that if the central death rates for the whole country based on the Census and on the deaths for the years 1920–22 (represented by m_x^s above) were applied to the 'scaled down' figures the total deaths would be 1000.

If P_x^s represents the number of occupied and retired civilian males enumerated in the age-group x, the number in the standard population for that age-group was taken as

$\dfrac{1000\, P_x^s}{\Sigma P_x^s m_x^s}$ where the summation extends over ages 20–65.

The rates of mortality actually observed for any given occupation or district were then applied to this standard population giving the index

$$\text{C.M.F.} = 1000 \frac{\Sigma P_x^s m_x^a}{\Sigma P_x^s m_x^s}$$

$$= 1000 \frac{\Sigma P_x^s m_x^s \dfrac{m_x^a}{m_x^s}}{\Sigma P_x^s m_x^s}.$$

It will be noticed that both the S.M.R. and the C.M.F. involve weighted means of the ratios m_x^a/m_x^s the weights being $P_x^a m_x^s$ in the case of the S.M.R. and $P_x^s m_x^s$ in the case of the C.M.F.

Example 2·1.

The figures of Table 2·6 are based on the Registrar-General's Report on the 1931 Census and although on this occasion the C.M.F. was constructed in a similar manner to that used for the 1921 Census, one-tenth of the index was printed in the tables to facilitate comparisons with the S.M.R.

TABLE 2·6

1931 *Census. Railway-engine drivers*

	Age-group					Total
	20–	25–	35–	45–	55–65	
Population in the occupation in 1931	302	2,613	12,210	13,991	10,515	—
Deaths from all causes in 3 years 1930–32	6	29	152	371	677	—
Occupational death-rate per cent p.a.	·662	·370	·415	·884	2·146	—
Standard population	17,436	31,422	25,779	23,630	18,116	—
Actual deaths p.a. in standard population	57	109	144	263	427	1,000
Calculated deaths p.a. based on occupational death-rates	115	116	107	209	389	936
Death-rate per cent p.a. for all men	·328	·346	·559	1·114	2·355	—
Calculated deaths in 3 years at these rates in the population in the occupation in 1931	3	27	205	468	743	1,446
Actual deaths in 3 years in the occupation	6	29	152	371	677	1,235

$$\text{C.M.F.} = 936. \quad \text{S.M.R.} = 100 \times \frac{1235}{1446} = 85.$$

It will be noticed that in the age-group '20–' i.e. for ages 20 last birthday to 24 last birthday inclusive, the occupational death-rate is ·662 % p.a. which compares very unfavourably with the corresponding rate of ·328 % p.a. for all men. The number of engine-drivers involved was only 302 with six deaths so that this group was relatively unimportant, a fact which was allowed for in the S.M.R. which, as we have seen, involves a system of weights $P^a_x m^s_x$ where P^a_x is the actual population (in this case 302).

The C.M.F. on the other hand gives this age-group the same relative importance as it has in the population as a whole and thus magnifies the effect of the adverse mortality at the younger ages.

2·14. The actuaries' investment index.

The Institute of Actuaries and the Faculty of Actuaries in connexion with the general question of investment research have organized an index of prices and average yields of some thirty-six groups of Stock Exchange Securities. Subscribers to the service are supplied with a detailed list of the individual securities included in the various groups. The group 'Electrical Manufacturing' for instance, includes twelve securities while 'Shipping' includes seven. The original intention was to revise the list every year, deleting securities which had been repaid or replaced (e.g. on amalgamation) and including new ones to allow for the increasing importance of certain industries such as aircraft manufacturing. On each revision figures on the old and new bases were given for comparison. For various reasons little alteration has taken place since 31st December 1938 but further revision is now contemplated. The base line is 100 on 31st December 1938.

The index is presented in two distinct sections (*a*) a price index (1938 = 100), and (*b*) figures for the average yield. Suppose a particular group consists of n securities the prices of which were $P_1, P_2, P_3 \ldots P_n$ on 31st December 1938 and are now $P'_1, P'_2, P'_3 \ldots P'_n$ The price index is defined as

$$100\left[\frac{P'_1}{P_1}\frac{P'_2}{P_2}\frac{P'_3}{P_3}\cdots\frac{P'_n}{P_n}\right]^{\frac{1}{n}}.$$

It is in fact a geometric mean of the n ratios P'/P with no allowance for the size or importance of individual securities.

When, however, two or more groups are combined the index is

formed by multiplying the factors P'/P for all the securities involved and taking the geometric mean of the combined data. Thus, if one group of seven securities were combined with a group of ten securities the resulting index would be of the form

$$100\left[\frac{P_1'}{P_1}\frac{P_2'}{P_2}\cdots\frac{P_7'}{P_7}\frac{Q_1'}{Q_1}\frac{Q_2'}{Q_2}\cdots\frac{Q_{10}'}{Q_{10}}\right]^{\frac{1}{17}},$$

where the Q's refer to the second group. In this way allowance is made in the combined averages for the numbers of securities in the various groups involved.

The average yield for each group, or combination of groups, is the ordinary average (described in the next chapter as the 'arithmetic mean') of the gross yields of the individual securities. As with the price index no attempt is made to allow for the relative importance of individual securities but in combining two or more groups allowance is automatically made for the relative numbers of securities involved.

Various difficulties of detail arise from time to time in connexion with such things as issues of new shares on bonus terms or the use of 'running' or 'redemption' yields and full details of the steps taken to deal with them are issued to subscribers.

EXERCISES 2

2·1 Represent the following data graphically as fully as you can.

Quantities of imported goods consumed per head

	1870	1875	1880	1885	1890	1895
Corn wheat and wheat-flour (bushels)	5·78	6·03	4·99	6·03	5·96	6·53
Cocoa (lb.)	·20	·30	·30	·41	·54	·63
Coffee (lb.)	·98	·98	·92	·91	·75	·70
Cotton (lb.)	35·23	37·52	40·73	33·86	42·10	39·72
Currants and raisins (lb.)	4·03	4·29	3·92	4·16	4·70	4·97
Meat (lb.)	101·42	109·46	114·09	112·52	124·09	123·73
Rice (lb.)	6·74	11·68	14·08	7·64	9·38	8·09
Sugar (lb.)	47·23	62·85	63·40	74·96	73·21	88·13
Tea (lb.)	3·81	4·44	4·57	5·06	5·17	5·67
Tobacco (lb.)	1·34	1·46	1·42	1·46	1·55	1·67
Wool (lb.)	10·09	10·72	10·72	10·13	11·32	13·15
Wine (gal.)	·49	·53	·45	·38	·40	·37
Spirits (gal.)	1·01	1·30	1·07	·96	1·02	1·00

2·2 Discuss the construction of index numbers from the data given in the above question. In particular, consider the construction of indices of consumption of special classes of goods, e.g. foodstuffs. In what ways are the data incomplete?

2·3 Let $p_0^{(j)}$ denote the price of commodity c_j in year '0' (base year), and $p_1^{(j)}$ its price in year '1' (current year). Let $q_0^{(j)}$, $q_1^{(j)}$ refer similarly to the quantities of this commodity produced in the two years. Discuss the following price indices for year '1' based on the k commodities $c_1, c_2, \ldots, c_k$:

(i) $100 \times \dfrac{p_1^{(1)} + p_1^{(2)} + \ldots + p_1^{(k)}}{p_0^{(1)} + p_0^{(2)} + \ldots + p_0^{(k)}}$.

(ii) $100 \times \dfrac{1}{k}\left[\dfrac{p_1^{(1)}}{p_0^{(1)}} + \dfrac{p_1^{(2)}}{p_0^{(2)}} + \ldots + \dfrac{p_1^{(k)}}{p_0^{(k)}}\right]$.

(iii) $100 \times \dfrac{\Sigma q_0 p_1}{\Sigma q_0 p_0}$, where $\Sigma q_0 p_1 = \sum_{j=1}^{k} q_0^{(j)} p_1^{(j)}$ and similarly for $\Sigma q_0 p_0$.

(iv) $100 \times \dfrac{\Sigma q_1 p_1}{\Sigma q_1 p_0}$.

(v) $100 \times \left[\Pi\left(\dfrac{p_1}{p_0}\right)\right]^{1/k}$.

(vi) $100 \times \left[\Pi\left(\dfrac{p_1}{p_0}\right)^{q_0}\right]^{1/\Sigma q_0}$.

Note. Each of the above indices may be represented by the symbol $100 I_{1/0}$. A method of computing an index is said to satisfy the *time reversal test* if $I_{1/0} = 1/I_{0/1}$, where $I_{0/1}$, of course, represents the index obtained if base year and current year are interchanged.

2·4 Which of (i)–(vi) in question 2·3 satisfy the time reversal test?

2·5 If the symbols 'p' and 'q' be interchanged indices of quantity will be obtained. The *factor reversal test* requires that

$$(\text{Price Index}) \times (\text{Quantity Index}) = \Sigma p_1 q_1 / \Sigma p_0 q_0.$$

Do any of (i)–(vi) satisfy the factor reversal test?

2·6 Show that the index number

$$100 \times \sqrt{\left(\frac{\Sigma q_0 p_1}{\Sigma q_0 p_0} \frac{\Sigma q_1 p_1}{\Sigma q_1 p_0}\right)}$$

satisfies both the time reversal test and the factor reversal test. This index is called Fisher's Ideal Index after its inventor, Irving Fisher.

2·7 Show that the index number

$$100 \times \frac{\Sigma(q_0 + q_1)\, p_1}{\Sigma(q_0 + q_1)\, p_0}$$

is a good approximation to the Ideal Index. Discuss the other properties of this index number.

2·8 State briefly, giving reasons, the types of diagram you consider most appropriate to use in dealing with each of the following classes of statistical data:

(i) Monthly production of pig iron over a period of 5 years.
(ii) Number of children per family for each family in a large town.
(iii) Maximum daily temperature for the 3 months at one meteorological station.
(iv) Daily rainfall for 3 months.
(v) Monthly rainfall for 5 years.
(vi) Monthly output of eggs, arranged in five grades of quality.
(vii) Total Panama Canal fees for 1 year, according to country of origin of ships using the canal.

2·9 Construct Z-charts for 1941 for those parts of the data below to which such charts are applicable.

Meteorological summary for London

	Mean temp. (° F.)		Rainfall			
			Days		Amount (in.)	
	1940	1941	1940	1941	1940	1941
Jan.	30·5	35·7	9	18	1·6	2·6
Feb.	37·6	40·5	13	17	1·3	1·6
Mar.	43·9	43·6	14	14	3·7	2·9
Apr.	48·6	46·1	16	8	1·8	1·7
May	55·8	50·7	9	11	1·1	1·4
June	62·7	62·1	8	7	·5	2·1
July	60·9	67·1	19	13	2·8	4·1
Aug.	62·5	60·6	3	23	·1	5·2
Sept.	57·4	61·0	7	2	1·1	·6
Oct.	51·5	53·5	17	9	2·3	·6
Nov.	46·3	45·9	18	15	6·3	2·5
Dec.	40·1	42·9	17	12	1·1	1·8

	Mean pressure (mb.)		Sunshine (%)		Average daylight per diem (hr.)
	1940	1941	1940	1941	
Jan.	1019·7	1010·6	14	5	8·4
Feb.	1012·5	1002·4	6	12	10·0
Mar.	1013·6	1012·5	29	19	11·8
Apr.	1013·2	1014·1	28	16	13·8
May	1016·3	1014·0	47	27	15·6
June	1018·3	1018·6	52	38	16·6
July	1013·6	1014·8	38	45	16·2
Aug.	1021·3	1010·9	41	36	14·6
Sept.	1016·3	1023·8	39	29	12·8
Oct.	1011·8	1021·3	25	29	10·8
Nov.	1007·6	1014·0	23	11	9·0
Dec.	1020·9	1024·4	10	12	8·0

2·10 Construct 'Pie' charts for the following data which should be suitably amalgamated so as to reduce the number of different categories to about ten. Comment on the results of comparing the charts for 1939–40 with those for 1946–47.

Panama canal traffic

Flag	1939–40		1946–47	
	No. of transits	Net tons	No. of transits	Net tons
British	1,073	5,773,000	892	4,915,200
Chilean	38	172,200	67	259,100
Danish	174	628,200	111	392,200
French	93	378,400	61	315,600
German	55	218,000	—	—
Greek	175	785,600	32	152,300
Honduran	81	127,000	195	279,200
Italian	46	319,400	9	45,900
Japanese	272	1,600,300	—	—
Netherland	340	626,600	161	441,900
Norwegian	557	2,537,300	248	1,235,200
Panamanian	243	464,000	217	728,600
Swedish	110	503,600	108	448,200
United States	1,997	9,688,700	1,974	10,494,200
Other	116	322,100	185	525,400
Total	5,370	24,144,400	4,260	20,233,000

2·11 The following table gives the number of persons killed and injured on the roads in America in 1947. Examine the data carefully and represent them diagrammatically so as to show clearly any points of interest.

	Persons killed	Percentage	Persons injured	Percentage
Exceeding speed limit	9,415	44·7	258,960	29·1
On wrong side of road	2,609	12·3	96,110	10·8
Did not have right of way	3,140	14·9	202,010	22·7
Cutting in	120	·6	23,140	2·6
Passing standing bus	60	·3	4,450	·5
Passing on curve or hill	100	·5	2,670	·3
Passing on wrong side	720	3·4	24,030	2·7
Failing to signal, etc.	550	2·6	76,530	8·6
Car ran away. No driver	40	·2	890	·1
Drove off roadway	1,030	4·9	29,360	3·3
Reckless driving	2,700	12·8	144,160	16·2
Miscellaneous	590	2·8	27,590	3·1
Total	21,074	100·0	889,900	100·0

2·12 The table below shows the population below age 80 of the administrative county of Lancashire, as enumerated in the 1911 census. The figures are correct to the nearest thousand.

Age last Birthday	Population (000's omitted)	
	Males	Females
0–4	257	255
5–9	239	241
10–14	228	231
15–19	217	229
20–29	399	458
30–39	363	399
40–49	268	291
50–59	177	199
60–69	98	118
70–79	34	51
Total	2,280	2,472

Represent this data by a population pyramid. Draw a histogram representing the distribution of age in the population regardless of sex.

BIBLIOGRAPHY

R. G. D. ALLEN. *Statistics for Economists* (Chapter 6). Hutchinson, London, 1949.

IRVING FISHER. *The Making of Index Numbers.* Houghton Mifflin, Boston and New York, 1922.

L. R. CONNOR. *Statistics in Theory and Practice* (Chapters 6 and 7). Sir Isaac Pitman and Sons Ltd., London. 3rd ed. 1937.

Examples of the use of statistical diagrams can be found from time to time in official publications such as *The Short Economic Survey*, 1948 and 1949 or *Our Money* (H.M. Stationery Office).

A comprehensive summary of Index Numbers is published in the *Monthly Digest of Statistics* (H.M.S.O.) and in the *Monthly Bulletin of Statistics* (Stat. Office of United Nations).

CHAPTER 3

DESCRIPTIVE STATISTICS. FUNDAMENTAL ANALYTICAL IDEAS

3·1. Central measures or measures of location.

Everyone is familiar with the idea of using an 'average' to represent a body of data, the purpose being to give some indication of where the middle or 'mean' lies. The word 'average' is, however, used in everyday language in several slightly different senses and in statistics it is usually replaced by one of the more carefully defined central measures dealt with in the following sections. It is instructive to consider for a moment some of the common uses of 'averages'. A batting average is obtained by dividing the total runs scored by the number of completed innings; the average age of a class is obtained by adding the ages of all the members and dividing by the number of members. This type of average is more precisely described as the *arithmetic mean.*

On the other hand the concept of 'average family' may be that of the type of family of most frequent occurrence. The phrase 'there are two children in the average family' may mean that the most frequent number of children per family is two. This idea of the most frequent event, or the most 'fashionable' leads to the definition of the *mode.*

We shall discuss other types of central measure, each of which has advantages in certain circumstances, and although we shall tend, in later chapters, to concentrate on the arithmetic mean, the student should bear in mind that this is not always the best measure. The phrase *measure of location* is sometimes used to cover all these 'averages' which indicate the location or general position of the body of data in the range of possible values.

There are certain fundamental properties which one feels intuitively that any central measure should possess.

If $M(x_1, x_2, \ldots, x_n)$ is a central measure of the observed values $x_1, x_2, \ldots, x_n$, these fundamental properties are:

(i) $M(x_1, x_2, \ldots, x_n)$ should be unaffected by a rearrangement of the x's in a different order.

(ii) $M(x_1, x_2, \ldots, x_n)$ should not be less than the smallest or greater than the greatest x. This implies, of course, that

$$M(X, X, \ldots, X) = X \quad \text{when} \quad x_1 = x_2 = \ldots = x_n = X.$$

(iii) If each x is increased by the same amount c, say, M should be increased by the same amount, i.e.

$$M(x_1 + c,\ x_2 + c, \ldots, x_n + c) = M(x_1, x_2, \ldots, x_n) + c.$$

The reader should verify that the various measures of location described below possess these fundamental properties.

It will be noticed that no measure of location gives any indication of the spread or scatter of the data.

3·2. The arithmetic mean.

This is the most important of the central measures and although it is more difficult to calculate than some others it readily lends itself to mathematical treatment and is therefore of great value in theoretical work.

If we have n values of the variable $x_1, x_2, x_3, \ldots, x_i, \ldots, x_n$ the arithmetic mean is defined as

$$m_1' = \frac{1}{n} \sum_{i=1}^{n} x_i. \tag{3·1}$$

We have here assumed that all the x's are different and although the same formula still applies if they are not it is often more convenient to replace it by

$$m_1' = \frac{1}{n} \Sigma f_i x_i, \tag{3·2}$$

where f_i is the number of times or *frequency* with which the value x_i is observed and $n = \Sigma f_i =$ total frequency.

For numerical work formulae (3·1) and (3·2) often involve laborious arithmetic which can usually be shortened considerably by the use of an arbitrary origin somewhere near the middle of the range of the measurements.

Let this arbitrary origin be denoted by a and let $x_i = a + hX_i$.

Then $$\frac{1}{n}\Sigma f_i x_i = \frac{1}{n}\Sigma f_i(a+hX_i)$$

$$= \frac{1}{n}(a\Sigma f_i + h\Sigma f_i X_i). \qquad (3\cdot 3)$$

Let $\frac{1}{n}\Sigma f_i X_i = \overline{X}$ be the arithmetic mean referred to the arbitrary origin selected with h taken as the new unit of measurement. Equation (3·3) then becomes

$$\frac{1}{n}\Sigma f_i x_i = a + h\overline{X}, \qquad (3\cdot 4)$$

since $$\Sigma f_i = n.$$

Thus we can calculate the arithmetic mean from any origin and using any 'scale' we please and deduce the mean from some other origin and using some other scale by means of equation (3·4). The artifice of using an arbitrary scale is particularly useful for calculations based on grouped data. Examples 3·1 and 3·2 will help to make this clear.

3·3. Geometric and harmonic means.

These are rarely used although they have certain specialized applications.

The geometric mean of n positive quantities $x_1, x_2, x_3, \ldots, x_n$ is

$$\sqrt[n]{(x_1 x_2 x_3 \ldots x_n)} \qquad (3\cdot 5)$$

or $$\{\Pi x_i^{f_i}\}^{1/n}$$

if the term x_i occurs with frequency f_i.

It may be noted that the logarithm of the geometric mean is the arithmetic mean of the logarithms of the quantities $x_1, x_2, \ldots, x_n$.

The harmonic mean H is defined by the equation

$$\frac{1}{H} = \frac{1}{n}\Sigma\frac{1}{x_i} \quad \text{or} \quad \frac{1}{n}\Sigma\frac{f_i}{x_i}. \qquad (3\cdot 6)$$

(Unless the contrary is indicated 'the mean' in the rest of this book refers to the *arithmetic* mean.)

3·4. The mode.

As was indicated in § 3·1 the mode is the value which occurs most often, i.e. the value with the greatest frequency. Paradoxically enough although this central measure is the simplest to define it is often the most difficult to determine in practice. No difficulty arises if the variable is discontinuous and each observed value is recorded separately but if the variable is continuous or the data are grouped for some other reason the determination of the mode is at best an approximation. In some distributions the frequency may rise to a peak and then decrease again at more than one point of the range thus giving rise to several 'local' modes instead of a unique central measure.

The lowest point of a U-shaped distribution is sometimes called the *antimode*.

3·5. The mid-point.

This is merely the value of the variable half-way between the greatest and the smallest values recorded and its great advantage is the ease with which it can be determined.

If the data are grouped it is often sufficient to assume that the lower limit of the lowest group and the higher limit of the uppermost group were actually observed values. However, if the group widths at the two ends of the distribution differ considerably, substantial errors may be introduced by this method.

3·6. The median and percentiles.

The median is the value of the variable which divides the total frequency into two equal parts. Thus if there were 104 observations we should find a value of the variable such that 52 observations fell below it and 52 above. Here a difficulty immediately arises; if the 52nd value occurred for a value x_1 and the 53rd for a different value x_2 any value between x_1 and x_2 would satisfy the requirements. The usual convention in such circumstances is to take $\frac{1}{2}(x_1+x_2)$ as the median. If the total frequency is an odd number this difficulty does not arise because the value corresponding to the central observation fulfils the requirements.

By an obvious extension of the same idea the *percentiles* are defined as values of the variable which subdivide the total frequency into various percentages. Particularly important are the median defined above, the *lower quartile* which has one-quarter of the total frequency below it and the *upper quartile* which has one-quarter of the total frequency above it.

We shall use the following notation:

$M_{\cdot 5}$ is the median with $\cdot 5$ of the total frequency below it.

$M_{\cdot 25}$ is the lower quartile with $\cdot 25$ of the total frequency below it.

$M_{\cdot 75}$ is the upper quartile with $\cdot 75$ of the total frequency below it.

$M_{\cdot 10}, M_{\cdot 20}, \ldots, M_{\cdot 90}$ are defined as the *deciles* and subdivide the total frequency into tenths. Generally M_x is a value with a fraction x of the total frequency below it.

3·7. Application of the calculus to continuous variables.

Later in this book we shall have to deal not only with observed data but also with idealized mathematical distributions for which various measures can be calculated as for actual observations and it is convenient to introduce them now. It will be seen that the same ideas apply as in §§ 3·1–3·6 and no proofs are needed.

The frequency with which values between x and $x+\Delta x$ occur is defined as $f(x)\,\Delta x$ (Δx is small). We shall assume $f(x)$ to be a continuous function of x.

If the range of variation of x is from a to b we have in the limit:

Total frequency $$n=\int_a^b f(x)\,dx. \tag{3·7}$$

The mean is $$\frac{\int_a^b xf(x)\,dx}{\int_a^b f(x)\,dx}=\frac{1}{n}\int_a^b xf(x)\,dx. \tag{3·8}$$

The mode is the value of x for which $f(x)$ is a maximum and is therefore found from the equation

$$\frac{df(x)}{dx}=0. \tag{3·9}$$

The mid-point is $\frac{1}{2}(a+b)$.

The median is given by the equation

$$\int_a^{M_{\cdot 5}} f(x)\,dx = \frac{n}{2} = \int_{M_{\cdot 5}}^b f(x)\,dx, \tag{3·10}$$

and the quartiles by the equations

$$\int_a^{M_{\cdot 25}} f(x)\,dx = \frac{n}{4}, \tag{3·11}$$

$$\int_a^{M_{\cdot 75}} f(x)\,dx = \frac{3n}{4}. \tag{3·12}$$

The equation of the ogive curve is $y = \int_a^x f(x)\,dx$.

Example 3·1.

The following example shows how the various central measures may be calculated when the variable is discontinuous and different values of the variable are not grouped together. In § 3·10 we shall deal with the more difficult problem of grouped data.

(i) As the frequencies are so small there is little to be gained by taking an arbitrary origin for the calculation of the arithmetic mean, but for purposes of illustration the marks shown in column (3) have been referred to 54 as a new origin. If the values in column (1) are denoted by x and those in column (3) by X, the relation

$$x = 54 + X$$

holds. This is of the form described in § 3·2 with $a = 54$, $h = 1$. Column (4) gives a total for Xf_x of -180 so that the arithmetic mean referred to 54 as origin is $-\frac{180}{52} = -3{\cdot}46$.

Referred to the original origin the value is $54 - 3{\cdot}46 = 50{\cdot}54$.

(ii) The mode is 48 (the mark occurring most frequently).

(iii) The mid-point is $\frac{1}{2}(22 + 74) = 48$.

(iv) Twenty-six candidates obtained 51 marks or less and the remaining twenty-six obtained 52 or over.

The median is therefore $51\frac{1}{2}$ using the convention described in 3·6. The 12th to the 14th candidates reckoned from the bottom all obtained 45 marks and hence the lower quartile is 45. (The fact that several observations occurred for this value does not affect the result.) Similarly the 13th and 14th candidates reckoned from the top both obtained 57 marks and 57 is therefore the upper quartile.

TABLE 3·1

Distribution of examination marks. (*Maximum possible* = 100)

Marks obtained (1)	Frequency (2)	Marks referred to 54 as origin (3)	(2) × (3) (4)
22	1	−32	−32
27	1	−27	−27
29	1	−25	−25
35	1	−19	−19
36	1	−18	−18
37	1	−17	−17
39	2	−15	−30
40	1	−14	−14
43	2	−11	−22
45	3	− 9	−27
46	1	− 8	− 8
47	2	− 7	−14
48	5	− 6	−30
50	3	− 4	−12
51	1	− 3	− 3
52	1	− 2	− 2
53	2	− 1	− 2
54	4	0	0
55	3	1	3
56	2	2	4
57	2	3	6
58	2	4	8
59	1	5	5
60	1	6	6
61	1	7	7
62	2	8	16
63	1	9	9
64	1	10	10
68	2	14	28
74	1	20	20
Total	52		−180

3·8. Approximate relationship between mean, median and mode.

It will often be found that if the data are represented by a histogram or a frequency polygon they produce a single-humped or 'cocked-hat' shape which is more or less symmetrical. In such circumstances the median usually lies between the mean and the mode and the relationship.

$$\text{Mean} - \text{mode} = 3\,(\text{mean} - \text{median}) \qquad (3\cdot13)$$

is often approximately satisfied.

This relationship can be used in suitable conditions for estimating the mode given the other two measures but generally speaking it is wiser to restrict its use to giving a rough check on three calculated values. In the above example the median does not lie between the other two central measures but the distribution is somewhat irregular and does not approximate very closely to a single-humped curve.

3·9. Merits of the various central measures.

In comparing the various central measures some of the points to be borne in mind will immediately occur to the reader such as, ease of calculation, the facility with which they can be handled in mathematical analysis, or the way in which they appeal to the reason or the imagination. Further, a measure which depends on all the observations is more likely to epitomize the data satisfactorily than one, such as the mid-point, which involves only two observations.

A very important but less obvious criterion is the extent to which the measure under consideration is sensitive to changes in the distribution. There is much to be said for a measure which changes slightly if any part of the data is altered but, for reasons which are to some extent immediately apparent and will become clearer when we deal with sampling problems, it is undesirable that it should be unduly influenced by freak observations. In other words, stability rather than extreme sensitiveness is desirable in any statistical measure such as we have been considering.

The dot diagrams shown in Figs. 3·1–3·4, although very elementary, serve to illustrate the way in which the measures reflect changes in the data. In Fig. 3·1 the mean, median, mode and mid-point are all zero. In Fig. 3·2 the ten observations for positive values

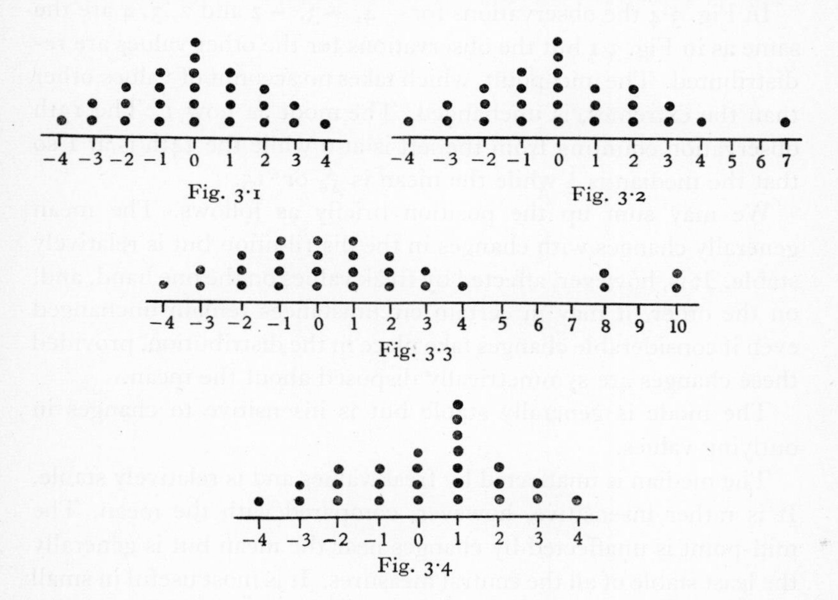

Fig. 3·1

Fig. 3·2

Fig. 3·3

Fig. 3·4

are scattered more widely while the others remain unchanged. It will be seen that

the median and the mode are unchanged,
the mid-point is altered to 1·5,
the mean is altered to $\frac{6}{26} = \cdot 23$ approx.

In this case the mean seems the best measure because, unlike the median and the mode, it reflects the very real change in the distribution but it is not so greatly affected as the mid-point.

Fig. 3·3 differs from Fig. 3·1 in the addition of the values at 8 and 10 and the elimination of two values at 0.

There are now twenty-eight observations but the 14th counting from the lower end is 0 while the 15th is 1 so that the median is now $\frac{1}{2}$. The mode is now indeterminate since the three values −1, 0 and 1 occur equally often. The mid-point is 3 and the mean is $\frac{36}{28}$ or

1·29. If the values at 8 and 10 were freaks the fact that the median is relatively unaffected is a point in its favour, and it should be noted that even if the freak values were 18 and 20 instead of 8 and 10 the median would still be $\frac{1}{2}$.

In Fig. 3·4 the observations for -4, -3, -2 and 2, 3, 4 are the same as in Fig. 3·1 but the observations for the other values are redistributed. The mid-point, which takes no account of values other than the extremes, is unchanged. The mode is now 1. The 13th observation counting from the left is at 0 while the 14th is at 1 so that the median is $\frac{1}{2}$ while the mean is $\frac{4}{26}$ or ·15.

We may sum up the position briefly as follows. The mean generally changes with changes in the distribution but is relatively stable. It is, however, affected by freak values on the one hand, and, on the other, it may in certain circumstances remain unchanged even if considerable changes take place in the distribution, provided these changes are symmetrically disposed about the mean.

The mode is generally stable but is insensitive to changes in outlying values.

The median is unaffected by freak values and is relatively stable. It is rather insensitive, however, compared with the mean. The mid-point is unaffected by changes near the mean but is generally the least stable of all the central measures. It is most useful in small samples consisting of five or ten observations. In these cases, however, little extra labour is needed to calculate the mean or median.

These conclusions are not always valid if the distribution is of unusual type and departs from the 'cocked hat' shape.

3·10. Grouped data.

Most of the special difficulties which arise with grouped data and the steps taken to deal with them are illustrated in the following example. Two points are of particular importance as they apply to nearly all grouped data.

The first is the precise definition of the limits of the group; these are not always clear from the way in which the data are given and further inquiries may be necessary. For instance, a group given as 2–5 in. may actually include all measurements from $1\frac{15}{16}$–$5\frac{1}{16}$ in. if all measurements were made to the nearest $\frac{1}{8}$ in.

The second important idea is the *class-interval* which is useful as a 'scale' if it is uniform for all groups; this is often the case. It is defined as the range of values covered by the group. It is convenient to take the class-interval as the unit in arithmetical work and to assume the whole frequency for any group to be concentrated at the mid-point of that group. There are, however, important qualifications to this latter convention which we shall deal with in § 3·23. If an arbitrary scale is used, as described in § 3·2, it is usual to take h equal to the class interval (or group width) and a, the arbitrary origin, equal to the central value of one of the groups.

Example 3·2.

Since nearest ages are given the true limits of the groups are $20\frac{1}{2}$–$25\frac{1}{2}$, $25\frac{1}{2}$–$30\frac{1}{2}$, etc. In column (3) an arbitrary origin has been taken near the estimated mean and the class interval of 5 has been taken as the unit. ($a=63$, $h=5$).

TABLE 3·2

Distribution of whole-life policies according to attained age

Nearest age x (1)	No. of policies f_x (2)	New variable X (3)	(2)×(3) Xf_x (4)	Cumulative frequency (5)
21– 25	44	−8	−352	44
26– 30	47	−7	−329	91
31– 35	66	−6	−396	157
36– 40	107	−5	−535	264
41– 45	147	−4	−588	411
46– 50	151	−3	−453	562
51– 55	208	−2	−416	770
56– 60	305	−1	−305	1075
61– 65	396	0	—	1471
66– 70	488	1	488	1959
71– 75	471	2	942	2430
76– 80	358	3	1074	2788
81– 85	222	4	888	3010
86– 90	104	5	520	3114
91– 95	18	6	108	3132
96–100	5	7	35	3137
Total	3137	—	681	—

Column (4) gives the values of Xf_x, where f_x is the frequency, i.e. the number of policies assumed to be concentrated at the value x. From the sum of column (4) we obtain the mean referred to the arbitrary origin

$$\tfrac{681}{3137} = \cdot 217 \text{ unit.}$$

Allowing for the scale the true value of the mean is

$$63 + 5 \times \cdot 217 = 64 \cdot 09 \text{ years.}$$

It is impossible to determine the mode with any great accuracy but the following device usually gives reasonable results for a continuous variable.

Assume that $f(y)$ in the notation of § 3·7 is equal to $a + by + cy^2$.

Taking a new origin at the middle of *the group of maximum frequency* ('66–70'), i.e. at the point 68 and still using the class interval as unit we have

$$\int_{-1\frac{1}{2}}^{-\frac{1}{2}} (a + by + cy^2)\, dy = 396, \quad \int_{-\frac{1}{2}}^{\frac{1}{2}} (a + by + cy^2)\, dy = 488,$$

$$\int_{\frac{1}{2}}^{1\frac{1}{2}} (a + by + cy^2)\, dy = 471$$

We thus obtain on integration:

$$a - b + \tfrac{13}{12}c = 396, \quad a + \tfrac{1}{12}c = 488, \quad a + b + \tfrac{13}{12}c = 471.$$

Solving we obtain

$$a = 492 \cdot 5, \quad b = 37 \cdot 5, \quad c = -54 \cdot 5.$$

At the mode $$\frac{df(y)}{dy} = 0, \quad \text{i.e.} \quad b + 2cy = 0.$$

Substituting for b and c this gives

$$y = \frac{37 \cdot 5}{109} = \cdot 344 \text{ unit.}$$

Referred to the true origin and scale the mode is therefore

$$68 + 5 \times \cdot 344 \quad \text{or} \quad 69 \cdot 72.$$

The median corresponds to the 1569th observation counting from either end. Now there are 1471 observations for (true) ages $65\frac{1}{2}$ and under while there are 488 in the next group $65\frac{1}{2}$–$70\frac{1}{2}$ (true ages).

The median therefore corresponds to the 98th observation in this group. If we assume *for this purpose only* that the observations are evenly spread over the group we may assume the median to be $\frac{98}{488}$ths of the way from the lower limit of the group, i.e. the median

$$M_{\cdot 5} = 65 \cdot 5 + 5 \times \tfrac{98}{488} = 66 \cdot 50.$$

Similarly we can find approximately the lower quartile $M_{.25}$ which lies in the group '56–60' and the upper quartile $M_{.75}$ which lies in the group '71–75'. Column (5) of the table obtained by summing column (2) downwards is useful in this connexion.

If we assume that there were observations at the extreme values $20\frac{1}{2}$ and $100\frac{1}{2}$ we obtain the mid-point 60·5.

It is interesting to note that the median lies between the mean and the mode and the distance between mean and mode, 5·63, is only about two and one-third times the distance between mean and median.

3·11. Graphic method for finding percentiles.

The ogive type of curve dealt with in § 2·6 affords a simple method of finding approximately the median, the quartiles and, in fact, any percentile. We first plot the cumulative frequencies against the values of the variable and join the points by a smooth curve.

The ordinate ranges up to N (the total frequency) and if we find the points on the curve with ordinates $\frac{1}{4}N$, $\frac{1}{2}N$ and $\frac{3}{4}N$, the corresponding abscissae will give us the lower quartile, median and upper quartile respectively.

In Fig. 3·5 the cumulative frequencies of Table 3·2 are joined by a smooth curve *OABCD*.

Taking points on the vertical scale representing one-quarter, one-half and three-quarters respectively of the total frequency (3137) we draw horizontal lines to meet the curve at A, B and C.

The abscissae of these three points are the lower quartile, the median and the upper quartile respectively.

The estimate of the median obtained in this way is 66·5, which agrees with the value of 66·50 calculated in § 3·10. The upper and lower quartiles are 74·7 and 56·0 approximately.

3·12. Formula for the central term.

For some purposes it may be desired to find the central term of a group in terms of the total frequency for that group and for each of the groups adjacent to it.

Let u_x be any function whose fourth and higher differences are negligible.

Let $w_{-1} = u_{-3m-1} + u_{-3m} + \dots\dots + u_{-m-2} + u_{-m-1}$,

$$w_0 = u_{-m} + u_{-m+1} + \dots + u_{-1} + u_0 + u_1 + \dots + u_{m-1} + u_m,$$

$$w_1 = u_{m+1} + u_{m+2} + \dots\dots + u_{3m} + u_{3m+1}.$$

w_{-1}, w_0 and w_1 are therefore three consecutive groups each of $2m+1$ values of u_x.

We wish to express u_0, the middle term of the middle group, in terms of w_{-1}, w_0 and w_1.

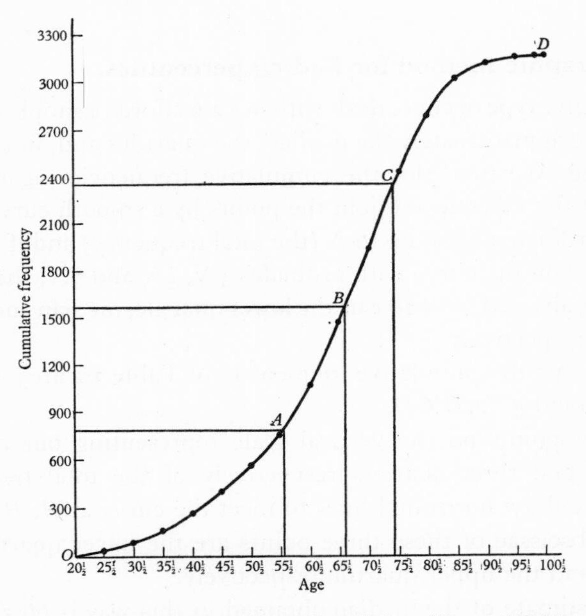

Fig. 3·5. Distribution of whole-life policies. (Data of Table 3·2.)

Stirling's interpolation formula is

$$u_x = u_0 + \frac{x}{2}(\Delta u_0 + \Delta u_{-1}) + \frac{x^2}{2}\Delta^2 u_{-1} + \frac{x(x^2-1)}{12}(\Delta^3 u_{-1} + \Delta^3 u_{-2}) + \dots$$

(*Mathematics for Actuarial Students*, Part II, p. 64).

Summing from $-m$ to $+m$:

$$w_0 \doteqdot (2m+1)\,u_0 + \Delta^2 u_{-1}(1^2 + 2^2 + \dots + m^2)$$

$$\doteqdot (2m+1)\,u_0 + \frac{m(m+1)(2m+1)}{6}\Delta^2 u_{-1}. \qquad (3\cdot14)$$

Summing from $-3m-1$ to $3m+1$:

$$w_{-1}+w_0+w_1 \doteqdot (6m+3)\,u_0+\frac{(3m+1)(3m+2)(6m+3)}{6}\Delta^2 u_{-1}$$

Hence $$w_{-1}-2w_0+w_1 \doteqdot (2m+1)^3\Delta^2 u_{-1}$$

Substituting for $\Delta^2 u_{-1}$ in (3·14) we obtain

$$w_0 \doteqdot (2m+1)\,u_0+\frac{m(m+1)}{6(2m+1)^2}(w_{-1}-2w_0+w_1),$$

or $$u_0 \doteqdot \frac{1}{2m+1}\left[w_0-\frac{m(m+1)}{6(2m+1)^2}(w_{-1}-2w_0+w_1)\right].$$

Putting $2m+1=n$, this may be written in the more usual form

$$u_0 \doteqdot \frac{1}{n}\left[w_0-\frac{n^2-1}{24n^2}\Delta^2 w_{-1}\right], \qquad (3·15)$$

where Δ now denotes the differencing of group totals and not individual u's.

When $n=5$, we have

$$u_0 \doteqdot \tfrac{1}{5}\left[w_0-\tfrac{1}{25}\Delta^2 w_{-1}\right]$$
$$\doteqdot \cdot 2w_0-\cdot 008\Delta^2 w_{-1}, \qquad (3·16)$$

which is the usual form of the expression. It was used by George King for Census data.

So far we have considered only odd values of n. If n is even ($=2r$ say), let

$$w_0=u_{-\frac{1}{2}(2r-1)}+u_{-\frac{1}{2}(2r-3)}+\dots+u_{-\frac{3}{2}}+u_{-\frac{1}{2}}+u_{\frac{1}{2}}+u_{\frac{3}{2}}+\dots+u_{\frac{1}{2}(2r-3)}+u_{\frac{1}{2}(2r-1)}.$$

Working as before we have

$$w_0 \doteqdot 2ru_0+\frac{r(2r-1)(2r+1)}{12}\Delta^2 u_{-1}$$
$$\doteqdot nu_0+\frac{n(n^2-1)}{24}\Delta^2 u_{-1}$$

corresponding to (3·14).

Formula (3·15) then follows as before, but it will be seen that

$$\frac{1}{n}\left[w_0-\frac{n^2-1}{24n^2}\Delta^2 w_{-1}\right]$$

no longer gives the central term of the middle group (there is no central term when n is even) but the value of u for an argument half-way between those of the two central terms. For instance, if the data are given for groups 40–43, 44–47 and 48–51 the application of the formula would give $u_{45\frac{1}{2}}$.

3·13. Formula for the central ordinate.

It is sometimes desired to find the ordinate at the mid-point of the range of a group in terms of the total frequency for that group and for each of the groups adjacent to it.

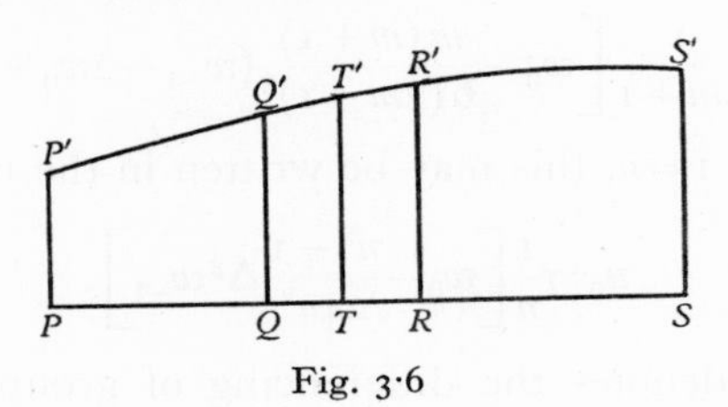

Fig. 3·6

Let $w_{-1}=\int_{-\frac{3}{2}n}^{-\frac{1}{2}n} f(x)\,dx$, represented by the area $PQQ'P'$,

$w_0=\int_{-\frac{1}{2}n}^{\frac{1}{2}n} f(x)\,dx$, represented by the area $QRR'Q'$,

$w_1=\int_{\frac{1}{2}n}^{\frac{3}{2}n} f(x)\,dx$, represented by the area $RSS'R'$.

The following formula gives the central ordinate u_0 in terms of the three areas, i.e. $f(0)$ in terms of w_{-1}, w_0 and w_1 assuming fourth and higher differences to be negligible. It can be applied only to continuous functions.

Let $$f(x)=a+bx+cx^2+dx^3.$$

Then $$w_0=\int_{-\frac{1}{2}n}^{\frac{1}{2}n} f(x)\,dx=na+\frac{n^3}{12}c,$$

$$w_{-1}+w_0+w_1=\int_{-\frac{3}{2}n}^{\frac{3}{2}n} f(x)\,dx=3na+\frac{9n^3}{4}c$$

and $$\Delta^2 w_{-1}=w_{-1}-2w_0+w_1=2n^3c,$$

where Δ is the operator for differencing grouped values.

Hence, $$w_0=na+\tfrac{1}{24}\Delta^2 w_{-1}.$$

Central ordinate $$TT'\,(=a)=\frac{1}{n}[w_0-\tfrac{1}{24}\Delta^2 w_{-1}]. \qquad (3·17)$$

3·14. Dispersion.

Consider the distributions represented by the dot diagrams Figs. 3·7 and 3·8 below. For either of these distributions the mean, the median and the mid-point between the extreme values are all

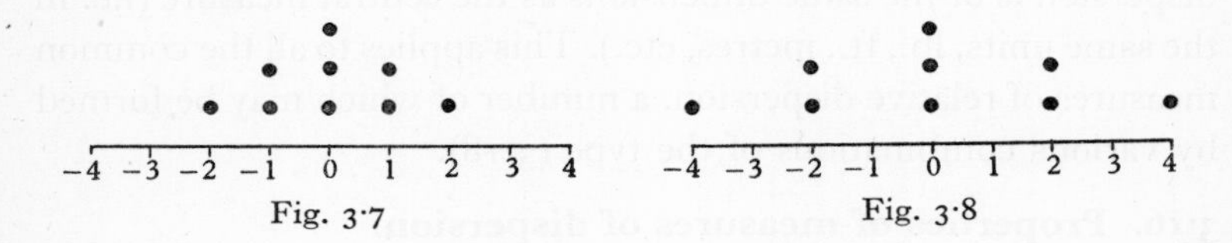

Fig. 3·7 Fig. 3·8

zero. A knowledge of any, or all, of these three quantities would not therefore enable us to distinguish between the two distributions although the second set of dots is clearly spread out twice as much as the first. If we had a quantity designed to measure the width or spread of a distribution it would enable us to make such a distinction. Such a quantity is called a measure of *dispersion*, *scatter*, or *variability*.

3·15. Relative dispersion.

A pure measure of dispersion should be unaltered if each measurement were increased by a constant amount. For example any measure of dispersion should have the same value for the

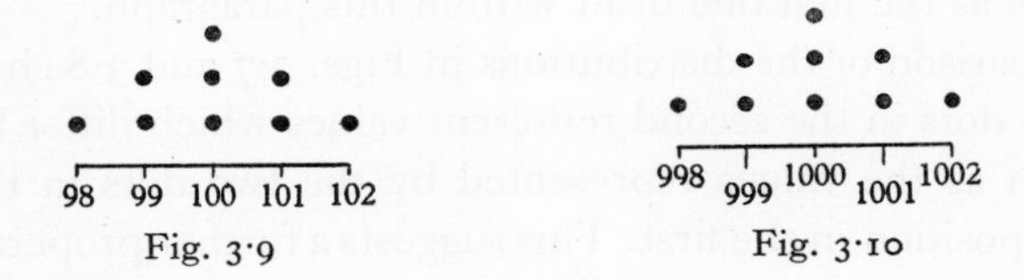

Fig. 3·9 Fig. 3·10

distribution of Fig. 3·7 and for the distributions shown in Figs. 3·9 and 3·10.

It may be argued that as the scatter of the values represented in Fig. 3·10 is less important, relative to their magnitude, than it is in Fig. 3·9, the measure of dispersion should reflect this fact and be smaller for Fig. 3·10. To provide quantities which allow for the relative size of the spread, coefficients of *relative dispersion* are constructed. These are of the form

$$\frac{\text{(Pure) measure of dispersion}}{\text{Central measure}}. \tag{3·18}$$

This ratio may be expressed as a percentage if the measure of dispersion is of the same dimensions as the central measure (i.e. in the same units, lb., ft., metres, etc.). This applies to all the common measures of relative dispersion, a number of which may be formed by various combinations of the type (3·18).

3·16. Properties of measures of dispersion.

The preceding paragraph leads immediately to two properties common to all the usual measures of dispersion. The first, and more fundamental of these, is that the measure should be unaffected by the addition of a fixed quantity to each observed value, or the subtraction of a fixed quantity from it. This arises from the requirement that any measure of dispersion should have the same value for distributions such as those shown in Figs. 3·7, 3·9 and 3·10. The second property is that the dimensions of the measure of dispersion shall be the same as those of the central measure. These latter, as we have already seen, are all of the same dimensions as the observations themselves. Hence the second property may be expressed as follows: any measure of dispersion should have the same dimensions as the observations on which it is based. This property is convenient for practical work but it is not of such importance as the first one dealt with in this paragraph.

Comparison of the distributions in Figs. 3·7 and 3·8 shows that any two dots in the second represent values which differ by twice as much as the values represented by the two dots in the same relative position in the first. This suggests a further property which is desirable in a measure of dispersion, namely, that a change in a constant ratio of the differences between observed values should result in the measure of dispersion being changed in the same ratio.

The properties which should be possessed by a measure of dispersion $D(x_1, \ldots, x_n)$ may be summarized as follows:

(i) $D(x_1+\delta, x_2+\delta, \ldots, x_n+\delta) = D(x_1, x_2, \ldots, x_n)$ whatever the size of δ.

(ii) $D(x_1, x_2, \ldots, x_n)$ should be in the same units as $x_1, x_2, \ldots, x_n$.

(iii) $D(\kappa x_1, \kappa x_2, \ldots, \kappa x_n) = |\kappa| D(x_1, x_2, \ldots, x_n)$ whatever the value of κ.

$|\kappa|$ is used instead of κ to ensure that D does not change sign.

A fourth property is implicit in properties (i) and (iii). Putting $\kappa = 0$ in (iii) we have $D(0, 0, \ldots, 0) = 0$.

Hence by (i) $D(\delta, \delta, \ldots, \delta) = 0$, that is, the measure of dispersion is zero if all the observations are equal.

3·17. Range.

The *range* of a distribution is defined as the difference between the greatest and least observed values. It is clearly unaffected if all observations are increased by a fixed amount and the dimensions of range are evidently the same as those of the observed values, since the range is a linear function of the observations. Finally, if the differences between observations are increased in a fixed ratio, the range, being a difference between two particular observations, will also be increased in this ratio. Thus, range is a measure of dispersion satisfying all three properties of § 3·16. We shall use the symbol w to denote range.

3·18. Inter-percentile distances.

In § 3·6 the percentiles M_α were defined. The difference between M_α and M_β is called an *inter-percentile distance* and by giving α and β various values an infinity of inter-percentile distances may be produced. Taking $\alpha = ·25$, $\beta = ·75$ we obtain the *inter-quartile distance* which is the most commonly used of this family of measures, and like the others is a measure of dispersion satisfying the three properties of § 3·16. One-half of the inter-quartile distance is sometimes called the *semi-interquartile range* or the *quartile deviation*.

3·19. Mean deviation.

The two previous sections deal with measures of dispersion which are each differences between two quantities. The spread of a distribution is, however, an over-all measure of space between the totality of the observations and it is reasonable therefore to consider using a measure of spread based explicitly on all the observed values.

The greater the dispersion of a distribution the greater will tend to be the size of the differences between the observations and any particular central measure. Thus a central measure of the distribution of absolute values (i.e. numerical values without regard to sign) of these differences seems to be an appropriate measure of dispersion. We shall now define such measures of dispersion in symbolic terms.

Let there be n observations in a distribution and let their values be $x_1, x_2, \ldots, x_n$. Further let C be the value of a central measure of these observations. We can then form a new distribution of absolute values of the difference between the x's and C. This distribution will consist of the n values $y_1, y_2, \ldots, y_n$, where

$$y_i = |x_i - C|.$$

The differences $x_i - C$ may be regarded as deviations of the x's from the central measure C.

Any central measure (except the mode) of the distribution of the y's might be taken as a measure of dispersion of the distribution of the x's. If the central measure chosen be the arithmetic mean, the corresponding measure of dispersion is $\frac{1}{n}\sum_{i=1}^{n}|x_i - C|$. This is called the *mean deviation from C*. If C is the arithmetic mean (of the x's) we have the *mean deviation from the arithmetic mean* or simply the *mean deviation* since this is the most frequently used of this type of measures of dispersion. In symbols the mean deviation may be written $\frac{1}{n}\sum_{i=1}^{n}|x_i - \bar{x}|$. We shall use the symbol m to denote this quantity.

3·20. Standard deviation.

A further possible average of the y's of the preceding section is the root mean square, $\sqrt{\left(\frac{1}{n}\sum_{i=1}^{n} y_i^2\right)}$ or, in terms of the x's

$$\sqrt{\left(\frac{1}{n}\sum_{i=1}^{n}(x_i - C)^2\right)}.$$

This may be called the *root mean square deviation* from C. If C be the arithmetic mean we have the measure of dispersion most frequently used. It is called the *standard deviation* and its square is called the *variance*. The standard deviation may be written in symbols

$$\sqrt{\left(\frac{1}{n}\sum_{i=1}^{n}(x_i-\bar{x})^2\right)}$$

and will be denoted by the symbol s.

The operations of squaring and later taking the square-root offset each other so that the standard deviation is of the same dimensions as the original observations.

It is possible to construct an infinity of measures of dispersion of the form $\sqrt[r]{\left(\frac{1}{n}\sum_{i=1}^{n}|y_i^r|\right)}$ but difficulties of computation, apart from theoretical reasons to be developed later, militate against the use of such quantities for values of r other than 1 or 2.

3·21. Comparison of measures of dispersion.

The object of a measure of dispersion is to sum up in a single value the spread of a set of observations. This is a collective property of the whole distribution. We should therefore expect the measures

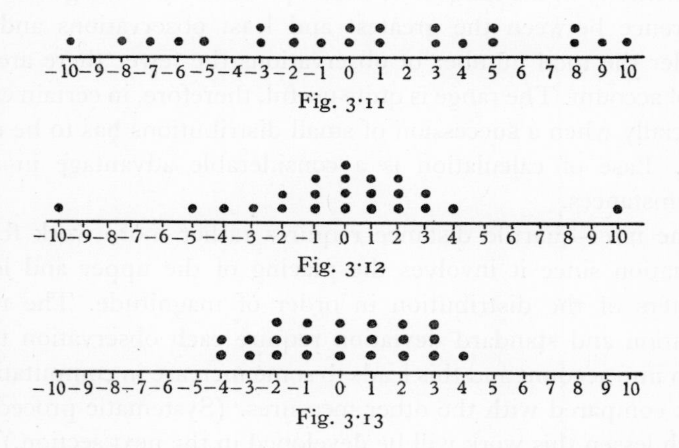

Fig. 3·11

Fig. 3·12

Fig. 3·13

of §§ 3·19 and 3·20, the mean deviation and standard deviation to be more effective than those considered earlier. The earlier measures, range and inter-percentile distances, do not require the actual values of all the observations for their computations. In fact, the values of many of the observations may be altered considerably without changing these measures of dispersion.

A study of the three distributions shown above will help to make this point clear. All three distributions have the same number (23) of observations. The first two have the same range, while the last two have the same inter-quartile distance. It should, however, be clear that the spread of Fig. 3·11 is greater than that of Fig. 3·12, and that the spread of Fig. 3·12, in turn, is greater than that of Fig. 3·13. The mean deviation and standard deviation, on the other hand, reflect this progressive diminution in spread as may be seen from Table 3·3.

TABLE 3·3

Distribution	Range	Inter-quartile distance	Mean deviation from the mean	Standard deviation
Fig. 3·11	20	8	4·5	5·5
Fig. 3·12	20	4	2·5	3·7
Fig. 3·13	8	4	2·0	2·3

If the number of observations is small (say less than ten) the lack of sensitivity in the range is of less importance. The range fixes the difference between the greatest and least observations and the smaller the total number of observations the fewer there are left out of account. The range is quite useful, therefore, in certain cases, especially when a succession of small distributions has to be dealt with. Ease of calculation is a considerable advantage in such circumstances.

The inter-quartile distance requires rather more work for its evaluation since it involves the placing of the upper and lower quarters of the distribution in order of magnitude. The mean deviation and standard deviation require each observation to be taken into account and this leads to some increase in computational work compared with the other measures. (Systematic procedures which lessen this work will be developed in the next section.) The amount of work involved is about the same for either and there is not much to choose between them on other grounds. The standard deviation is, however, open to the objection that it gives more weight to the outlying observations than does the mean deviation since it involves the squares of the distances from the arithmetic mean. A comparison of the figures for the distributions in Figs. 3·12 and 3·13 bears out this statement. The mean deviation does not give undue weight to occasional large deviations. It is also more easily understood as it is a simple mean of absolute values of differences between the observations and the arithmetic mean. On the other hand, the standard deviation is more easily dealt with algebraically and has considerable theoretical importance.

A rough but useful result is

$$\text{mean deviation} = \tfrac{4}{5}\,(\text{standard deviation.})$$

This holds approximately for a wide variety of distributions.

3·22. Computation.

Mean deviations and standard deviations may be computed directly by first finding separately the deviation of each observation from the arithmetic mean and then combining them as required by the formulae. It is possible to reduce the amount of work involved by means of the methods developed below.

In the case of mean deviation we have

$$m = \frac{1}{n}\sum_{i=1}^{n} |x_i - \bar{x}|.$$

This sum can be divided into two parts according as x_i is greater than or less than $\bar{x}$. Let n_G be the number of observations greater than $\bar{x}$ and n_L the number less than $\bar{x}$; and let $\sum_G$ denote summation over observations greater than $\bar{x}$ and $\sum_L$ summation over those less than $\bar{x}$.

Then $$m = \frac{1}{n}\{\sum_G (x_i - \bar{x}) + \sum_L (\bar{x} - x_i)\}. \qquad (3·19)$$

Since $$\sum_{i=1}^{n} (x_i - \bar{x}) = 0, \quad \sum_G (x_i - \bar{x}) + \sum_L (x_i - \bar{x}) = 0. \qquad (3·20)$$

Hence $$m = \frac{1}{n}\{2\sum_G (x_i - \bar{x})\} = \frac{2}{n}\{\sum_G x_i - n_G\bar{x}\}. \qquad (3·21)$$

Similarly $$m = \frac{2}{n}\{n_L\bar{x} - \sum_L x_i\}. \qquad (3·22)$$

It should be noted that observations which happen to be equal to the mean need not be assigned to either group, since their contribution to the sum $\sum_{i=1}^{n} |x_i - \bar{x}|$ is zero.

These formulae enable the mean deviation to be calculated from two simple sums of observations, and avoid the necessity for separate determination of each deviation from the arithmetic mean.

For the standard deviation we have

$$
\begin{aligned}
s^2 &= \frac{1}{n}\sum_{i=1}^{n}(x_i - \bar{x})^2 \\
&= \frac{1}{n}\left\{\sum_{i=1}^{n} x_i^2 - 2\bar{x}\sum_{i=1}^{n} x_i + n\bar{x}^2\right\} \\
&= \frac{1}{n}\left\{\sum_{i=1}^{n} x_i^2 - 2\bar{x}\,n\bar{x} + n\bar{x}^2\right\} \\
&= \frac{1}{n}\sum_{i=1}^{n} x_i^2 - \bar{x}^2. \qquad (3\cdot23)
\end{aligned}
$$

Once again the need for the evaluation of each deviation separately has been removed. This time only the sum of all the observations and the sum of squares of all the observations (referred to some convenient origin) are required.

If the data are grouped with class-interval h and an arbitrary origin is taken at a, the computation of s^2 may be carried out wholly in terms of the class-interval as unit with a final correction for scale much on the same lines as in § 3·10.

Let X_i be the value on the arbitrary scale corresponding to an observed value x_i, i.e.

$$x_i = a + hX_i. \qquad (3\cdot24)$$

Taking arithmetic means

$$\bar{x} = a + h\bar{X}. \qquad (3\cdot25)$$

It follows that $x_i - \bar{x} = h(X_i - \bar{X})$,

and

$$\frac{1}{n}\sum_{i=1}^{n}(x_i - \bar{x})^2 = h^2\frac{1}{n}\sum_{i=1}^{n}(X_i - \bar{X})^2, \qquad (3\cdot26)$$

i.e.

$$s_x^2 = h^2 s_X^2, \qquad (3\cdot27)$$

the subscripts of the s's denoting the variables with respect to which they are evaluated.

3·23. Adjustments for grouping.

When data are grouped the calculation of the mean, mean deviation and standard deviation involves the replacement of observed values by the central value of the group to which they belong. Clearly this will in general affect the value of the functions so computed and it is desirable, as far as possible, to make a correction. Without details of the actual values, exact adjustment cannot be made but corrections have been worked out which, under certain conditions will, on the average, reduce the discrepancies between values of functions calculated from the grouped and the ungrouped data. An important set applicable in certain fairly common circumstances (see Appendix 1) are called *Sheppard's adjustments* after W. F. Sheppard, who investigated this problem. It should be noted that while these corrections are designed to be of use in the long run, it is quite possible that in a particular case they may produce greater discrepancies than were present before they were applied.

The mean needs no correction but in suitable cases s^2 should be adjusted by deducting $\frac{1}{12}h^2$ where h is the class-interval. The correction for the mean deviation is rather more complicated and does not appear to have been dealt with hitherto in standard text-books. In the first place we calculate m by formula (3·21) or (3·22) on the assumption that the total frequency in each group is concentrated at the mid-point of that group but corrections are needed for two reasons.

The frequency of the group* in which the mean lies should be split into two parts, one assumed to apply to values less than $\bar{x}$ and the rest to values greater than $\bar{x}$. These sections should be treated separately as each makes a positive contribution to m whereas if we assume the frequency to be concentrated at the mid-point these contributions will tend to cancel out and in the extreme case where the mean happens to be the mid-point, the group will contribute nothing at all to m.

The second correction is similar to that devised by Sheppard

* It should be noted that this is not necessarily the same as the group containing the origin of the arbitrary scale.

for the standard deviation and is due to much the same considerations. The total correction is given approximately by

$$\frac{\text{Frequency in group containing the mean}}{\text{Total frequency}}\left\{\frac{(X-\bar{x})^2}{h}-|X-\bar{x}|+\frac{h}{12}\right\}, \tag{3·28}$$

where X is the central value of the group containing the mean, h is the class-interval and $|X-\bar{x}|$ indicates that the difference is to be taken as positive.

A proof of this adjustment and also of Sheppard's adjustments will be found in Appendix 1.

Example 3·3.

To illustrate the way in which grouped data are usually dealt with in practice we proceed to calculate the range, mean deviation, standard deviation and inter-quartile distance of the data given in Table 3·2 and reproduced below.

TABLE 3·4

Distribution of whole-life policies according to attained age

Nearest age x (1)	No. of policies (2)	New variable X (3)	(2)×(3) $=Xf_x$ (4)	(4)×(3) $=X^2f_x$ (5)	(5)×(3) $=X^3f_x$ (6)	(6)×(3) $=X^4f_x$ (7)
21– 25	44	−8	− 352	2,816	−22,528	180,224
26– 30	47	−7	− 329	2,303	−16,121	112,847
31– 35	66	−6	− 396	2,376	−14,256	85,536
36– 40	107	−5	− 535	2,675	−13,375	66,875
41– 45	147	−4	− 588	2,352	− 9,408	37,632
46– 50	151	−3	− 453	1,359	− 4,077	12,231
51– 55	208	−2	− 416	832	− 1,664	3,328
56– 60	305	−1	− 305	305	− 305	305
61– 65	396	0	−3,374	—	−81,734	—
66– 70	488	1	488	488	488	488
71– 75	471	2	942	1,884	3,768	7,536
76– 80	358	3	1,074	3,222	9,666	28,998
81– 85	222	4	888	3,552	14,208	56,832
86– 90	104	5	520	2,600	13,000	65,000
91– 95	18	6	108	648	3,888	23,328
96–100	5	7	35	245	1,715	12,005
Total	3,137	—	+4,055	27,657	+46,733	693,165

Again we take our origin for calculation at the mid-point of the group '61–65' which we assume to be age 63 exact and take the class-interval 5 as our unit. Assuming as before that there are observations at the two extremes we have

$$\text{The range} = 100\tfrac{1}{2} - 20\tfrac{1}{2} = 80.$$

Column (4) is the same as before except that the total of the negative terms has been inserted opposite the value $x=0$ and the total of the positive terms is shown at the foot.

Using formula (3·21), $m = \frac{2}{3137}\{4055 - 1666 \times \cdot 217\} = 2\cdot 355$ units, or using formula (3·22), $m = \frac{2}{3137}\{(1471 \times \cdot 217) + 3374\} = 2\cdot 355$ units. (The mean has already been shown to be ·217 unit referred to this origin.)

Since X is zero the correction (formula (3·28)) becomes

$$\tfrac{396}{3137}\{(\cdot 217)^2 - \cdot 217 + \tfrac{1}{12}\}\text{ unit} = -\cdot 011\text{ unit.}$$

Alternatively if we expressed X, $\bar{x}$ and the unadjusted m in the original scale and referred to the given origin the correction would be

$$\frac{396}{3137}\left\{\frac{(63 - 64\cdot 09)^2}{5} - (64\cdot 09 - 63) + \frac{5}{12}\right\} = -\cdot 055\text{ year.}$$

The adjusted mean deviation is therefore

$$m = 2\cdot 344\text{ units or }11\cdot 72\text{ years.}$$

To find the standard deviation we first construct column (5) all the items of which are essentially positive since they are of the type $X^2 f_x$.

We thus find $\qquad \frac{1}{n}\Sigma X^2 f_x = \frac{27,657}{3,137} = 8\cdot 816.$

Hence $\qquad s^2 = 8\cdot 816 - (\cdot 217)^2 = 8\cdot 769$

and $\qquad s = \sqrt{(8\cdot 769)} = 2\cdot 961$ units,

$\qquad = 14\cdot 80$ years.

If we apply Sheppard's correction for s^2 we obtain

$$s^2\,(\text{corrected}) = 8\cdot 769 - \tfrac{1}{12}$$

and $\qquad s = 2\cdot 947$ units.

$\qquad = 14\cdot 73$ years.

It will be noticed, however, that the conditions as to negligible differential coefficients are not satisfied at the lower end.

As we have seen earlier the lower quartile lies in the range '56–60' and it is found to be $55\cdot 5 + 5 \times \frac{14\frac{1}{4}}{305} = 55\cdot 73$ years.

Similarly the upper quartile is $70\cdot 5 + 5 \times \frac{393\frac{3}{4}}{471} = 74\cdot 68$ years.

The inter-quartile distance is therefore 18·95 years, or the quartile deviation 9·47 years.

(The columns (6) and (7) of the Table will be referred to in a continuation of this example later in the Chapter.)

3·24. Coefficient of variation, etc.

We now return to the question of relative dispersion mentioned in § 3·15. The measure commonly used is the ratio of the standard deviation to the arithmetic mean, i.e. $s/\bar{x}$, which is known as the *coefficient of variation*. For example suppose that the average height of a number of men is 5 ft. 9·2 in. (=69·2 in.) and the standard deviation of their heights is 2·1 in.; the coefficient of variation is 2·1/69·2=·0303 or about 3 %. The coefficient of variation is rarely used unless the characteristic measured is always of the same sign and the arithmetic mean is somewhat greater than the standard deviation. Coefficients of variation greater than 30 % in magnitude are rarely encountered. If the arithmetic mean is negative the coefficient of variation is also negative. It is, however, the absolute size of the ratio which is important as a measure of relative dispersion.

Another coefficient of relative dispersion is the ratio of the inter-quartile distance to the median. All the quantities involved may be obtained by simply placing the observations in order of magnitude. No summation or squaring of all the observations is required.

Whatever coefficient of relative dispersion is used, comparison of different distributions should be based on the use of the same coefficient for each distribution.

3·25. Moments.

The quantity $\frac{1}{n}\sum_{i=1}^{n} x_i^r$ is called the *rth moment of the distribution about zero*, and is denoted by m_r'. More generally $\frac{1}{n}\sum_{i=1}^{n}(x_i-A)^r$ is called the rth moment of the distribution about A.* This may be denoted by ${}_Am_r'$; in this notation ${}_0m_r'=m_r'$.

* The cases $r=1$ and 2 are respectively analogous to moment and moment of inertia in mechanics.

${}_{A}m'_r$ is in fact the arithmetic mean of the quantities $(x_i - A)^r$.

We have $$m'_0 = \frac{1}{n}\sum_{i=1}^{n} x_i^0 = \frac{1}{n}\sum_{i=1}^{n} 1 = 1,$$

$$m'_1 = \frac{1}{n}\sum_{i=1}^{n} x_i = \bar{x}.$$

Also we have already shown in § 3·22 that

$$s^2 = \frac{1}{n}\sum_{i=1}^{n} x_i^2 - \bar{x}^2.$$

s^2 may therefore be expressed in terms of moments about zero, as follows:

$$s^2 = m'_2 - m_1'^2. \qquad (3{\cdot}29)$$

By definition $$s^2 = \frac{1}{n}\sum_{i=1}^{n} (x_i - \bar{x})^2,$$

that is s^2 is the second moment about the arithmetic mean, ${}_{\bar{x}}m'_2$. A moment about the arithmetic mean is termed a *central moment*. The rth central moment is $\frac{1}{n}\sum_{i=1}^{n} (x_i - \bar{x})^r$ and is denoted by m_r. Thus ${}_{\bar{x}}m'_r = m_r$ and in particular ${}_{\bar{x}}m'_2 = m_2$. We have therefore proved that

$$s^2 = m_2 = m'_2 - m_1'^2. \qquad (3{\cdot}30)$$

This is a particular case of the general relationship between moments about zero and central moments to be developed in § 3·28 by means of which one set may be found from the other. We have in fact already made use of it to simplify our calculation of s.

If $x_i - A$ be replaced by its modulus $|x_i - A|$ in the expression for ${}_{A}m'_r$ we have the *rth absolute moment about A* which we shall denote by ${}_{A}n'_r$. For absolute moments about zero we write ${}_{0}n'_r = n'_r$ and for absolute central moments ${}_{\bar{x}}n'_r = n_r$. Evidently the mean deviation, m, is represented in this scheme by n_1.

An obvious relation between absolute and ordinary moments is

$${}_{A}n'_r = {}_{A}m'_r$$

if r is even.

3·26. Skewness.

We have seen that the first moment about zero provides a central measure of a distribution and the square-root of the second central moment a measure of dispersion. We now consider what properties of a distribution are reflected in its third central moment.

Unlike the second central moment, which cannot be negative, the third central moment may be either positive or negative. It may be positive if the positive deviations from the arithmetic mean are few and large, while the negative deviations are many and small because the cubes of the deviations are used and the larger

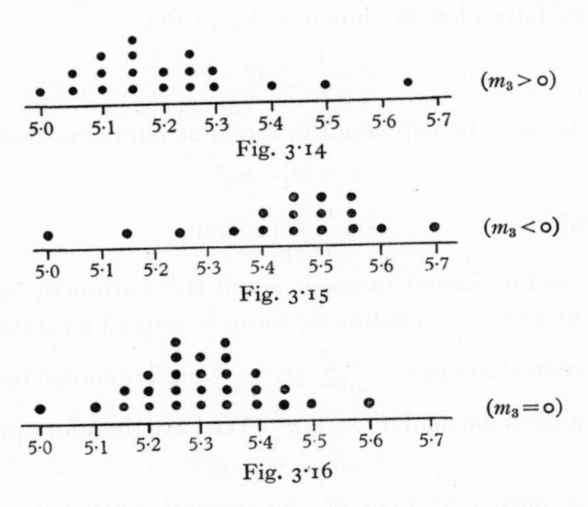

Fig. 3·14

Fig. 3·15

Fig. 3·16

deviations are thus given much more weight than the smaller. For the distribution of Fig. 3·14, m_3 is positive while for Fig. 3·15 the situation is reversed and m_3 is negative.

In the first case the positive third central moment reflects the fact that the distribution has a longer 'tail' in the positive direction from the mean while the negative m_3 for the second distribution corresponds to the case of a longer negative tail.

If, to each positive deviation from the arithmetic mean, there corresponds a negative deviation of equal magnitude (as in Fig. 3·16), m_3 is zero since the terms of the sum $\sum_{i=1}^{n} (x_i - \bar{x})^3$ cancel out in pairs.

Such a distribution is said to be *symmetrical* and departure from symmetry is called *skewness*. The two distributions of Figs. 3·14 and 3·15 exhibit different types of skewness which are each associated with non-zero values of m_3, in one case positive, in the other, negative. It seems therefore that m_3 might be used as a measure of skewness. In fact distributions for which m_3 is positive are said to be *positively skew*; if m_3 is negative they are said to be *negatively skew*.

Clearly m_3 is also affected by the spread of the distribution for if each observation is doubled m_3 is multiplied by eight. Skewness, however, is a property unaffected by spread, since it depends only upon the relative sizes of positive and negative deviations from the arithmetic mean. It is desirable, therefore, that any measure of skewness should be unaltered if each observation were multiplied by a constant factor. Such a measure of skewness may be constructed by dividing m_3 by the third power of a measure of dis-

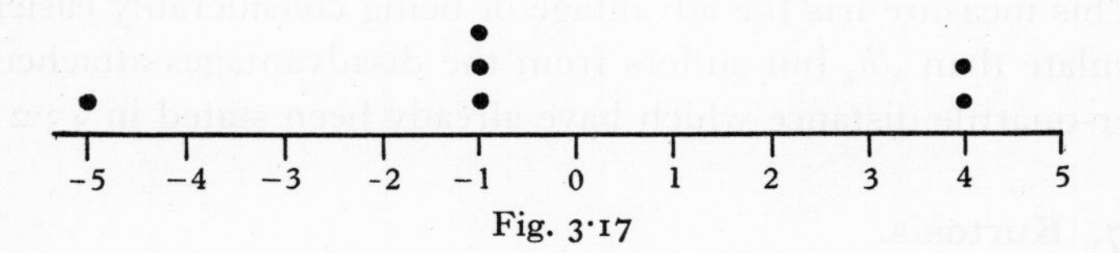

Fig. 3·17

persion. The measure of skewness most frequently used is formed by using the standard deviation in the denominator. The measure obtained in this way is

$$\sqrt{b_1} = \frac{m_3}{s^3} = \frac{m_3}{m_2^{\frac{3}{2}}}. \qquad (3\cdot31)$$

The symbol $\sqrt{b_1}$ is the conventional one and owes its origin to certain historical and theoretical reasons. Positive and negative values of $\sqrt{b_1}$ correspond to positive and negative skewness, i.e. positive and negative values of m_3.

$\sqrt{b_1}$ is zero for symmetrical distributions but it should be noted that the converse is not necessarily true. If $\sqrt{b_1}$ is zero it does not necessarily follow that the distribution is symmetrical as defined above. The distribution of Fig. 3·17 has $\sqrt{b_1}=0$, but clearly the deviations from the arithmetic mean (which is zero) are not equal and of opposite sign in pairs.

A truly symmetrical distribution would have all its odd central moments zero but the fifth central moment of the above distribution is -1080. On the other hand the zero value of $\sqrt{b_1}$ does reflect the fact that there is no large excess of either positive or negative tail.

An alternative measure of skewness, requiring only the arrangement of the observations in order of magnitude, is

$$\frac{(\text{Upper quartile} - \text{median}) - (\text{Median} - \text{lower quartile})}{\text{Inter-quartile distance}}, \quad (3{\cdot}32)$$

or, in the notation developed in § 3·6

$$\frac{(M_{\cdot 75} - M_{\cdot 5}) - (M_{\cdot 5} - M_{\cdot 25})}{M_{\cdot 75} - M_{\cdot 25}},$$

that is

$$\frac{M_{\cdot 75} + M_{\cdot 25} - 2M_{\cdot 5}}{M_{\cdot 75} - M_{\cdot 25}}. \quad (3{\cdot}33)$$

This measure has the advantage of being considerably easier to calculate than $\sqrt{b_1}$ but suffers from the disadvantages attached to inter-quartile distance which have already been stated in § 3·21.

3·27. Kurtosis.

We now consider what additional information about a distribution is provided by the fourth central moment m_4. We can form a moment ratio independent of spread analogous to $\sqrt{b_1}$ by taking the ratio of m_4 to s^4. This quantity is conventionally represented by the symbol b_2.

Hence

$$b_2 = \frac{m_4}{s^4} = \frac{m_4}{m_2^2}. \quad (3{\cdot}34)$$

Quantities such as $\sqrt{b_1}$ and b_2 which are independent of the magnitude and spread of the observations and are affected only by the shape of the distribution are sometimes called *shape-factors*. Evidently b_2 is always positive. Moreover:

$$m_4 - m_2^2 = \frac{1}{n}\sum_{i=1}^{n}(x_i - \bar{x})^4 - s^4$$

$$= \frac{1}{n}\sum_{i=1}^{n}\{(x_i - \bar{x})^2 - s^2\}^2,$$

since the product term is

$$-\frac{2}{n}\sum_{i=1}^{n}(x_i - \bar{x})^2 s^2 = -2s^4.$$

$m_4 - m_2^2$ is therefore essentially positive and we have

$$b_2 \geqslant 1. \quad (3{\cdot}35)$$

It is rather more difficult to appreciate what properties of the distribution are reflected in the value of b_2 than it has been to interpret the central measures and measures of dispersion and skewness. The point to notice is that in m_4 the larger deviations have even greater relative weight than in m_2.

A distribution which is composed of values evenly spread will have a smaller fourth central moment than a distribution having the same standard deviation but containing a concentration of observations near the arithmetic mean counterbalanced by a number of deviations larger on the average than those in the first distribution.

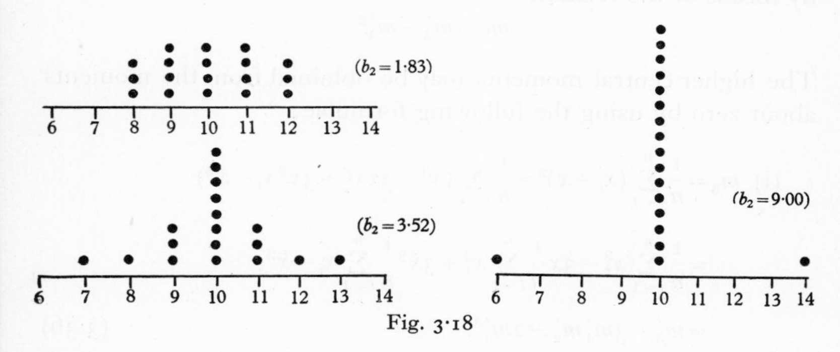

Fig. 3·18

The value of b_2 will therefore be smaller for the first distribution than for the second. The three distributions above are in order of increasing b_2, each having the same mean, 10, and the same standard deviation, $\frac{4}{3}$.

These three distributions are all symmetrical so that we have to proceed as far as the fourth central moment before we find one to distinguish between them.

The value $b_2 = 3$ is taken as a standard and departures from this standard are said to measure *kurtosis*. Distributions for which $b_2 < 3$ are said to be *platykurtic* and those for which $b_2 > 3$ are said to be *leptokurtic*.

The interpretation of the central moments becomes increasingly subtle as the order of the moments increases and orders higher than the fourth are rarely considered. It is indeed usually unnecessary to proceed so far; the amount of numerical work involved is an important consideration in this connexion. Skewness is of some importance but often a general impression gained from a diagram is sufficient. Central measures and measures of dispersion, however, should usually be calculated.

3·28. Computation of moment ratios.

As a preliminary to the computation of $\sqrt{b_1}$ and b_2 the first four central moments must be obtained. We have already seen how to calculate the mean and the moments about zero. We can obtain the second central moment from the first two moments about zero by means of the relation

$$m_2 = m_2' - m_1'^2.$$

The higher central moments may be obtained from the moments about zero by using the following formulae:

$$\text{(i)}\ m_3 = \frac{1}{n}\sum_{i=1}^{n}(x_i - \bar{x})^3 = \frac{1}{n}\sum_{i=1}^{n}(x_i^3 - 3\bar{x}x_i^2 + 3\bar{x}^2 x_i - \bar{x}^3)$$

$$= \frac{1}{n}\sum_{i=1}^{n} x_i^3 - 3\bar{x}\frac{1}{n}\sum_{i=1}^{n} x_i^2 + 3\bar{x}^2\frac{1}{n}\sum_{i=1}^{n} x_i - \bar{x}^3$$

$$= m_3' - 3m_1' m_2' + 2m_1'^3, \qquad (3·36)$$

$$\text{(ii)}\ m_4 = \frac{1}{n}\sum_{i=1}^{n}(x_i - \bar{x})^4 = \frac{1}{n}\sum_{i=1}^{n}(x_i^4 - 4\bar{x}x_i^3 + 6\bar{x}^2 x_i^2 - 4\bar{x}^3 x_i + \bar{x}^4)$$

$$= \frac{1}{n}\sum_{i=1}^{n} x_i^4 - 4\bar{x}\frac{1}{n}\sum_{i=1}^{n} x_i^3 + 6\bar{x}^2\frac{1}{n}\sum_{i=1}^{n} x_i^2 - 4\bar{x}^3\frac{1}{n}\sum_{i=1}^{n} x_i + \bar{x}^4$$

$$= m_4' - 4m_1' m_3' + 6m_1'^2 m_2' - 3m_1'^4. \qquad (3·37)$$

The values of m_1', m_2', m_3' and m_4' are calculated first, using a convenient origin, and the values of m_2, m_3 and m_4 are then obtained from them by means of these formulae. In general

$$m_k = m_k' - k m_1' m_{k-1}' + \binom{k}{2} m_1'^2 m_{k-2}' + \ldots + (-1)^{k-1}(k-1)\, m_1'^k.$$

If an arbitrary scale be used (see § 3·22) the relation $x_i = a + hX_i$ entails $x_i - \bar{x} = h(X_i - \bar{X})$ and we have

$$m_{3.x} = h^3 m_{3.X}; \quad m_{4.x} = h^4 m_{4.X}$$

and in general $m_{r.x} = h^r m_{r.X}$. Hence

$$\sqrt{b_{1.x}} = \frac{m_{3.x}}{m_{2.x}^{\frac{3}{2}}} = \frac{h^3 m_{3.X}}{h^3 m_{2.X}^{\frac{3}{2}}} = \frac{m_{3.X}}{m_{2.X}^{\frac{3}{2}}} = \sqrt{b_{1.X}},$$

$$b_{2.x} = \frac{m_{4.x}}{m_{2.x}^2} = \frac{h^4 m_{4.X}}{h^4 m_{2.X}^2} = \frac{m_{4.X}}{m_{2.X}^2} = b_{2.X}.$$

The moment ratios therefore require no correction for arbitrary scale.

The Sheppard's adjustment for m_3 is zero.

The correction for m_4 is (see Appendix 1)

$$-\tfrac{1}{2}h^2 m_2 + \tfrac{7}{240}h^4. \tag{3·38}$$

The following example shows how the work involved in calculating the moment ratios for a grouped distribution may be set out.

Example 3·3 (*cont.*).

In Table 3·4 the last two columns are needed in finding m_3 and m_4. The method of construction is obvious and it will be noted that in column (6) positive and negative terms have again been added separately:

$$m_3' = \tfrac{1}{3137}(46{,}733 - 81{,}734)$$
$$= -11·16 \text{ in terms of the scale adopted,}$$

and we have previously found that $m_1' = ·217$ and $m_2' = 8·816$.

Hence from (3·36)

$$m_3 = -11·16 - 3(·217)(8·816) + 2(·217)^3$$
$$= -16·88 \quad \text{(no Sheppard's adjustment required).}$$

Similarly $$m_4' = \frac{693{,}165}{3{,}137} = 220·96.$$

From (3·37) we then obtain

$$m_4 = 220·96 + 4(·217)(11·16) + 6(·217)^2(8·816) - 3(·217)^4$$
$$= 233·14 \text{ ignoring Sheppard's correction.}$$

In applying Sheppard's correction we must bear in mind that all our calculations are in terms of the class interval as unit so that we must take $h = 1$

$$m_4\,(\text{corrected}) = 233·14 - \tfrac{1}{2}(8·769) + \tfrac{7}{240}$$
$$= 228·78.$$

Finally, $$\sqrt{b_1} = -\frac{16·88}{(8·686)^{\frac{3}{2}}} = -·659 \quad \text{(negative skewness),}$$

and $$b_2 = \frac{228·78}{(8·686)^2} = 3·032 \quad \text{(very slightly leptokurtic).}$$

Example 3·4.

As a further example we shall deal with the following data compiled by London Transport for the Ministry of Transport's campaign to stagger working hours (*The Times*, 3rd Jan. 1947).

TABLE 3·5

Passengers entering a.m.

Time (1)	Number (2)	Variable X (3)	$\frac{(2)\times(3)}{100}$ (4)	(4)×(3) (5)	(5)×(3) (6)	(6)×(3) (7)
7.15–7.30	35,500	−5	−1,775	8,875	−44,375	221,875
7.30–7.45	50,500	−4	−2,020	8,080	−32,320	129,280
7.45–8.00	71,000	−3	−2,130	6,390	−19,170	57,510
8.00–8.15	62,000	−2	−1,240	2,480	−4,960	9,920
8.15–8.30	63,000	−1	−630	630	−630	630
8.30–8.45	94,000	0	−7,795	—	−101,455	—
8.45–9.00	114,000	1	1,140	1,140	1,140	1,140
9.00–9.15	103,500	2	2,070	4,140	8,280	16,560
9.15–9.30	90,000	3	2,700	8,100	24,300	72,900
9.30–9.45	61,500	4	2,460	9,840	39,360	157,440
Total	745,000		+8,370	49,675	+73,080	667,255

Passengers leaving p.m.

Time (8)	Number (9)	Variable X (10)	$\frac{(9)\times(10)}{100}$ (11)	(11)×(10) (12)	(12)×(10) (13)	(13)×(10) (14)
4.30–4.45	48,500	−4	−1,940	7,760	−31,040	124,160
4.45–5.00	67,500	−3	−2,025	6,075	−18,225	54,675
5.00–5.15	118,000	−2	−2,360	4,720	−9,440	18,880
5.15–5.30	114,500	−1	−1,145	1,145	−1,145	1,145
5.30–5.45	131,000	0	−7,470	—	−59,850	—
5.45–6.00	111,000	1	1,110	1,110	1,110	1,110
6.00–6.15	101,500	2	2,030	4,060	8,120	16,240
6.15–6.30	69,000	3	2,070	6,210	18,630	55,890
6.30–6.45	46,000	4	1,840	7,360	29,440	117,760
6.45–7.00	31,500	5	1,575	7,875	39,375	196,875
Total	838,500		+8,625	46,315	+96,675	586,735

It will be noticed that the frequencies have been divided by 100 to reduce the number of figures but the results are, of course, unaffected. In general the frequencies may be replaced by any quantities bearing a constant ratio to them.

It may be assumed that the limits of the groups are exactly those stated and we obtain the following results which should be carefully checked by the reader:

a.m. passengers

$$\text{Mean} = 8 \text{ hr. } 37\tfrac{1}{2} \text{ min.} + 15\left(\tfrac{575}{7450}\right) \text{ min.}$$
$$= 8 \text{ hr. } 38{\cdot}66 \text{ min.}$$

p.m. passengers

$$\text{Mean} = 5 \text{ hr. } 37\tfrac{1}{2} \text{ min.} + 15\left(\tfrac{1155}{8385}\right) \text{ min.}$$
$$= 5 \text{ hr. } 39{\cdot}57 \text{ min.}$$

This is an example where the mode, corresponding to the 'rush-hour peak', would be more interesting than the mean and the reader is advised to calculate the two modes. We proceed to calculate the higher moments omitting, from time to time, some of the intermediate steps which should, however, be traced by those who are trying to obtain a thorough grasp of the subject by verifying these examples. Sheppard's corrections have been applied, although the requirements with regard to high contact at each end of the distribution are not fulfilled.

a.m. passengers	p.m. passengers
$m_2' = \frac{49{,}675}{7450} = 6{\cdot}6678$	$m_2' = \frac{46{,}315}{8385} = 5{\cdot}5236$
$m_2 = 6{\cdot}5785$ in units	$m_2 = 5{\cdot}4213$ in units
$s = 38{\cdot}5$ min.	$s = 34{\cdot}9$ min.
$m_3' = -\frac{28{,}375}{7450} = -3{\cdot}8087$	$m_3' = \frac{36{,}825}{8385} = 4{\cdot}3918$
$m_3 = -5{\cdot}3516$ in units	$m_3 = 2{\cdot}1144$ in units
$m_4' = \frac{667{,}255}{7450} = 89{\cdot}564$ in units	$m_4' = \frac{586{,}735}{8385} = 69{\cdot}974$ in units
$m_4 = 87{\cdot}718$	$m_4 = 65{\cdot}500$

All the above with the exception of the s's are in terms of the class-interval (15 min.) as unit.

$\sqrt{b_1} = \dfrac{m_3}{m_2^{\frac{3}{2}}} = -{\cdot}317$ for a.m. passengers and ${\cdot}167$ for p.m. passengers.

$b_2 = \dfrac{m_4}{m_2^2} = 2{\cdot}027$ for a.m. passengers and $2{\cdot}229$ for p.m. passengers.

It will be noticed: (i) that the values of s indicate that the data are more concentrated at the evening rush-hour than in the morning, (ii) that the values of $\sqrt{b_1}$ indicate negative skewness in the morning, greater in extent than the positive skewness of the evening figures, and (iii) that the values of b_2 show little difference in kurtosis.

It should be noted that both distributions are truncated, i.e. movements of passengers outside the hours mentioned are ignored.

3·29. Calculation of moments by successive summations.

The moments of a distribution can be derived from successive summations of the data by the following method which is particularly useful in conjunction with some of the modern tabulating machines. These have several 'counters' which can be so arranged that the machine automatically prints the columns giving successive summations as the operator tabulates the observations.

Consider the following scheme in which the origin is taken at the first observation and the frequencies are denoted by

$$f_r \ (r=0, 1, \dots, n-1).$$

It is essential that the values of r should be at regular intervals but the moments, when calculated, can be adjusted by the methods already described to allow for change of origin and scale and Sheppard's adjustments can be applied (where appropriate) if the data have been grouped.

r	f_r (1)	Σ (1) (2)	Σ (2) (3)	Σ (3) (4)	Σ (4) (5)
0	f_0	$\sum_{r=0}^{n-1} f_r$	—	—	—
1	f_1	$\vdots$	$\sum_{r=1}^{n-1} r f_r$	—	—
2	f_2	$\vdots$	$\vdots$	$\sum_{r=2}^{n-1} r_{(2)} f_r$	—
3	$\vdots$	$\vdots$	$\vdots$	$\vdots$	$\sum_{r=3}^{n-1} r_{(3)} f_r$
$\vdots$	$\vdots$	$\vdots$	$\vdots$	$\vdots$	$\vdots$
t	f_t	$\sum_{r=t}^{n-1} f_r$	$\sum_{r=t}^{n-1} (r-t+1) f_r$	$\sum_{r=t}^{n-1} (r-t+2)_{(2)} f_r$	$\sum_{r=t}^{n-1} (r-t+3)_{(3)}$
$\vdots$	$\vdots$	$\vdots$	$\vdots$	$\vdots$	$\vdots$
$n-3$	f_{n-3}	$f_{n-3}+f_{n-2}+f_{n-1}$	$f_{n-3}+2f_{n-2}+3f_{n-1}$	$f_{n-3}+3f_{n-2}+6f_{n-1}$	—
$n-2$	f_{n-2}	$f_{n-2}+f_{n-1}$	$f_{n-2}+2f_{n-1}$	$f_{n-2}+3f_{n-1}$	—
$n-1$	f_{n-1}	f_{n-1}	f_{n-1}	f_{n-1}	—

Column (1) gives the observed data and column (2) is obtained from it by adding the items successively from the bottom upwards. Thus the item in column (2) on the line $r=n-2$ is the sum of the last two items of column (1), while the item in column (2) for $r=t$ is the sum of the last $n-t$ items of column (1). Similarly column (3) is obtained from column (2), column (4) from column (3) and so on, the general rule being that a given item in any column is equal to the sum of the values in the previous column for all values of r equal to or greater than the one considered.

Consider the successive entries on the line $r=t$. The first is, of course, f_t and the second $\sum_{r=t}^{n-1} f_r$. The frequency f_r will appear in column (2) at the line where f_r appears in column (1) and at each line above it. Hence when column (3) is formed the term on the line $r=t$ will include f_r with coefficient $r-t+1$, i.e. it will be equal to $\sum_{r=t}^{n-1} (r-t+1)f_r$.

Now consider the term involving f_r in the corresponding item in the next column. Its coefficient will be equal to

$$1+2+3+\ldots+(r-t+1)=(r-t+2)_{(2)}.$$

In the notation used here

$$x_{(s)}=\frac{x(x-1)(x-2)\ldots(x-s+1)}{s(s-1)\ldots 2.1},$$

and it can be proved that

$$\sum_{x=0}^{n} x_{(s)}=\left[x_{(s+1)}\right]_0^{n+1}=(n+1)_{(s+1)} \tag{3·39}$$

(see *Mathematics for Actuarial Students*, Pt. II, p. 100).

Still considering the same line of the table we see that in column (5) the coefficient of the term involving f_r will be

$$\sum_{x=0}^{r-t+2} x_{(2)}=(r-t+3)_{(3)} \quad \text{from} \quad (3·39).$$

This process can clearly be continued for subsequent columns. The top item in column (2) is the total frequency N.

Putting $t=1$ we see that the second item in column (3)

$$=\sum_{r=1}^{n-1} rf_r=Nm_1'.$$

Putting $t=2$ we see that the third item in column (4)

$$=\sum_{r=2}^{n-1} r_{(2)}f_r = N(m_2'-m_1')/2!$$

Putting $t=3$ we see that the fourth item in column (5)

$$=\sum_{r=3}^{n-1} r_{(3)}f_r = N(m_3'-3m_2'+2m_1')/3!$$

Putting $t=4$ we see that the fifth item in column (6)

$$=\sum_{r=4}^{n-1} r_{(4)}f_r = N(m_4'-6m_3'+11m_2'-6m_1')/4!$$

(It will be noticed that the lower limits of the summations could be altered to zero without affecting the results because the coefficients vanish for values of r between 0 and the lower limits.)

From these results m_1', m_2', m_3' and m_4' can be found and hence $m_2, m_3, m_4, \sqrt{b_1}$ and b_2.

If the method is used in the manner described some very large figures may arise and to overcome this difficulty some very elegant variations have been devised. For details the reader is referred to Aitken's *Statistical Mathematics* (see Bibliography).

Example 3·5.

Let us consider the data of Table 3·5 relating to a.m. passengers. They are set out in Table 3·6 with the origin taken in the middle of the range 7·15–7·30 and with the frequencies expressed in hundreds.

TABLE 3·6

(Part of the data of Table 3·5)

r	Frequency (1)	Σ(1) (2)	Σ(2) (3)	Σ(3) (4)	Σ(4) (5)	Σ(5) (6)
0	355	**7,450**	45,275	185,025	600,325	—
1	505	7,095	**37,825**	139,750	415,300	—
2	710	6,590	30,730	**101,925**	275,550	—
3	620	5,880	24,140	71,195	**173,625**	—
4	630	5,260	18,260	47,055	102,430	**199,145**
5	940	4,630	13,000	28,795	55,375	96,715
6	1,140	3,690	8,370	15,795	26,580	41,340
7	1,035	2,550	4,680	7,425	10,785	14,760
8	900	1,515	2,130	2,745	3,360	3,975
9	615	615	615	615	615	615
Total	7,450	45,275	185,025	600,325	(199,145)	

It will be noticed that in every column but the last, the summations have been continued to the top line. This has been done so that the work can be checked at each stage, the top item in each column being equal to the sum of all the items in the preceding column. It is not necessary to construct column (6) at all if only moments up to the fourth are needed. The required value (199,145, in this example) could be obtained by adding the values in the previous column up to, but not including, the one in heavy type. The construction of column (6) enables this sum to be checked; the total 199,145 is shown in brackets to indicate that it is not the total of the whole column. Similarly each of the values in heavy type could have been checked by comparing it with the sum of the values in the preceding column for the same or greater values of r.

We then proceed as follows:

Total frequency $N=7450$.

$$Nm'_1=37{,}825 \quad \text{whence} \quad m'_1=5{\cdot}077,$$

$$N(m'_2-m'_1)=2!\times 101{,}925 \quad \text{whence} \quad m'_2=32{\cdot}440,$$

$$N(m'_3-3m'_2+2m'_1)=3!\times 173{,}625 \quad \text{whence} \quad m'_3=226{\cdot}997,$$

$$N(m'_4-6m'_3+11m'_2-6m'_1)=4!\times 199{,}145 \quad \text{whence} \quad m'_4=1677{\cdot}148.$$

The values of m_2, m_3, m_4, $\sqrt{b_1}$ and b_2 can then be deduced as before.

EXERCISES 3

In Exercises 3·1–3·4 inclusive calculate the mean, mean deviation, standard deviation, $\sqrt{b_1}$ and b_2 of the given distributions, applying corrections for grouping where necessary.

3·1 *Distribution of Intelligence Quotients of pupils in a Los Angeles Junior High School*

I.Q.	No.	I.Q.	No.
50–54	1	105–109	285
55–59	7	110–114	257
60–64	16	115–119	193
65–69	40	120–124	178
70–74	68	125–129	86
75–79	112	130–134	61
80–84	157	135–139	29
85–89	244	140–144	20
90–94	307	145–149	14
95–99	349	150–154	3
100–104	363	155–159	7
		160–164	3

Total No. 2800.

(Humm and Humm, *J. Educ. Psychol.* 1933.)

3·2 *Age of becoming a widower (British peerage)*

Age	No.	Age	No.
18–22	5	53–57	88
23–27	43	58–62	76
28–32	108	63–67	82
33–37	107	68–72	59
38–42	130	73–77	41
43–47	109	78–82	16
48–52	115	83–87	8

Total No. 987.

(T. Sprague, *J. Inst. Actu.* vol. 22, p. 81, 1880.)

3·3 *Distribution of mean gross weekly expenditure per 'adult male' upon all foodstuffs (Brisbane)*

Class interval 12 pence	No.	Class interval 12 pence	No.
49–60	2	193–204	11
61–72	3	205–216	13
73–84	4	217–228	7
85–96	16	229–240	6
97–108	15	241–252	6
109–120	23	253–264	—
121–132	34	265–276	4
133–144	24	277–288	1
145–156	39	289–300	1
157–168	25	301–312	—
169–180	36	313–324	—
181–192	29	325–336	1

Total No. 300.

(*Commonwealth of Australia, Final Report of the Advisory Council on Nutrition*, 1938.)

3·4 *Distributions of ages of members of the Presbyterian Church of England Ministers' Widows and Orphans Fund in 1881 and 1902 respectively.*

Age	No. of members in	
	1881	1902
20–24	1	1
25–29	12	15
30–34	40	56
35–39	43	66
40–44	51	62
45–49	40	69
50–54	29	44
55–59	28	40
60–64	14	40
65–69	—	29
70–74	—	13
75	—	8
Total	258	443

(*J. Inst. Actu.* vol. 39, 1905.)

3·5 Define range, mean deviation and standard deviation, and compare their merits as descriptive measures of dispersion.

3·6 Summarize formally the fundamental properties which should be possessed by

(i) any central measure,
(ii) any measure of dispersion,
(iii) any measure of skewness.

3·7 Comment on the following extract from a discussion on statistics in the electrical industry:

'In the supply section of the industry, we use a statistic known as the load factor which is the ratio between the maximum half-hourly load and the average of all the half-hourly loads occurring in the period under review. Obviously, the longer the period the more likely it is that an extreme value will be obtained, so that the set of weekly load factors occurring in any one year is vastly different from the set of monthly load factors calculated for the same year. It appears that much better statistics than these could be invented.'

3·8 Using the methods and notation of § 3·12 obtain a correction for grouping for the second moment of the distribution of a discontinuous variable which can take values at intervals of $h/(2m+1)$ and which is grouped in sets of $(2m+1)$ successive possible values.

*3·9 From the following table of the exposed to risk in central form and the corresponding deaths per annum, find the values of μ_x and q_x for ages 32, 37, 42 and 47. How would you find the same functions for ages 27 and 52?

Age-group	Exposed to risk in central form	No. of deaths per annum
25–30	7,300	44
30–35	10,500	74
35–40	14,700	118
40–45	15,400	140
45–50	14,000	154
50–55	12,300	160

3·10 The following table shows the number of deaths (in thousands) among the male population in England and Wales in the years 1930–32:

Age at death	No. of deaths	Age at death	No. of deaths	Age at death	No. of deaths
0–	97	35–	18	70–	84
5–	12	40–	24	75–	72
10–	7	45–	33	80–	45
15–	13	50–	44	85–	20
20–	17	55–	57	90–	5
25–	16	60–	68	95–	1
30–	16	65–	81	100–	0

Total 730.

Calculate the mean age at death, the standard deviation of the age at death and two coefficients of skewness. Can you suggest a reason for the difference between the two measures of skewness?

3·11 A distribution is said to be 'truncated above' if all values greater than a certain amount A_1 are omitted, and 'truncated below' if all values less than a certain amount A_2 are omitted. What is the effect of (i) truncation above, (ii) truncation below, (iii) both combined, likely to be on the various central measures and measures of dispersion, skewness and kurtosis associated with the distribution? Apply your reasoning to the distributions of Example 3·3.

*3·12 Show that for any distribution of positive values

$$f(r) = m_r'^{\,1/r} \ (r \neq 0), \qquad f(0) = \lim_{r \to 0} f(r)$$

is a non-decreasing function of r. Hence show that the harmonic, geometric and arithmetic means are either equal or in ascending order of magnitude.

3·13 Construct cumulative charts and estimate the median and upper and lower quartiles of the following distributions. Suggest possible sources of error in your estimates.

Number of innings

Runs in innings	Hayward	Jessop	Tunnicliffe	Warner
0–19	53	68	64	44
20–39	36	24	34	15
40–59	22	21	18	14
60–79	18	11	9	13
80–99	9	3	6	5
100–119	8	1	2	2
120–139	5	—	3	2
140–159	6	—	—	1
160–179	3	1	—	1
180–199	2	—	—	—
200–219	4	1	—	2
220–239	—	1	—	—
240–259	2	—	—	—
Total	168	131	136	99

(From 'Cricket Scores and some Skew Correlation Distributions', by Sir William Elderton, F.I.A., *J.R. Statist. Soc.* vol. 108, parts I–II, p. 2.)

3·14 Show that ${}_An'_1$ is a minimum if A is the median of the observations. Obtain a formula suitable for computation of this minimum value.

3·15 The distribution of values of a certain characteristic which cannot be negative is symmetrical. What can you say of the distribution of the logarithms of these values?

BIBLIOGRAPHY

YULE AND KENDALL. *An Introduction to the Theory of Statistics* (Chapters 7, 8 and 9). Griffin and Co., London, 14th ed., 1948.

E. G. CHAMBERS. *Statistical Calculations*. Cambridge University Press, 1940.

A. C. AITKEN. *Statistical Mathematics*. Oliver and Boyd, Edinburgh. 1945.

CHAPTER 4

DESCRIPTIVE STATISTICS. CORRELATION AND LINEAR REGRESSION

4·1. Hitherto we have considered only a single variable and the frequencies with which values, or ranges of values, of the variable occur. When we investigate two variables x and y, and the frequencies with which pairs of values occur together, we meet the phenomenon of correlation.

In Table 4·1, for instance, are set out the pairs of marks obtained in a certain examination by forty-eight candidates, x being the number of marks obtained on the first paper and y the number obtained on the second.

This is an example of the simplest type of correlation table, which consists merely of a list of observed values of x and the corresponding values of y. These values need not necessarily be arranged according to a definite scheme, and if there happen to be two pairs of observations for which a given value of x was associated with a given value of y they would appear as two separate items in the list. For instance, in Table 4·1 we have two candidates with 67 marks on the first paper and 49 on the second. These are represented by two separate entries in the table.

In the more general type of table the data are extensive and are usually grouped to show the frequencies with which values of x within a given range are associated with values of y within the various ranges adopted in grouping the y's. This is analogous to the procedure adopted for single variables.

Table 4·2, showing how male adult mortality and infantile mortality are associated in 147 parental occupations, is an example of such a table. As frequencies as well as values of the variables have to be shown a double-entry table is used; the analogy with the grouped frequency distributions of Chapter 3 will at once be apparent. The particulars have been extracted from Table A of the Registrar-General's *Decennial Supplement*, *England and Wales*,

1921, Part II and, as the values quoted in that table are given to the nearest integer, it should be borne in mind that the real limits of the groups differ by ·5 from those shown. Thus the group 81–110 really includes all values from 80·5 to 110·5.

TABLE 4·1

No. of marks obtained on		No. of marks obtained on	
First paper	Second paper	First paper	Second paper
71	83	44	68
65	76	73	76
58	60	73	65
33	59	58	66
48	54	55	57
57	60	39	64
68	77	66	67
55	59	58	49
75	67	66	58
69	69	62	88
61	68	88	82
67	49	92	82
51	68	69	74
70	76	74	75
63	59	85	66
81	72	67	65
60	74	61	70
67	49	68	68
66	56	79	78
79	59	80	79
76	84	56	68
83	88	70	74
89	70	72	73
56	71	59	78

We often desire to examine to what extent one variable varies with another. As a matter of convention:

(*a*) if large values of x tend to be associated with large values of y there is said to be positive correlation.

(*b*) if large values of x tend to be associated with small values of y and small values of x tend to be associated with large values of y there is said to be negative correlation.

The figures in Table 4·2 suggest positive correlation.

Sometimes the position is more complex; for instance over one section of the range the values of x and y may seem to increase or decrease together while over another section they may seem to

TABLE 4·2

Male mortality (for ages 20–65) and infantile mortality for 147 occupations

(Data taken from the Registrar-General's Decennial Supplement 1921. Part II. Occupations with less than 10,000 persons have been ignored.)

Infantile mortality (1921)† y	Standardized mortality ratio* male lives aged 20–65 (1921–23) x						
	21–50	51–80	81–110	111–140	141–170	171–200	Total
21– 40	—	2	4	—	—	—	6
41– 60	3	14	13	2	1	—	33
61– 80	3	8	35	7	2	—	55
81–100	1	4	16	10	4	2	37
101–120	—	2	2	7	2	—	13
121–140	—	—	—	1	1	—	2
141–160	—	—	—	1	—	—	1
Total	7	30	70	28	10	2	147

* The Standardized Mortality Ratio (S.M.R.) is the ratio (expressed as a percentage) of the deaths recorded to those which would have occurred if the mortality rate at each age-group in the several occupations had been the same as that for all occupied and retired civilian males.

† The figures for infantile mortality relate to 1921 only and represent the deaths of legitimate infants under 1 year of age per 1000 legitimate births.

move in opposite directions, an increase in the value of one being associated with a decrease in the value of the other. This leads to the study of non-linear regression (Chapter 16).

The assessment of the magnitude of correlation requires considerable analysis and often involves the calculation of an index known as the coefficient of correlation. This will be developed in § 4·4 but before we proceed to the analytical details there are certain general principles to be borne in mind. The application of these principles to a given set of data may sometimes indicate that the usual analytical processes are unnecessary or unsuitable and liable to produce misleading results.

In the first place it is important to see that the pairs of observations have some definite link quite apart from the association which it is desired to measure. That is to say their association should not be merely fortuitous.

Technically this means that values of the two characters measured on the *same* individual are paired. In Table 4·1 the individuals are the candidates, in Table 4·2 the individuals are the occupations.

Secondly, although some index of correlation may be calculated as a measure of association, it should be remembered that the data as set out in tabular form (as for instance in Table 4·2) actually give more information than any single index can do. Careful examination of the data will often, therefore, give useful information which is submerged in subsequent analytical work. An example of this will be given later.

Finally, it must never be assumed that correlation implies causation. Because x and y show a marked tendency to vary together it must on no account be inferred that a change in x will cause a change in y or vice versa.

An example will make this clear. An investigation of cases of sunstroke in a series of years and the amount of home-grown wheat in those years might show a marked degree of correlation between the two factors although neither could be said to *influence* the other in any way. The true explanation would almost certainly be that a hot summer tends to produce a bumper harvest and many cases of sunstroke. Two variables which are correlated are, in fact, very often both affected by a common cause, or combination of causes, but only rarely is one affected directly by the other.

4·2. Scatter-diagrams.

When we are dealing with two variables it is not usually convenient to represent the data by an extension of the dot-diagrams of Chapter 3, in which the variable corresponded to the horizontal distance and the frequency was represented by the number of dots set out vertically. To allow for a second variable we should have to represent the pairs of values observed by points scattered over a plane and the frequency by dots set out in 'columns' perpendicular to the plane. Such a 'model' may be useful as an aid to the imagination.

If the data are of the type shown in Table 4·1 they can be represented by a *scatter-diagram* such as Fig. 4·1, where the figure '(2)' against the dot representing $x=67$, $y=49$, indicates that that particular value occurs twice.

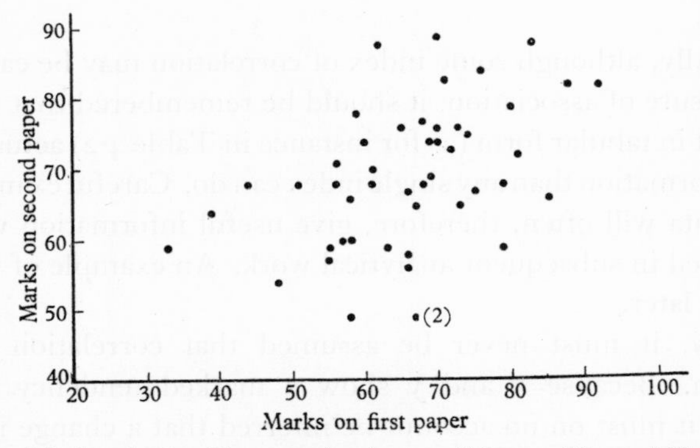

Fig. 4·1. Marks obtained by examination candidates. (Data of Table 4·1.)

If several of the pairs of values occur more than once or if the data are grouped as in Table 4·2 this simple diagram is no longer satisfactory but a rough indication of frequency can be obtained by replacing the dots by small circular disks of area roughly proportionate to the frequency. Thus, Fig. 4·2 represents the data of Table 4·2, the frequency for each group being assumed to be concentrated at the centre of that group, e.g. the frequency 35 is assumed to correspond to $x=95·5$, $y=70·5$.

In a table such as Table 4·2 it is usual to refer to each horizontal row of data (corresponding to a fixed value or range of values of y) as an *x-array* and each column of data as a *y-array*. (Note that an x-array is an array of values of x for a fixed value of y.) In order to 'condense' the data we next calculate the mean value of each x-array and the mean value of each y-array and it is helpful to plot these on the scatter-diagram.

The means of the x-arrays of Table 4·2 from top to bottom will be found to be 85·5, 81·0, 93·9, 110·1, 116·3, 140·5 and 125·5 respectively. These are shown in Fig. 4·2 as dots surrounded by rings thus ⊙. The means of the y-arrays are represented by crosses.

When the data are extensive the simplification thus achieved by plotting the means is considerable and the means themselves will

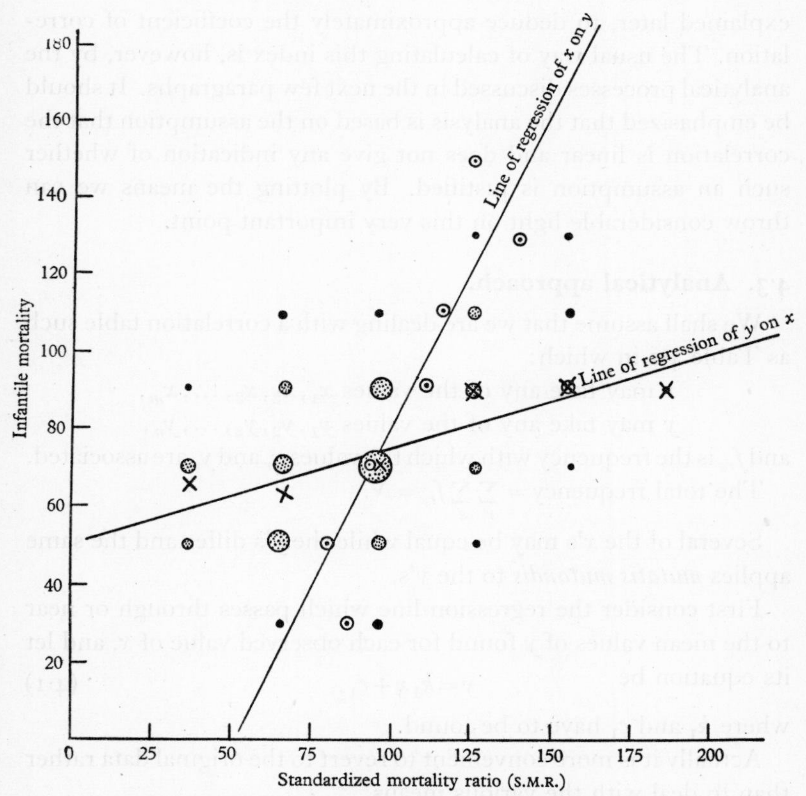

Fig. 4·2. Male mortality (1921–23) for ages 20–65 and infantile mortality (1921) for 147 occupations. (Data of Table 4·2.)

usually be found to lie on or near a smooth curve known as a *regression curve*. In the simplest examples the regression curves are assumed to be straight lines and the correlation is said to be linear. Even in more complex cases the assumption of linear regression is often useful as a first approximation.

In what follows, unless the contrary is stated, it will always be assumed that linear correlation is under discussion.

In Fig. 4·2 the data are so scanty that an attempt to fit a more elaborate curve would be unjustified and the lines of regression have been roughly sketched in.

Having drawn the regression lines it is possible, as will be explained later, to deduce approximately the coefficient of correlation. The usual way of calculating this index is, however, by the analytical processes discussed in the next few paragraphs. It should be emphasized that the analysis is based on the assumption that the correlation is linear and does not give any indication of whether such an assumption is justified. By plotting the means we can throw considerable light on this very important point.

4·3. Analytical approach.

We shall assume that we are dealing with a correlation table such as Table 4·2 in which:

x may take any of the values $x_1, x_2, x_3, \ldots, x_m$,

y may take any of the values $y_1, y_2, y_3, \ldots, y_n$,

and f_{rs} is the frequency with which the values x_r and y_s are associated.

The total frequency $= \sum_r \sum_s f_{rs} = N$.

Several of the x's may be equal while the y's differ and the same applies *mutatis mutandis* to the y's.

First consider the regression line which passes through or near to the mean values of y found for each observed value of x, and let its equation be

$$y = k_1 x + c_1, \tag{4·1}$$

where k_1 and c_1 have to be found.

Actually it is more convenient to revert to the original data rather than to deal with the various means.

The pair of values (x_r, y_s) denoted by P in Fig. 4·3 occurs with frequency f_{rs}.

The ordinate through P cuts the line $y = k_1 x + c_1$ at Q, the ordinate of which is $k_1 x_r + c_1$.

Hence the distance $QP = y_s - k_1 x_r - c_1$.

As the line $y = k_1 x + c_1$ approximately represents the mean values of y for the various values of x the point Q may be regarded as representing an estimate of the value of y corresponding to x_r and QP represents the error involved as regards the particular observation represented by P.

If the line is to 'fit' the data satisfactorily one obvious requirement is that the total of all distances such as QP should be small, allowing

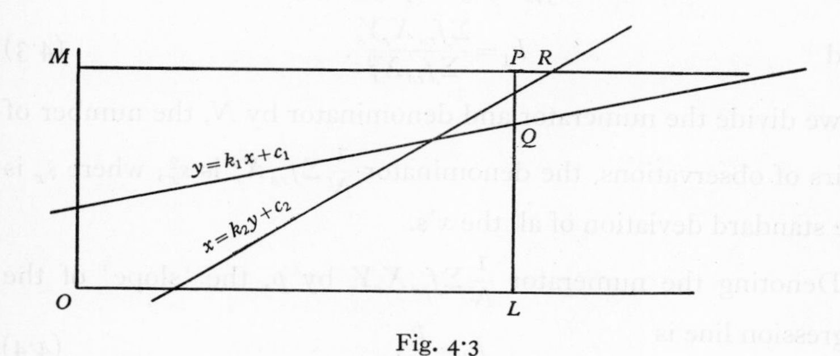

Fig. 4·3

for different signs cancelling and also for the frequencies involved, i.e. we should expect $\Sigma f_{rs}(y_s - k_1 x_r - c_1)$ to be small when the summation extends over all the observations. If we make this sum zero we obtain

$$\Sigma y_s f_{rs} = k_1 \Sigma x_r f_{rs} + c_1 \Sigma f_{rs},$$

or, dividing by N, $\frac{1}{N}\Sigma y_s f_{rs} = \frac{k_1}{N}\Sigma x_r f_{rs} + \frac{c_1}{N}\Sigma f_{rs}$,

i.e.

$$\bar{y} = k_1 \bar{x} + c_1, \tag{4·2}$$

where $\bar{y}$ is the mean of all the y's and $\bar{x}$ is the mean of all the x's.

Thus the regression line passes through the point $(\bar{x}, \bar{y})$ the centre of gravity (centroid) of the data, which we take as a new origin, writing $x_r = \bar{x} + X_r$ and $y_s = \bar{y} + Y_s$. (X_r and Y_s are not to be confused with the symbols for the arbitrary scale values used in Chapter 3.)

The equation of the regression line is now $Y = k_1 X$ and the distance

$$QP = Y_s - k_1 X_r.$$

The expression $\Sigma f_{rs}(Y_s - k_1 X_r)^2$ where the summation extends over all the observations is essentially positive, but if the 'fit' is good it should be small. We therefore choose k_1 so as to make it a minimum.

For a minimum (k_1 being the variable)

$$\frac{d}{dk_1}\Sigma f_{rs}(Y_s - k_1 X_r)^2 = 0,$$

i.e.
$$-2\Sigma f_{rs} X_r (Y_s - k_1 X_r) = 0,$$

or
$$\Sigma f_{rs} X_r Y_s = k_1 \Sigma f_{rs} X_r^2,$$

and
$$k_1 = \frac{\Sigma f_{rs} X_r Y_s}{\Sigma f_{rs} X_r^2}. \tag{4·3}$$

If we divide the numerator and denominator by N, the number of pairs of observations, the denominator $\frac{1}{N}\Sigma f_{rs} X_r^2$ is s_x^2, where s_x is the standard deviation of all the x's.

Denoting the numerator $\frac{1}{N}\Sigma f_{rs} X_r Y_s$ by p, the 'slope' of the regression line is

$$k_1 = \frac{p}{s_x^2}. \tag{4·4}$$

The equation of the line is

$$Y = \frac{p}{s_x^2} X,$$

or, referred to the original axes,

$$y - \bar{y} = \frac{p}{s_x^2}(x - \bar{x}). \tag{4·5}$$

This is known as the *line of regression* of y on x.

Similarly, the line of regression passing through or near the mean values of x found for each value of y is known as the regression line of x on y.

Denote this equation by $x = k_2 y + c_2$.

In Fig. 4·3 the line MPR parallel to the axis of x cuts this line at R.

The distance $RP = x_r - k_2 y_s - c_2$.

For a good fit we make

$$\Sigma f_{rs}(x_r - k_2 y_s - c_2)^2 \quad \text{a minimum.}$$

Partial differentiation with respect to c_2 leads to

$$\bar{x} = k_2 \bar{y} + c_2, \tag{4·6}$$

so that the second regression line also passes through the centroid $(\bar{x}, \bar{y})$ and the expression to be made a minimum may be written

$$\Sigma f_{rs}(X_r - k_2 Y_s)^2.$$

Differentiating with respect to the variable k_2 and proceeding as before, we obtain

$$k_2 = \frac{\Sigma f_{rs} X_r Y_s}{\Sigma f_{rs} Y_s^2}$$

$$= \frac{p}{s_y^2}, \tag{4·7}$$

where s_y is the standard deviation of the y's.

Referred to the original axes the regression line of x on y is therefore

$$x - \bar{x} = \frac{p}{s_y^2}(y - \bar{y}). \tag{4·8}$$

The expressions $\frac{p}{s_x^2}$ and $\frac{p}{s_y^2}$ are known as *coefficients of regression* or *regression coefficients.*

Before proceeding to the coefficient of correlation let us consider exactly what the lines of regression enable us to do.

Take, for instance, the line of regression of y on x (equation 4·5). For any value of x the equation gives an 'estimate' of the corresponding average value of y. If x happens to be one of the values tabulated it is unlikely that the resulting value of y will coincide with any of those actually observed in conjunction with that value of x or with the mean of these values. This is because it takes into account all the observed pairs of values and not merely a particular y-array.

To answer the question: 'What infantile mortality would you expect to correspond to an S.M.R. of 110?' we should use the line of regression of y on x. Similarly the line of regression of x on y would provide an answer to the question: 'What S.M.R. would you expect to find if the infantile mortality were 80 per 1000 live births?' In each case it is assumed that the question related to an experience similar to that from which the lines of regression were calculated.

4·4. Coefficient of correlation.

As was stated in §4·1 correlation is said to be:

(i) positive if high (low) values of x tend to correspond with high (low) values of y;

(ii) negative if high (low) values of x tend to correspond with low (high) values of y.

Very often, however, there is no apparent tendency for x and y to vary together. Any given value of x seems to occur equally often in conjunction with high and low values of y, and similarly any given value of y is associated with high and low values of x. Correlation is then likely to be small, but we cannot be sure that it is negligible. Tests will be described in Vol. II, chapter 16, which are designed to aid our judgement in this respect.

If we take our origin at the means of x and y and denote the values referred to this origin by X and Y as above, then

(i) for positive correlation the values of the product XY will tend to be large and positive because positive values of X will tend to be associated with positive values of Y and negative values of X with negative values of Y;

(ii) for negative correlation the values of the product XY will tend to be large and negative because positive values of X will tend to be associated with negative values of Y and vice versa;

(iii) for a small degree of correlation the values of XY will be small and fairly evenly divided between positive and negative terms.

In other words, if f_{rs} is the frequency with which the values X_r and Y_s are observed together and $\Sigma f_{rs} = N$, the expression

$$p = \frac{1}{N} \Sigma f_{rs} X_r Y_s$$

offers a useful measure of the extent and sign of the correlation.

Unfortunately p reflects the scales used for x and y. By altering the scale of either variable we alter p, while the correlation is of course the same as before. Scale can be allowed for by measuring the x's in terms of s_x and the y's in terms of s_y.

If we take $\dfrac{p}{s_x s_y}$ as our measure of correlation it will be seen that a change in the scale adopted for either x or y affects numerator and denominator alike and the expression can claim to be an absolute (as distinct from merely relative) measure of the correlation. It is of course symmetrical in x and y and is known as the *coefficient of correlation* (usually denoted by r).

The coefficient of correlation is thus defined as

$$r=\frac{p}{s_x s_y}. \tag{4·9}$$

In view of the above remarks about scale it seems more logical to write the equation of the lines of regression in the form:

$$\frac{y-\bar{y}}{s_y}=\frac{p}{s_x s_y}\frac{x-\bar{x}}{s_x}, \tag{4·10}$$

and

$$\frac{x-\bar{x}}{s_x}=\frac{p}{s_x s_y}\frac{y-\bar{y}}{s_y}. \tag{4·11}$$

It will now be seen that the first factor on the right-hand side is r in both equations and the coefficients of regression can be written in the more usual forms:

$$k_1 \text{(coefficient of regression of } y \text{ on } x)=r\frac{s_y}{s_x}, \tag{4·12}$$

$$k_2 \text{(coefficient of regression of } x \text{ on } y)=r\frac{s_x}{s_y}, \tag{4·13}$$

and finally we have

$$r=\sqrt{(k_1 k_2)}. \tag{4·14}$$

In practical work it is very desirable to set out the calculations in tabular form in such a way that $\bar{x}$, $\bar{y}$, s_x, s_y and p can all be derived in turn.

The student is already familiar with the method of calculating the first four of these values by selecting a convenient origin and scale and making subsequent adjustments. The same devices are useful in calculating p.

By definition $p=\frac{1}{N}\Sigma f_{rs}X_rY_s$, where X_r and Y_s are measured from their respective means.

We first calculate $\frac{1}{N}\Sigma f_{rs}x_ry_s$. This is generally called the 'product moment' about the origin chosen, or, more correctly, about the axes chosen.

Now

$$\begin{aligned}\frac{1}{N}\Sigma f_{rs}x_ry_s &= \frac{1}{N}\Sigma f_{rs}(X_r+\bar{x})(Y_s+\bar{y})\\ &=\frac{1}{N}\{\Sigma f_{rs}X_rY_s+\bar{x}\Sigma f_{rs}Y_s+\bar{y}\Sigma f_{rs}X_r+\bar{x}\bar{y}\Sigma f_{rs}\},\end{aligned}$$

since $\bar{x}$ and $\bar{y}$ are constants, viz. the distances of the centroid from the axes chosen.

Since X_r and Y_s are measured from the centroid,

$$\Sigma f_{rs}X_r = \Sigma f_{rs}Y_s = 0,$$

and we have

$$\frac{1}{N}\Sigma f_{rs}x_r y_s = p + \bar{x}\bar{y}, \qquad (4{\cdot}15)$$

$$p = \frac{1}{N}\Sigma f_{rs}x_r y_s - \bar{x}\bar{y}. \qquad (4{\cdot}16)$$

In other words, we find the product moment, using any convenient origin, and then derive p by deducting $\bar{x}\bar{y}$, where $\bar{x}$ is the distance of the mean of the x's from the origin and $\bar{y}$ is the distance of the mean of the y's from the origin (allowing for sign).

The following examples should make this clearer, and it is essential that they should be closely studied and every stage of the working verified. It will be noticed that if all the work is done in class units or some other convenient scales r does not need adjustment to allow for this, although the regression coefficients do need adjustment.

Example 4·1.

Calculate the coefficient of correlation for the series of observations shown in Table 4·3.

TABLE 4·3

Year	Average yield of Consols during year	Average index number of wholesale commodity prices during year	Year	Average yield of Consols during year	Average index number of wholesale commodity prices during year
1810	4·5	171	1823	3·8	107
1811	4·7	164	1824	3·3	106
1812	5·1	147	1825	3·5	124
1813	4·9	138	1826	3·8	108
1814	4·5	137	1827	3·6	108
1815	5·0	131	1828	3·6	97
1816	4·8	109	1829	3·3	95
1817	4·1	141	1830	3·5	97
1818	3·9	160	1831	3·8	99
1819	4·2	135	1832	3·6	94
1820	4·4	124	1833	3·4	90
1821	4·0	113	1834	3·3	94
1822	3·8	106			

This is typical of the simpler problems where frequencies need not be specifically introduced as they are all unity, the table being simply a list. Take as origins:

Average yield of Consols during year = 4·0 (variable x).
Average index number during year = 120 (variable y).

Taking ·1 as the unit of x, the work can be arranged as shown in Table 4·4.

TABLE 4·4

x		y		x^2	y^2	xy	
+	−	+	−			+	−
5		51		25	2,601	255	
7		44		49	1,936	308	
11		27		121	729	297	
9		18		81	324	162	
5		17		25	289	85	
10		11		100	121	110	
8			11	64	121		88
1		21		1	441	21	
	1	40		1	1,600		40
2		15		4	225	30	
4		4		16	16	16	
			7	—	49	—	
	2		14	4	196	28	
	2		13	4	169	26	
	7		14	49	196	98	
	5	4		25	16		20
	2		12	4	144	24	
	4		12	16	144	48	
	4		23	16	529	92	
	7		25	49	625	175	
	5		23	25	529	115	
	2		21	4	441	42	
	4		26	16	676	104	
	6		30	36	900	180	
	7		26	49	676	182	
62	58	252	257	784	13,693	2,398	148

It will be noticed that positive terms are shown on the left and negative terms on the right of each column. This facilitates the additions and lessens the risk of arithmetical errors.

Since the number of observations is 25 we have, working in class units,

$$\bar{x}=\frac{62-58}{25}=\cdot 16,$$

$$\bar{y}=\frac{252-257}{25}=-\cdot 20,$$

$$s_x^2=\frac{784}{25}-(\cdot 16)^2=31\cdot 3344,$$

$$s_x=5\cdot 6,$$

$$s_y^2=\frac{13{,}693}{25}-(-\cdot 20)^2=547\cdot 68,$$

$$s_y=23\cdot 4,$$

$$p=\frac{2398-148}{25}-(\cdot 16)(-\cdot 20)=90\cdot 03.$$

Coefficient of correlation $r=\dfrac{90\cdot 03}{(5\cdot 6)(23\cdot 4)}=\cdot 69$ approx.

All the work has been done in class units, but if the mean yield of Consols and the standard deviation are required in terms of the original scale and origin we have

Mean yield of Consols $=4\cdot 0+(\cdot 16)(\cdot 1)=4\cdot 016$.
Standard deviation $=5\cdot 6\times\cdot 1=\cdot 56$.
The mean index number is $120-\cdot 20=119\cdot 8$.

Example 4·2.

As a second example let us consider the data of Table 4·2 which has been represented graphically earlier in this chapter.

The chief difficulty arises in determining the product moment

$$\frac{1}{N}\Sigma f_{rs}x_r y_s$$

and two methods will be explained, one in this example and the other in Example 4·3.

In Table 4·5 the original data are reproduced but new variables have been taken with the class interval as unit and with origins at the mid-points of the groups 81–110 (S.M.R.) and 61–80 (Infantile Mortality) respectively. These new variables will, for convenience, be denoted by x and y respectively.

To find the mean value of x when y is fixed at y_s we need to find

$$\sum_r x_r f_{rs},$$

and since the values of x for all the values in any given column are the same we multiply the total frequencies for the various columns by the appropriate values of x to form the line marked $x_r \sum_s f_{rs}$ and a further multiplication by the same values of x produces the line $x_r^2 \sum_s f_{rs}$. A horizontal cast of these rows produces $\sum_r \sum_s x_r f_{rs}$ and $\sum_r \sum_s x_r^2 f_{rs}$ for the whole body of the data, viz. 10 and 144 respectively.

Similarly the last two columns on the right enable $\sum_r \sum_s y_s f_{rs}$ and $\sum_r \sum_s y_s^2 f_{rs}$ to be obtained (viz. 28 and 180 respectively).

Hence, working in class units,

$$\bar{x} = \tfrac{10}{147} = \cdot 068,$$

$$\bar{y} = \tfrac{28}{147} = \cdot 190,$$

$$s_x^2 = \tfrac{144}{147} - (\cdot 068)^2 = \cdot 975,$$

$$s_y^2 = \tfrac{180}{147} - (\cdot 190)^2 = 1\cdot 188.$$

To find $\sum_r \sum_s x_r y_s f_{rs}$ a convenient procedure is as follows:

First rule heavy lines along the borders of the column for which $x=0$ and the row for which $y=0$. Clearly the observations within these lines contribute nothing to $\sum_r \sum_s x_r y_s f_{rs}$.

The remaining data fall into four sections: in the upper left-hand and the lower right-hand sections the product $x_r y_s$ is always positive since x_r and y_s have the same sign. In the other two sections the signs are all negative. It is convenient therefore to deal with each of the sections separately and although positive and negative signs have been inserted in Table 4·5 they are not really necessary.

The product $x_r y_s$ is next inserted slightly above and to the left of each frequency and then the value of $x_r y_s f_{rs}$ slightly below and to the right. The total $\sum_r \sum_s x_r y_s f_{rs}$ for each section separately is then found by addition mentally and the four sums are inserted in the corresponding segments with a ring round them as indicated.

Finally for the given data

$$\sum_r \sum_s x_r y_s f_{rs} \text{ over the whole table} = 24 + 59 - 4 - 10$$

$$= 69.$$

Hence $$p = \tfrac{69}{147} - (\cdot 068)(\cdot 190) = \cdot 4564$$

and $$r = \frac{\cdot 4564}{\sqrt{(\cdot 975 \times 1\cdot 188)}} = \cdot 424.$$

As previously indicated, r needs no adjustment for scale if the same units are used throughout.

TABLE 4·5

Male mortality and infantile mortality. (Data of Table 4·2.)

Male mortality (x) / Infantile mortality (y)

y \ x	−2	−1	0	1	2	3	$\sum_r f_{rs}$	$y_s \sum_r f_{rs}$	$y_s^2 \sum_r f_{rs}$
−2	(+24)	$^{+2}$ 2 $_{+4}$	4		(−4)		6	−12	24
−1	$^{+2}$ 3 $_{+6}$	$^{+1}$ 14 $_{+14}$	13	$^{-1}$ 2 $_{-2}$	$^{-2}$ 1 $_{-2}$		33	−33	33
0	3	8	35	7	2		55	—	—
1	$^{-2}$ 1 $_{-2}$	$^{-1}$ 4 $_{-4}$	16	$^{+1}$ 10 $_{+10}$	$^{+2}$ 4 $_{+8}$	$^{+3}$ 2 $_{+6}$	37	37	37
2		$^{-2}$ 2 $_{-4}$	2	$^{+2}$ 7 $_{+14}$	$^{+4}$ 2 $_{+8}$	(+59)	13	26	52
3	(−10)			$^{+3}$ 1 $_{+3}$	$^{+6}$ 1 $_{+6}$		2	6	18
4				$^{+4}$ 1 $_{+4}$			1	4	16
$\sum_s f_{rs}$	7	30	70	28	10	2	147	28	180
$x_r \sum_s f_{rs}$	−14	−30	—	28	20	6	10		
$x_r^2 \sum_s f_{rs}$	28	30	—	28	40	18	144		

The symbol $\sum_r$ is used to denote summation within the x-arrays and similarly $\sum_s$ is used to denote summation within the y-arrays.

No adjustment has been made for the error involved in assuming the frequencies to be concentrated at the mid-points of the intervals. Such an adjustment is not usually made in calculating a coefficient of correlation. The Sheppards' adjustment to p is zero. The s's could be corrected but it should be noted that it is possible to obtain values of r greater than unity if this is done.

The coefficient of correlation could be obtained approximately from the diagram by reference to the lines of regression which were roughly sketched in Fig. 4·2. These lines intersect at the centroid $(\bar{x}, \bar{y})$ and their slopes give the coefficients of regression.

The line of regression of y on x is

$$y - \bar{y} = r\frac{s_y}{s_x}(x - \bar{x}),$$

and hence the tangent of the angle which it makes with the x-axis is

$$r\frac{s_y}{s_x} = k_1.$$

Similarly, the tangent of the angle which the other regression line makes with the y-axis is

$$r\frac{s_x}{s_y} = k_2.$$

The product $k_1 k_2$ gives r^2; cf. equation (4·14).

Example 4·3.

When the data are extensive the process used in the previous example of inserting $x_r y_s$ and hence $x_r y_s f_{rs}$ against each group frequency becomes rather laborious and is liable to lead to error. The rather more elaborate

TABLE 4·6

Ages and diastolic blood pressures of a group of men accepted for life assurance on ordinary terms

Age next birthday	Diastolic blood-pressure (in mm. of mercury)									
	Up to 57	58–62	63–67	68–72	73–77	78–82	83–87	88–92	93–97	98–102
18–22	4	11	6	31	23	53	15	5	2	—
23–27	2	13	11	60	44	128	33	23	2	—
28–32	1	7	7	51	51	116	37	26	1	—
33–37	2	5	5	55	38	127	39	33	7	2
38–42	—	4	4	29	37	100	32	31	4	2
43–47	—	2	2	18	12	59	28	26	4	—
48–52	—	—	—	10	8	35	21	24	3	3
53–57	—	1	—	5	4	21	12	16	3	—
58–62	—	—	1	2	5	11	9	10	2	1
63–67	—	—	—	—	1	4	2	—	3	—

method in the following example has the great merit that checks on the accuracy of the arithmetic are available and the mean of each x-array and each y-array are obtained, as 'by-products'. The importance of the latter point will become clearer when we deal with more complicated types of regression.

It may be assumed that the readings of blood-pressure are to the nearest millimetre and that the exact ages included in any group are evenly spread over the range. Thus, in the age-group 28–32 we shall assume that all ages from just over 27 to just under 32 occur equally often although there is some tendency for policies to be taken out just before a birthday so that a uniform spread is not strictly justified.

Two further points are of interest. The lowest y-array 'up to 57' actually included one reading of 48 mm. and two of 50 mm. but it will be sufficient for our purposes to assume the limits of the group to be 53–57 mm. (nearest), i.e. 52·5–57·5 mm. exact. The second point relates to the grouping of the blood-pressures. There is a well-known tendency, particularly important in Census data, for people to prefer even numbers to odd numbers and numbers ending in 0 or 5 to those adjoining. This tendency was noticeable to a marked degree in the doctors' readings and the grouping adopted is designed to reduce the effect as far as possible; thus if readings which should have been 79 or 81 were recorded as 80 the error is immaterial if the group embraces all these readings.

As usual the class interval is taken as unit. Arbitrary origins are taken at the middle of the 78–82 group for blood-pressures (x) and the middle of the group (33–37) for ages (y). The work is then arranged as shown in Table 4·7.

The columns headed $\sum_r f_{rs}$, $y_s \sum_r f_{rs}$ and $y_s^2 \sum_r f_{rs}$ are similar to those of Example 4·2 and do not call for special comment. The next column of $\sum_r x_r f_{rs}$ is different from anything we have met hitherto. Taking each x-array in turn, each frequency is multiplied by the appropriate value of x and the products are added to give the figure tabulated, e.g. taking the second array (corresponding to $y=-2$) we have

$$2\times(-5)+13\times(-4)+11\times(-3)+60\times(-2)+44\times(-1)$$
$$+33\times 1+23\times 2+2\times 3=-174.$$

The final column is obtained from the preceding one by multiplying each item by the value of y for all observations in that x-array. For instance, the value of -174 just calculated is multiplied by -2 to give 348 as the contribution to $\sum_r \sum_s x_r y_s f_{rs}$ from all the observations in that particular x-array. The total of the last column gives $\sum_r \sum_s x_r y_s f_{rs}$ for the whole data. The row marked $\sum_s y_s f_{rs}$ is constructed from the y-arrays in

TABLE 4·7

$y \backslash x$	−5	−4	−3	−2	−1	0	1	2	3	4	$\sum_r f_{rs}$	$y_s \sum_r f_{rs}$	$y_s^2 \sum_r f_{rs}$	$\sum_r x_r f_{rs}$	$y_s \sum_r x_r f_{rs}$
−3	4	11	6	31	23	53	15	5	2	—	150	−450	1350	−136	408
−2	2	13	11	60	44	128	33	23	2	—	316	−632	1264	−174	348
−1	1	7	7	51	51	116	37	26	1	—	297	−297	297	−115	115
0	2	5	5	55	38	127	39	33	7	2	313	—	—	−59	—
1	—	4	4	29	37	100	32	31	4	2	243	243	243	−9	−9
2	—	2	2	18	12	59	28	26	4	—	151	302	604	30	60
3	—	—	—	10	8	35	21	24	3	3	104	312	936	62	186
4	—	1	—	5	4	21	12	16	3	—	62	248	992	35	140
5	—	—	1	2	5	11	9	10	2	1	41	205	1025	27	135
6	—	—	—	—	1	4	2	—	3	—	10	60	360	10	60
$\sum_s f_{rs}$	9	43	36	261	223	654	228	194	31	8	1687	−9	7071	−329	1443
$x_r \sum_s f_{rs}$	−45	−172	−108	−522	−223	—	228	388	93	32	−329				
$x_r^2 \sum_s f_{rs}$	225	688	324	1044	223	—	228	776	279	128	3915				
$\sum_s y_s f_{rs}$	−17	−54	−34	−139	−76	−45	108	182	50	16	−9				
$x_r \sum_s y_s f_{rs}$	85	216	102	278	76	—	108	364	150	64	1443				

much the same way as $\sum_r x_r f_{rs}$ was constructed from the x-arrays. Thus the third column of data gives the term

$$6\times(-3)+11\times(-2)+7\times(-1)+4\times1+2\times2+1\times5=-34.$$

The last row is readily derived from this row and the total 1443 is obtained.

The following checks on the numerical work are immediately available:

(i) Σf_{rs} must be the same whether we add the totals of the x-arrays or the totals of the y-arrays.

(ii) The total of the column headed $y_s \sum_r f_{rs}$ gives $\sum_r \sum_s y_s f_{rs}$ for the whole data and must agree therefore with the total of the row marked $\sum_s y_s f_{rs}$. Similarly the total for the row marked $x_r \sum_s f_{rs}$ must agree with the total of the column headed $\sum_r x_r f_{rs}$.

(iii) The values of the total $\sum_r \sum_s x_r y_s f_{rs}$ derived from the last row and the last column must agree.

There is no automatic check in this scheme for the totals $\sum_r x_r^2 f_{rs}$ and $\sum_s y_s^2 f_{rs}$, but such checks could be devised if necessary.

We shall see later (Chapter 15) that the column $\sum_r x_r f_{rs}$ and the row $\sum_s y_s f_{rs}$ have another important application. The mean of each x-array and of each y-array can be deduced by dividing by the total frequency in the array considered and, as has been stated previously, these means are of importance in dealing with non-linear regression.

From the table we obtain the following results which the student should verify:

$$\bar{x}=-\frac{329}{1687}=-\cdot195, \qquad \bar{y}=-\frac{9}{1687}=-\cdot005,$$

$$s_x^2=\frac{3915}{1687}-(\cdot195)^2, \qquad s_y^2=\frac{7071}{1687}-(\cdot005)^2,$$

$$s_x=1\cdot511, \qquad s_y=2\cdot047,$$

$$p=\frac{1443}{1687}-(-\cdot195)(-\cdot005)=\cdot8544,$$

$$r=\frac{\cdot8544}{1\cdot511\times2\cdot047}=\cdot276.$$

The lines of regression are

$$(y+\cdot 005)=\cdot 276\frac{2\cdot 047}{1\cdot 511}(x+\cdot 195)$$

and

$$(x+\cdot 195)=\cdot 276\frac{1\cdot 511}{2\cdot 047}(y+\cdot 005).$$

In terms of the original scales and axes of measurement the estimate of the average blood-pressure X for a given age Y is derived from the equation

$$(X-79\cdot 025)=\cdot 204(Y-34\cdot 475),$$

i.e.

$$X=\cdot 204\,Y+72\cdot 00.$$

Note that we have for convenience used x, y for values on the arbitrary scale and X, Y for values on the original scale. This is the reverse of the notation used in the previous chapter (§ 3·2 et seq.).

4·5. Some properties of the correlation coefficient.

In § 4·3 the coefficient of regression k_1 was found by making

$$\sum_r\sum_s f_{rs}(Y_s-k_1X_r)^2 \qquad (4\cdot 17)$$

a minimum.

Substituting for k_1, this expression becomes

$$\sum_r\sum_s f_{rs}\left(Y_s-r\frac{s_y}{s_x}X_r\right)^2=\sum_r\sum_s f_{rs}Y_s^2-2r\frac{s_y}{s_x}\sum_r\sum_s f_{rs}Y_sX_r$$

$$+r^2\frac{s_y^2}{s_x^2}\sum_r\sum_s f_{rs}X_r^2. \qquad (4\cdot 18)$$

If there are N pairs of observations the first and last terms are clearly

$$Ns_y^2 \quad\text{and}\quad r^2\frac{s_y^2}{s_x^2}Ns_x^2 \quad\text{respectively.}$$

Also

$$\sum_r\sum_s f_{rs}Y_sX_r=Np=Nrs_xs_y.$$

Hence the expression (4·18) reduces to

$$N\{s_y^2-2r^2s_y^2+r^2s_y^2\}$$

$$=N(1-r^2)s_y^2. \qquad (4\cdot 19)$$

But since f_{rs} is always positive the expression (4·17) and its equivalent (4·19) are essentially positive, or zero.

Hence $1-r^2$ must be positive or zero and

$$-1\leqslant r\leqslant 1. \qquad (4\cdot 20)$$

In other words r cannot be numerically greater than 1.

The expression $$Y_s - r\frac{s_y}{s_x}X_r,$$

previously denoted by $$Y_s - k_1 X_r,$$

gives the difference between the value Y_s associated with X_r and the ordinate of the point on the regression line $Y = k_1 X$ with the same abscissa.

Hence $\sum_r \sum_s f_{rs}(Y_s - k_1 X_r)^2$, which we have seen reduces to

$$N(1 - r^2)s_y^2,$$

gives the sum of the squares of these differences or deviations.

If $r = \pm 1$ each of the deviations must be zero, since no term of the summation can be negative. That is to say, when there is no 'scattering' but all the observations lie on the regression lines, the correlation is perfect and $r = \pm 1$ according as correlation is positive or negative (s_y is not zero by hypothesis).

If $r = 0$ the expression (4·19) reduces to Ns_y^2, i.e. the sum of the squares of the deviations from $\bar{y}$.

This will happen if the regression line is parallel to the axis of x so that the average value of y for *every* value of x is $\bar{y}$.

In this case there is no correlation and the points of the scatter-diagram do not tend to cluster round any straight line inclined to the x-axis.

4·6. Approximate methods.

The reader will now realize that the calculation of the coefficient of correlation and the determination of the equations of the regression lines involve a considerable amount of arithmetical work which may not be justified if an approximate result is sufficient for the particular problem under consideration.

The graphic approach illustrated in Fig. 4·2 is often very useful since it indicates whether the correlation is likely to prove linear.

It will be remembered that this method entails the calculation of the mean of each x-array, which is then plotted against the corresponding value of y and the regression line of x on y is then found by 'fitting' a straight line to the series of points thus obtained. The other regression line is found by first calculating the mean of each y-array. The fitting of the regression lines by eye involves a considerable element of guess-work and the method also suffers from the objection that the calculation of the means involves a good deal of arithmetical labour.

Since two points are sufficient to fix a straight line a simple method of approximation is to calculate the means of only two x-arrays and two y-arrays. To give a good indication of the slope these arrays should not be close together and it is usually unwise to go to the other extreme by selecting the two end arrays which usually involve only very scanty data.

In Table 4·7 the x-arrays for $y=-3$ and $y=5$ respectively include adequate data and the means of $-\cdot 91$ and $\cdot 66$ lead to a regression line

$$\frac{x+\cdot 91}{\cdot 66+\cdot 91}=\frac{y+3}{5+3},$$

i.e.

$$x=\cdot 20y-\cdot 321,$$

or referred to the original axes and adjusted for scale

$$X=\cdot 20Y+71\cdot 4.$$

The more accurate equation found in Example 4·3 is

$$X=\cdot 204Y+72\cdot 00.$$

Similarly from two y-arrays it is possible to find approximately the equation of the regression line of Y on X, although the reader will appreciate that estimating an average age for a given blood-pressure would serve little useful purpose.

Another method which involves rather more work than the last is as follows. Instead of singling out two y-arrays suppose we split the whole data into two 'master' arrays, one including all data for which x is less than the mean $\bar{x}$ and one for which x is greater than $\bar{x}$. The equation of the line joining the centroids of these two sections treated separately is a good approximation to the regression line of y on x.

Similarly if we divide the data into two sections according as y is greater or less than $\bar{y}$ and find the centroids of these two sections, the line joining them is a good approximation to the regression line of x on y. If f_L is the total frequency for $x<\bar{x}$ and $(\bar{x}_L, \bar{y}_L)$ the mean of this data and f_G, $(\bar{x}_G, \bar{y}_G)$ refer similarly to the rest of the data we must have

$$\bar{x}=\frac{f_G\bar{x}_G+f_L\bar{x}_L}{f_G+f_L} \quad \text{and} \quad \bar{y}=\frac{f_G\bar{y}_G+f_L\bar{y}_L}{f_G+f_L},$$

and this point clearly lies on the straight line joining $(\bar{x}_G, \bar{y}_G)$ and $(\bar{x}_L, \bar{y}_L)$. In other words the regression line found in this way passes through the mean as it should. The same applies of course to the other regression line found by subdividing the data according as y is greater than or less than $\bar{y}$.

It is left as an exercise to the reader to calculate the regression lines in this way for the data of Table 4·6 and to show that they do in fact pass through the mean.

4·7. Conclusion.

Most of this chapter has been concerned with linear regression, and the more general type of regression and correlation will be dealt with in Volume II. Some of the ideas already developed are, however, of general application. The data as tabulated give some indication of correlation but the calculation of the means of the x-arrays and the y-arrays is always helpful. Consideration of the results may for instance suggest that the means of the x-arrays lie on a second degree curve. If we can find the equation of a curve passing near the means we are in a position to form an 'estimate' of the value of x corresponding to a given y and this 'estimate' will be based on the whole of the data and not merely on a single array.

The reader will now be in a position to appreciate (and criticize) the following definitions of correlation:

(1) If two quantities vary in sympathy so that a movement in one tends to be accompanied by a movement in the other, they are said to be correlated.

(2) Two variables are said to be correlated when we do not find a fixed value of the one variable equally likely to be associated with different values of the other.

We close this chapter with an example which presents many points of interest.

Example 4·4.

The following data have been collected for the purpose of investigating the correlation between the duration of life of married and widowed women and the number of children. Calculate the correlation coefficient and mention any approximate measures which might be used to indicate the extent of correlation, stating the objections to these measures.

TABLE 4·8

Table showing ages at death in quinquennial age-groups, of 1095 wives and widows, with particulars of the number of children				Table showing the distribution of the deaths according to number of children	
Central age at death	No. of deaths	Total no. of children	Average no. of children	No. of children	No. of deaths
20	29	36	1·2	0	24
25	87	151	1·7	1	130
30	99	261	2·6	2	122
35	109	478	4·4	3	134
40	90	450	5·0	4	111
45	87	437	5·0	5	106
50	64	370	5·8	6	85
55	54	331	6·1	7	91
60	69	430	6·2	8	81
65	73	447	6·1	9	77
70	83	547	6·6	10	58
75	77	590	7·7	11	23
80	78	547	7·0	12	24
85	59	398	6·7	13	15
90	26	212	8·2	14	6
95	7	50	7·1	15	2
100	4	35	8·8	16	2
—	—	—	—	17	2
—	—	—	—	18	2
Total	1095	5770	—	—	1095

Find an equation for the regression of the number of children on the length of life of the mother and plot this on a graph together with any information from the given data which will show whether the regression line is satisfactory. On consideration of your graph state whether the correlation coefficient may be regarded as the best measure in this particular case.

The following additional information is given:

Mean age at death	53·292
Standard deviation of age at death calculated on a unit of 5 years	4·091
Standard deviation of number of children ...	3·409

(Faculty of Actuaries examinations, April, 1931)

To investigate correlation we should expect the data to be given in the form of a double-entry table with (say) age at death along the top (x) and number of children down the left-hand side (y), the class-interval for x being taken as 5 years.

Actually we are not given the data to fill in the squares but we are given the total of each y-array, i.e. the number of deaths for a specified central age at death, and also the total of each x-array, i.e. the number of deaths for a specified number of children.

The column 'Average number of children' need not have been provided since it can be obtained by dividing the 'Total number of children' at each central age by the number of deaths at that age. It will, however, be found useful later on.

In our previous notation we are given $\sum_s f_{rs}$ for each y-array and also $\sum_r f_{rs}$ for each value of y, i.e. the total frequency for each number of children irrespective of age of mother at death. Hence we could calculate $\bar{x}$, s_x, $\bar{y}$ and s_y in the usual way; three of these values are given, but they should be checked as an exercise.

The only difficulty is in finding the product moment $\sum_r \sum_s f_{rs} x_r y_s$.

The method normally used breaks down because we do not know the individual values of f_{rs} for every pair of associated values of x and y. We are given the total number of children for each central age at death but not how many mothers dying at that age left 0, 1, 2, 3, ... children.

The given data are in fact the values of $\sum_s y_s f_{rs}$ for each central age at death, where y_s represents the number of children and f_{rs} the frequency; these values correspond to the last row but one of Table 4·7.

We assume the frequencies concentrated at the mid-point of the intervals and take the class-interval as the unit. The origin of x (the age) is taken at 55. There is little to be gained by altering the origin of y. The work is as shown in Table 4·9.

Clearly $\bar{y}$ (the mean number of children per death) $= \frac{5770}{1095} = 5·269$.

There is thus no need to refer to the last two columns given in the question unless it is desired to check the given value of s_y.

The product-moment about the chosen origins is $\frac{5678}{1095}$.

The values of the means are

$$\bar{x} = \tfrac{1}{5}(53{\cdot}292 - 55) \text{ class units, measured from } 55$$
$$= -{\cdot}3416 \text{ class unit,}$$
$$\bar{y} = 5{\cdot}269.$$

Therefore p (the product-moment about the means)

$$= \frac{5678}{1095} + ({\cdot}3416)\,(5{\cdot}269)$$
$$= 6{\cdot}985.$$

TABLE 4·9

Age x (1)	No. of deaths $\sum_s f_{rs}$ (2)	No. of children $\sum_s y_s f_{rs}$ (3)	(1)×(3) $x_r \sum_s y_s f_{rs}$ (4) −	+
−7	29	36	252	
−6	87	151	906	
−5	99	261	1305	
−4	109	478	1912	
−3	90	450	1350	
−2	87	437	874	
−1	64	370	370	
0	54	331		
1	69	430		430
2	73	447		894
3	83	547		1641
4	77	590		2360
5	78	547		2735
6	59	398		2388
7	26	212		1484
8	7	50		400
9	4	35		315
Total	1095	5770	−6969	+12,647 = 5678

Coefficient of correlation

$$= \frac{p}{s_x s_y} = \frac{6{\cdot}985}{(4{\cdot}091)(3{\cdot}409)}$$
$$= {\cdot}50.$$

An approximate value of r can be obtained as follows:

For each value of x we are given not the frequencies with which each number of children was observed but the average number of children. We cannot therefore draw a scatter-diagram, but we can at once plot the mean value of y for each value of x and try to fit a straight line by inspection. As x increases from 20 to 100, i.e. 16 units of 5 years, the mean value of y increases from 1·2 to 8·8, i.e. by 7·6.

Hence k_1, the slope of the regression line, is roughly $\frac{7\cdot6}{16}$.

Since $k_1 = r\frac{s_y}{s_x}$ this gives

$$r = \frac{7\cdot6}{16} \cdot \frac{4\cdot091}{3\cdot409} = \cdot57.$$

The observations at ages 20 and 100 are, however, very scanty, and it seems preferable to base an estimate on the figures for ages 30 and 90, taking the mean value at age 90 as 8·0 to get a better run of figures there.

On this basis

$$k_1 = \frac{5\cdot4}{12} \quad \text{and} \quad r = \frac{5\cdot4}{12} \cdot \frac{4\cdot091}{3\cdot409} = \cdot54.$$

The objection to both these estimates is of course that they are based on observations at two ages only and not on the general run of the means.

The equation of the regression line of y on x is

$$y - \bar{y} = r\frac{s_y}{s_x}(x - \bar{x}),$$

or

$$y - 5\cdot269 = \cdot5\frac{3\cdot409}{4\cdot091}(x + \cdot3416).$$

Reverting to the original axes, this becomes

$$Y - 5\cdot269 = \cdot5\frac{3\cdot409}{4\cdot091}\left(\frac{X - 55}{5} + \cdot3416\right),$$

or

$$Y = \cdot083X + \cdot83, \text{ approx.}$$

This line is drawn in Fig. 4·4 together with the points representing the mean values of Y for each value of X.

A glance at these means shows that they cannot in fact be represented satisfactorily by a straight line, i.e. that the regression is non-linear. The coefficient of correlation calculated is therefore an inadequate measure of the nature of the association.

The curve shown seems to be a reasonably good approximation to the run of the values and may be taken as the curve of regression.

From general considerations we should expect that from age 20–45 the number of children would increase with the age at death, since the size of family must depend to a large extent on the duration of life during the child-bearing period.

The average number of children increases fairly regularly throughout. The explanation is almost certainly to be found in the fact that the given data relate in all probability to the deaths of married women and widows over a short period of time; if the average age at motherhood is taken as 30, this means that women dying at 90 had their children 60 years ago when large families were the rule rather than the exception. Similarly, those dying at 60 had their children on the average about 30 years ago.

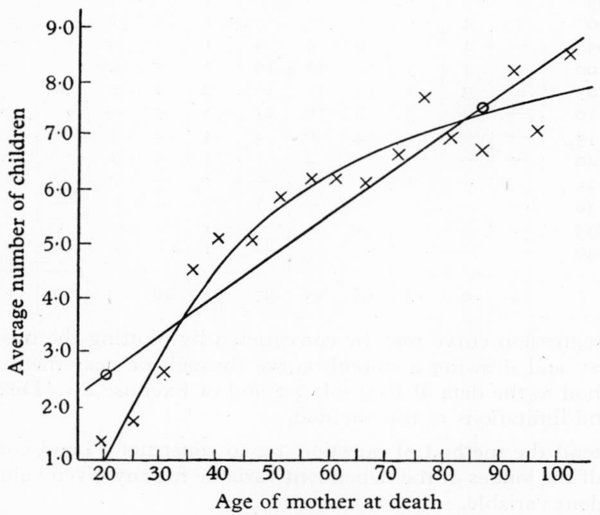

Fig. 4·4. Regression of number of children on length of life of mother.

Thus the regression curve reflects the variation of number of children not so much with age of mother at death as with the period when the children were born. The chief factor operating has thus been a steadily falling birth-rate.

This example incidentally illustrates the difficulties involved in interpreting the results of an investigation into correlation.

EXERCISES 4

4·1 Fit a regression line to the following data relating to changes in the proportion of old people (i.e. over 65 years of age) and in the rate of pauperism between the years 1871 and 1881 for 236 rural areas of England. The figures are in each case the ratio of the 1881 values to the corresponding 1871 values, expressed as percentages. (Yule, *J.R. Statist. Soc.* 1899.)

Pauperism and percentage of old people (1871–81), *Rural*

Pauperism ratio

Ratio of percentage of old	15–25	25–35	35–45	45–55	55–65	65–75	75–85	85–95	95–105	105–115	115–125	Total
70–75	—	—	—	1	—	—	—	—	1	—	—	2
75–80	—	—	—	—	—	—	1	—	—	—	—	1
80–85	1	—	—	—	—	—	1	—	—	—	—	2
85–90	—	1	—	1	—	—	1	1	1	—	—	5
90–95	—	1	1	6	4	4	1	1	—	—	—	18
95–100	—	1	5	14	12	10	7	5	—	—	—	54
100–105	—	3	1	10	11	16	7	2	—	1	—	51
105–110	—	—	3	8	16	21	8	5	—	—	—	61
110–115	—	—	1	4	6	4	4	4	1	—	—	24
115–120	—	—	—	—	4	1	1	2	1	—	—	9
120–125	—	—	1	—	2	—	1	—	—	—	1	5
125–130	—	—	—	—	—	1	—	—	—	—	—	1
130–135	—	—	—	—	—	—	1	—	—	1	—	2
135–140	—	—	—	—	—	—	1	—	—	—	—	1
Total	1	6	12	44	55	57	34	20	4	2	1	236

4·2 A regression curve may be constructed by plotting the medians of each array and drawing a smooth curve through or near them. Apply this method to the data of Example 4·2 and of Exercise 4·1. Discuss the merits and limitations of this method.

4·3 Extend the method of question 4·2 to construct a band containing about half the values of the dependent variable for any given value of the independent variable.

4·4 On each of n individuals the values of three characters X_1, X_2 and X_3 are measured. The correlation between X_1 and X_2 is $r_{1,2}$; between X_2 and X_3, $r_{2,3}$, between X_1 and X_3, $r_{1,3}$. Show that

$$r_{1,2}+r_{2,3}+r_{1,3}> -\tfrac{3}{2}.$$

4·5 Examine the following data showing how age is associated with size of farm (from 'An Economic Survey of Agriculture in the Eastern Counties of England, 1933'. University of Cambridge, Dept. of Agriculture).

Size of farm	Percentage of occupiers whose ages are:						
	Under 25 yrs.	25–34	35–44	45–54	55–64	65–74	Over 74 yrs.
Acres	%	%	%	%	%	%	%
20–50	2	12	25	28	23	8	2
50–100	1	7	21	36	26	7	2
100–150	1	10	29	28	24	6	2
150–300	1	9	21	36	21	10	2
Over 300	nil	5	19	39	22	11	4

4·6 Define correlation. If you were asked to investigate the question whether there is correlation between the rate of pulse and the height of lives accepted at ordinary rates by a life assurance company, how would you proceed? It may be assumed that the measurements of both quantities are recorded in the papers. (Institute of Actuaries Examinations, May 1928.)

4·7 The following figures give the maximum stress tolerated by twelve samples of steel at temperatures of 15 and 600° C.

Maximum stress in tons per square inch

At 15° C.	At 600° C.	At 15° C.	At 600° C.
56·5	34·0	68·0	42·6
48·3	24·2	36·6	15·5
63·0	42·0	57·8	44·9
54·0	36·5	48·5	32·7
58·0	45·0	68·0	45·3
61·0	41·0	63·0	39·5

Obtain a regression line of the maximum stress at 600° C. on the maximum stress at 15° C.

Make any comments on the data which occur to you. Suggest possible uses of the regression line.

4·8 Using a *graphic* process find approximately the equation of the line of regression of x on y from the following data. It may be assumed that the variables are continuous and that the limits of the class intervals are exact, e.g. the class 63–68 includes all values 63 or over and less than 68.

Values of y	Values of x									Totals
	63–68	68–73	73–78	78–83	83–88	88–93	93–98	98–103	103–107	
113–118	1	20	11	22	3	—	—	—	—	57
118–123	11	86	56	162	35	19	1	—	—	370
123–128	5	23	37	105	20	12	1	2	—	205
128–133	6	32	49	149	75	50	4	—	—	365
133–138	2	6	13	57	31	29	10	1	—	149
138–143	—	1	14	83	27	43	5	5	—	178
143–148	1	1	2	9	18	24	4	—	—	59
148–153	—	3	—	5	11	25	2	6	2	54
153–158	—	—	1	1	4	4	4	1	1	16
158–163	—	—	—	3	4	7	8	6	1	29
163–168	—	—	—	—	—	2	1	1	4	8
Totals	26	172	183	596	228	215	40	22	8	1490

Hence find approximately the coefficient of correlation, given that the equation of the line of regression of y on x is

$$y = \cdot 7556x + 69\cdot 22.$$

(Institute of Actuaries Examinations, Nov. 1947.)

4·9 The table below gives the observed values of the mean and standard deviation of a variable y, arranged according to the value of another variable x.

Value of x	No. of observations	Mean value of y	Standard deviation of y
46·0–47·9	22	17·21	3·61
48·0–49·9	57	22·09	4·22
50·0–51·9	160	25·22	3·12
52·0–53·9	287	29·03	3·34
54·0–55·9	333	32·79	3·51
56·0–57·9	318	36·30	3·65
58·0–59·9	246	40·04	3·17
60·0–61·9	121	43·94	3·22
62·0–63·9	60	48·11	3·26
64·0–65·9	30	51·23	2·98
66·0–67·9	19	55·97	4·01

Calculate the least squares regression line of y on x and give a graphical representation of your results.

4·10 The following data relate to pairs of observed values of two variables x and y in three groups:

	Group I	Group II	Group III
Number of pairs in groups	75	100	200
Arithmetic mean of x	22·71	24·98	24·21
Arithmetic mean of y	31·02	30·52	30·90
Standard deviation of x	·311	·420	·271
Standard deviation of y	·277	·351	·255
Correlation coefficient between x and y	·761	·811	·833

Calculate the correlation coefficient between x and y for the whole 375 pairs of observations combined.

4·11 Using the previous exercise as an illustration discuss the effect of heterogeneity on the correlation coefficient.

4·12 Making use of the relationship

$$(x-y)^2 = x^2 - 2xy + y^2$$

show how the calculation of the correlation coefficient and of the constants of the regression straight line can be based on the evaluation of the first and second moments of three distributions, no product moments being calculated directly.

Prepare a set of computing instructions for the application of this method.

Suggest a method of checking the calculations.

4·13 Apply the method of the previous Exercise to the data of Exercise 4·1.

BIBLIOGRAPHY

YULE AND KENDALL. *An Introduction to the Theory of Statistics* (Chapter 10). Griffin and Co., London, 14th ed., 1948.

W. PALIN ELDERTON. *Frequency Curves and Correlation.* C. and E. Layton, London, 1938.

M. EZEKIEL. *Correlation Analysis* (Chapters 1–5). New York, J. Wiley and Son. London, Chapman and Hall, 1942.

CHAPTER 5

THE PROBLEM OF STATISTICAL INFERENCE

5·1. Introduction.

The last three chapters have been devoted to methods of presenting the salient features of observational data in a concise manner. These methods do not tell us anything which was not contained in the original data but they sum up the most important information in a few simple measures.

We have not yet considered, however, why we wish to have this information or, in fact, why the original data were collected and tabulated. However, we often wish to obtain knowledge of the distributions of values of the characteristics measured among individuals of the populations concerned. For instance, statistics are being collected giving for each birth registered, the age of the mother and the duration of the marriage. The purpose in view is not a mere record of events but it is hoped to find out something about births in general, i.e. to find out for the 'population' (in the wider sense discussed in Chapter 1) how births are distributed according to the characteristics, 'age of mother' and 'duration of marriage'.

This leads us to inquire how accurately we can expect our data to provide the desired information. There must nearly always be some inaccuracy in our conclusions, if only because of the occurrence of errors in the observations. Apart from this, however, our observations often do not cover all the individuals in the population concerned. There is thus a gap in our knowledge which we try to bridge by making, from the available data, inferences which we hope will apply to the population. There is evidently considerable scope for inaccuracy.

For example, an assurance company may be investigating the mortality of its annuitants, the data available consisting of the exposed to risk and deaths over a certain period. It may be supposed that the data represent the facts accurately, i.e. that there have been no recording errors. Nevertheless, these annuitants constitute a portion only of all annuitants of the same age, social class, etc., since others will have chosen other companies. Further, some persons of the same category may not have effected annuities. To this extent the company's information is incomplete as a record of the 'population' experience. This applies still more forcibly if the mortality figures obtained are to be used as a basis for estimates of the mortality of future purchasers of annuities who will not, in general, be among the individuals included in the investigation.

5·2. Samples.

The situation in which information is available in respect of only part of a population is very common and constitutes a central problem of statistical theory. Indeed, as has been indicated in Chapter 1, it may occur even when apparently complete information is available, if the purpose of the investigation is taken into account.

The part of the population for which data are available is called a *sample*, and the individuals in a sample are called *members* of the sample. The values assumed by a given characteristic in respect of the members of a sample form a distribution which is called the *sample distribution* if it is desired to stress its connexion with the sample. Similarly, the distribution of values for the whole population is called the *population distribution* if it is desired to stress its connexion with the population. Values of indices such as the arithmetic mean, range, mean deviation, etc., calculated from these distributions may be specified in the same way: e.g. sample mean, sample range, population mean, etc. An index based on a population distribution is called a *parameter*, an index calculated from a sample distribution is called a *statistic*. This last term is in general use, although it is a little unfortunate that its plural may be confused with the title of the subject. The plural 'statistics' signifies, of course, a number of indices calculated from one or more samples.

Example 5·1.

A box contains fifty tickets numbered 1–50. Six tickets are drawn from the box. It is observed that the numbers on these tickets are

42, 5, 38, 36, 24 and 19. The set of fifty tickets may then be regarded as a population and the set of six tickets may be regarded as a sample from this population.

The population arithmetic mean is $25\frac{1}{2}$ and the population range is 49. These are parameters.

The sample arithmetic mean is $27\frac{1}{3}$ and the sample range is 37. These are statistics.

Usually the parameters are unknown and we are, in fact, attempting to make inferences about them from the statistics of the sample. We approach this problem by investigating what sort of samples we might expect to obtain from different populations and thus providing ourselves with a background of knowledge about the relations between sample and population over a range of typical cases. This knowledge is useful as an aid to judgement in dealing with the data of particular samples.

5·3. Notation.

It is important to keep in mind, not only the distinction between statistics and parameters but also the connexion between certain statistics and the corresponding parameters. A conventional system of notation has been devised with these rather conflicting aims in view. It is governed by two simple rules:

(*a*) Statistics are denoted by small Roman letters, parameters by small Greek letters.

(*b*) If a statistic and a parameter correspond, the appropriate Roman and Greek letters correspond according to a scheme of pairing. The scheme most commonly used is shown in Table 5·1.

To aid the reader, the English name of each Greek letter is also given.

TABLE 5·1

$a\ \alpha$	alpha	$f\ \phi$	phi	$p\ \pi$	pi	$w\ \omega$	omega
$b\ \beta$	beta	$k\ \kappa$	kappa	$^*q\ \chi$	chi	$x\ \xi$	ksi
$c\ \gamma$	gamma	$l\ \lambda$	lambda	$r\ \rho$	rho	$y\ \eta$	eta
$d\ \delta$	delta	$m\ \mu$	mu	$s\ \sigma$	sigma	$y\ {}^*\theta$	theta
$e\ \epsilon$	epsilon	$n\ \nu$	nu	$t\ \tau$	tau	$z\ \zeta$	zeta

* These combinations are not in general use but are sometimes convenient in actuarial theory.

For example, we denote the standard deviation calculated from a sample by s. The standard deviation calculated from a population is denoted by σ which is paired with s in Table 5·1.

Although this system of notation is of great value there are departures from it in the standard notations of statistical theory. Two of the most important of these departures are the use of χ^2 to denote a statistic (see Chapter 13) and the use of capital Roman letters to denote certain parameters.

5·4. Types of population.

It is clear that when, on the basis of experience, we ascribe to a population a particular distribution of values of a certain characteristic we are to some extent guessing. We are attempting to replace a distribution over which we do not exercise complete control by one which we have designed in such a way as to be amenable to theoretical treatment. We are, in fact, using a concept of our own minds as a representation of something which we might observe given sufficient time and patience. It is not expected that the concept and the observations would agree exactly, but it is hoped that they would correspond closely. This method of replacing an observation by a concept is not peculiar to statistics but is common to all scientific theory. Simple examples are the concept 'circle' applied to the curve drawn with a pair of compasses, and the concept of 'purity' in chemistry.

Very often, not only is the population distribution of values a concept, but the population itself is also imaginary in the sense that it is thought of at a time when its individuals do not all exist. For example, three tossings of a penny may be regarded as a sample of three from all tossings (past and future) of an ideal coin. Further, in the case of an assurance company estimating annuitants' mortality, already referred to in this chapter, the observed annuitants may be considered as a sample from all possible similar annuitants, including those who have not yet effected such a contract. As a convenient classification, populations may be termed *concrete* if all individuals in the populations could have been measured, and *imaginary* if this does not apply. Clearly a concrete population must be finite, i.e. contain a finite number of individuals;

an imaginary population may be finite or infinite. Often the population concerned, though finite, is very large and is considered, for purposes of approximation, as infinite.

The choice of population to be considered in any particular problem will naturally depend upon what is known of the conditions giving rise to the distribution of values of the character to be dealt with. A suitable choice is of great importance for an efficient treatment of the problem, making good use of the data available. In choosing the population, knowledge of the conditions of the problem is blended with knowledge of possible populations, and ability to develop and use the appropriate theoretical background. A combination of practical experience in the subject concerned with theoretical knowledge and experience in the use of statistical method is therefore required. The greatest care should be taken not to ignore any possible contribution from any of these sources to the solution of the problem of choice of population.

5·5. Methods of sampling.

In order to study the relation between sample and population it is necessary to make some assumption about the method by which the sample is obtained. The collection of a sample is fundamentally a human action. In order to reduce the effect of the variable human element various systems of sampling have been proposed. They are of the nature of ideals which are rarely attained, but theory developed on the basis of these systems may be usefully applied to the results of practical sampling. This is, again, an example of the substitution of a concept for practical conditions, referred to in the previous section. In the case of sampling there is the additional factor of the effort to make the observational method approximate to the concept.

5·6. Random sampling.

The most widely applied concept in the theory of sampling is that of the random sample which is based in turn on the idea of *randomness*. Randomness may be described as 'lack of purpose', yet it provides a basis for a system of sampling which seeks to ensure that no one individual in the population is more likely to be included in a sample than any other. This lack of purpose in the selection of a sample is difficult of attainment in practice owing to latent personal preferences. For this reason various mechanical devices are used to help in the selection of random samples. A simple method, applicable if the number of individuals is not too great, is to assign a number to each and to choose the sample by drawing numbered tickets from a box. This method is commonly employed in drawing for prizes in raffles, etc., but it is rather cumbersome for everyday use. There are also possibilities of the randomness of the method being disturbed by physical causes such as lack of thoroughness in mixing the tickets. To avoid the necessity of making a special drawing each time a sample is to be taken, tables have been prepared giving in effect the results of a large number of drawings. These are known as tables of random numbers and references to the best known sets are given at the end of this chapter. Special precautions, which are described in the relevant literature, were taken in their selection.

Tables of random numbers consist of blocks of digits. The compilers of these tables may be supposed to have chosen the digits 0–9 at random. Fig. 5·1 shows a typical block.

7261
0993
4571
8020
4137

Fig. 5·1

The way in which these tables are used depends in detail on the kind of population concerned, but always involves the numbering of members of the population and subsequently the selection of individuals corresponding to the numbers in a section of the table of random numbers. For example, there may be 3137 persons holding whole-life assurances with a certain office and further information may be required in respect of a sample of 100 of these persons. The selection of the sample might proceed as follows: the persons are numbered 1–3137 and those selected correspond to successive four-figure numbers in the table, ignoring four-figure numbers greater than 3137. Thus, using the figures in Fig. 5·1 and reading horizontally, we should select no. 993. If we read vertically passing from the foot of each column to the top of the next, we select nos. 169, 3107. It should be noted that only one of these procedures should be used in any one sampling problem, as the numbers chosen by the two systems are not independent.

All numbers from 3138 to 9999 are rejected by this system but various modifications can be designed so as to reduce the proportion of these rejected numbers. We might, for instance, deduct 5000 from all numbers greater than that figure and accept the result if it were not greater than 3137; in this way we should make use of all numbers in the table from 1 to 3137 inclusive and from 5001 to 8137 inclusive. Various other devices will readily occur to the student; they are not of importance in themselves since the published tables of sampling numbers are sufficiently extensive for all practical purposes but it is a valuable exercise to examine how the numbers can be adapted for special needs.

5·7. Proportional sampling.

If, in the example above, the ages of the lives assured were known, it might be felt desirable to choose the sample in such a way that the distribution of lives by quinquennial age-groups should be approximately the same in the population as in the sample. Thus if the age distribution of the assured lives were as shown in column (2) of Table 5·2 the nearest proportionate allocation of the sample to the different age-groups would be that in column (3).

A random sample might approximate to this apportionment, but this could not be relied on. If the numbers shown in column (3) are to be ensured, there must be some departure from purely random sampling. This does not mean, however, that tables of random numbers cannot be used; in fact the sample may be formed either by proceeding as for a purely random sample and omitting all individuals in excess of the quota for the age-groups concerned, or by treating each age-group as a separate population and drawing a separate random sample for it.

Methods of sampling of this kind are intended to produce a sample which shall be a small-scale representation of the population from which it is drawn. It is seen that these methods of selection may contain some elements of randomness. Such methods require more detailed knowledge of the structure of the population than does the random method and they are also rather more complicated

TABLE 5·2

Distribution of assured lives according to attained age

(These data are taken from Table 3·2)

Nearest age (1)	Number of lives in population (2)	Number in sample (3)
21–25	44	1
26–30	47	1
31–35	66	2
36–40	107	3
41–45	147	5
46–50	151	5
51–55	208	7
56–60	305	10
61–65	396	13
66–70	488	16
71–75	471	15
76–80	358	11
81–85	222	7
86–90	104	3
91–95	18	1
96–100	5	
Total	3137	100

since they entail a preliminary subdivision of the population. However, in the cases where they can be used, they are likely to lead to more accurate results than the random method, because they make fuller use of knowledge of the population.

5·8. A practical example of sampling.

In 1924 and 1928 respectively two interesting papers were read to the Royal Statistical Society, giving particulars of sampling investigations carried out on an extensive scale to obtain information about unemployment in Great Britain. Some of the principal points are set out in this section but for fuller details the reader should refer to the original papers.*

The first investigation with which we shall deal was based on a one per cent sample of 'insured workpeople unemployed' in the latter part of 1923. The required information could be obtained only by a personal interview carried out by the manager of the Employment Exchange in the case of men or boys or by the senior woman official in the case of women or girls and the whole of this work had to be completed during the week, Monday 5th to Saturday 10th November.

Any method of sampling based on random selection by the Exchange Authorities was rejected because it would probably lead to over-representation of the more approachable claimants or those known personally because of frequent visits or with complex cases. A form of purposive sampling was therefore used based on the card-index kept at each Employment Exchange of all unemployed registered on their books. It would have been a simple matter to instruct each manager to 'tab' every hundredth card and arrange for the interview of those people when they next presented themselves but there were serious theoretical and practical objections to such a plan.

At each Exchange the cards were kept in order of occupation, occupation No. 1 for instance being 'carpenters and joiners'. Hence, if the 'tabbing' of cards always started at the beginning of the file carpenters and joiners would be over-represented since there would probably be one at least for every Exchange with a claimant in that category. To overcome this difficulty each Exchange was given a different starting-point as 'the first claim in Occupation Classification No....', care being taken to obtain an even distribution over the whole occupational classification. The manager was also told how many men, women, boys and girls should be interviewed and was instructed to tab every Xth card where

$$X = \frac{\text{Total cards in the category}}{\text{Number of returns required}}$$

(X was not necessarily 100) and when he reached the end of the file

* 'Enquiry by Sample', *J.R.S.S.* Vol. LXXXVII and 'Some Further Enquiries by Sample', *J.R.S.S.* Vol. XCI, by John Hilton.

of cards to continue at the beginning until the whole quota had been marked. If there were no claims in the occupation designated, the instruction was to 'take the next forward in which there are claims'.

The practical difficulties were of two kinds:

On a strictly proportional basis the large Exchanges would have had an impossible task; Birmingham Exchange, for instance, would have been called on for reports on about 150 men and 50 women in one week. It was decided therefore to have the upper limit of 30 men or 40 individuals in all at any given place, the medium and small Exchanges being required to contribute proportionately more to make up the required total. In the second place the person 'tabbed' might fail to turn up during the week owing to illness, death, moving to a new district, or having found employment. Permission was given therefore to include the five cards on each side of the one 'tabbed' and to interview the first of these eleven people who 'signed on'.

Both the relaxations were subjected to criticism. It was realized that the first would 'under-weight' big industrial centres such as Sheffield but no geographical comparisons were contemplated and it was hoped that difficulties would not arise on that score. Actually this 'under-weighting' was unfortunate because such 'heavy' industries as iron and steel were not fully represented. Dr Bowley suggested that a better plan would have been to reduce the sample to one in 300 but to adhere rigidly to that proportion.

It was agreed that the margin of five on each side of the 'tabbed' card was too wide and in subsequent investigations it was reduced to three and one respectively. The wider margin had one unexpected result; the proportion registered on the books but not eligible for unemployment benefit was underestimated and this was traced to the fact that such people were required to 'sign on' only once a week while those receiving benefit had to sign every day or several days a week. Obviously the more often a man appeared the more likely was he to be interviewed.

One other aspect of those sampling investigations may be mentioned briefly. For juveniles the effect of school terms was very marked and it was essential to choose a suitable week for the investigation. Eventually a week towards the end of the summer term was taken as most representative of the average for the whole year and as the numbers were small every *tenth* card in an alphabetical index of claimants was tabbed. This is an example of 'time sampling' in conjunction with 'case sampling'.

5·9. Statistical inference.

The problem of reaching conclusions about populations, starting from the data given by measurements of a character for each of the members of a sample is one which admits of no unique solution except in trivial cases. Such a trivial case arises for example if a box contains a number of cards, each of which is known to be marked with the same number. A sample of one is then sufficient to determine the number on each card uniquely. If we now suppose that the numbers may differ, one sample will give no information whatever about the numbers on the remaining cards. Clearly this corresponds to the cases usually met with in practical work. It seems therefore that no conclusion about the distribution in the whole population can be reached on the basis of the sample alone. This is indeed the case, unless some assumption about the nature of the distribution in the population is made. Even if such an assumption is made, we can still only consider the relationship of the observed sample to a hypothetical population. Any inferences to be made from the sample will be based on such comparisons of sample and supposed population and will therefore be uncertain in two ways:

(i) they will depend upon the populations chosen;
(ii) even for a given population we can consider only *how likely* it is that the observed sample would have been drawn from it.

The first of these sources of uncertainty is minimized by taking care in the choice of population. The necessity for this has already been pointed out in § 5·4. The second source of uncertainty is inherent in the conditions of the problem and cannot be removed. It can, however, be more clearly understood and measured by applying probability theory in a suitable manner to the problem. Statistical inference is, in fact, uncertain inference and so may sometimes be wrong. In practical applications the important property of a system of statistical inference is not its logical certainty, but the proportion of times it leads to effectively correct conclusions. It is hoped to show that the probability theory developed in the next three chapters enables estimates to be made of this proportion.

5·10. Conclusion.

The problem of statistical inference has been propounded in this chapter and the conditions of its solution sketched out. It is seen that these call for a combination of practical knowledge of the particular subject concerned, knowledge of probability theory applied to a variety of theoretical populations and appreciation of the ideas involved in the use of this theory to aid personal judgement. This book does not, of course, provide practical knowledge, which can only be attained by close contact with the problems to be considered. The purpose in the next four chapters is to supply a basic knowledge of theory and an idea of the principles of its application which will be sufficient to provide an adequate background for the simpler statistical tests. These chapters may at present appear to the reader as an unnecessarily long detour. It must be borne in mind, however, that their object is to produce a specialized habit of thought which can be applied without hesitation to the problems presented by observed data. Although this habit of thought is only a development of normal common sense it is in some ways unfamiliar and considerable thought and study is needed to attain facility in, and understanding of, its use.

The first three of the following chapters are concerned with development of theory applicable to abstract populations. As we shall be dealing with idealized distributions we shall be able to treat the subject with all the exactitude which mathematics makes possible. Chapter 9, however, which deals with the application of the theory to observational data and may appear to be couched in somewhat vague terms, reflects the greater complexity of the world of experience as compared with the world of ideas, and our conse quent ignorance of much of the former. The difference already noted between our conceptual population and the reality it is supposed to represent is a particular example of this difference between experience and ideas or concepts.

EXERCISES 5

5·1 Discuss the following situations indicating where you think it is practicable and preferable to perform 100% examination rather than to use some sampling system:

(*a*) Testing ammunition for firing efficiency according to some specified requirements.
(*b*) Checking the soundness of wheels of railway carriages.
(*c*) Testing milk for freedom from certain types of bacteria.
(*d*) Checking a set of mathematical tables.

5·2 A Broadcasting Company has used the following methods to find out how the programmes are appreciated:

(*a*) Inviting casual passers-by to speak into a portable microphone at a busy street corner and express their likes and dislikes.
(*b*) Scrutiny of letters in the Press and letters received by the Company from listeners.
(*c*) Door-to-door inquiries in selected areas by a trained staff of canvassers.
(*d*) Employment of a small body of paid listeners who are required to report on reception, interference and other technical matters as well as on the programmes themselves.

Criticize briefly each of these methods. (Institute of Actuaries Examinations, May 1945.)

5·3 Describe the practical advantages of proportional sampling.

It is well known that if a random sample is drawn no substitution should be allowed of one individual for another on account of the difficulty of measuring any of the chosen individuals. How far, if at all, does this requirement apply in proportional sampling?

5·4 In a certain group of 100 men it is known that the ages of 15 of them are 42, 47, 43, 31, 51, 51, 44, 40, 44, 35, 48, 55, 42, 40 and 37 respectively.

What can you say about the average age in the group:

(*a*) with certainty,
(*b*) assuming that no man can be older than 120,
(*c*) assuming that the mean deviation of the ages of the 100 men is no more than that of the 15 whose ages are known?

5·5 Consider what sampling methods might be devised to help in investigating the following problems:

(*a*) The management of a gas works wish to analyse the coal supplied from various collieries (i) by railway wagons and (ii) by barges.
(*b*) A manufacturing chemist requires to know the purity of the common salt supplied to him in 5 cwt. sacks.
(*c*) An excise officer has to measure the alcohol content in whisky produced by a certain distillery.

5·6 A farmer intending to grow wheat in a very large field desires to have an analysis made of the soil so that appropriate fertilizers may be applied. Criticize the following methods of investigating the problem by sampling:

(i) A handful of soil is taken from various parts of the field by a labourer walking about 'at random'. Each handful is analysed separately.

(ii) The field is divided into quarters and equal measured amounts of soil are taken from each quarter (*a*) from the surface and (*b*) from about 12 in. below the surface. These eight samples are carefully mixed and a small quantity is taken from the mixture for analysis.

(iii) A tennis ball is thrown into the field from each boundary in turn. A measured sample is then taken from the spot where the ball comes to rest. The four samples are amalgamated and the whole of the resulting mixture is analysed.

(iv) A scale map of the field is divided into 200 ruled rectangles which are numbered. By a table of sampling numbers ten rectangles are selected, and a measured sample of soil is taken from each of the points in the field corresponding as nearly as can be measured to the centre of a rectangle. The ten samples are carefully mixed and a small quantity is then taken for analysis.

(v) As in (iv), but every tenth rectangle is chosen starting with one in a corner.

5·7 A Life Assurance Company wishes to know how many policies on the average are effected on each separate life. The available records include (*a*) a list of policies in numerical order with particulars of the person on whose life each policy was issued and (*b*) a card index in alphabetical order of surnames of the various lives with particulars on each card of all policies issued on that life.

How would you proceed to investigate the problem by sampling and what precautions would you take to avoid bias?

5·8 Construct sets of 'random numbers' using the following kinds of apparatus:

(1) A stop-watch.
(2) A pack of cards.
(3) A series of gas or electric meter readings.
(4) Sets of numerical data published in newspapers (e.g. bond drawings in *The Times*).
(5) A telephone directory.

In each case give a critical appraisal of the method you use.

5·9 In the following table fatal road accidents in America in 1947 are analysed according to the weather conditions at the time of the accident. Criticize the method of presentation, and state what further information you would require to enable useful conclusions to be drawn.

Fatal road accidents in America, 1947

Weather	No. of fatal accidents	Percentage
Dry	21,670	74·7
Wet	5,070	17·5
Snowy	960	3·3
Icy	1,300	4·5
Total	29,000	100·0

BIBLIOGRAPHY

L. H. C. Tippett. *Statistics* (Home University Library). Oxford, Clarendon Press. 3rd ed. 1943.

F. Yates. *Sampling Methods for Censuses and Surveys* (Chapters 1–5). Griffin and Co., London, 1949.

M. G. Kendall and B. Babington Smith. *Tables of Random Sampling Numbers*. Cambridge University Press, 1939.

CHAPTER 6

PROBABILITY: FUNDAMENTALS

6·1. Introduction.

The preceding chapter has described the value of a theoretical background as an aid in the interpretation of observational data. We shall now consider in more detail the nature of the theory required. We recall, first of all, that the subject of statistics deals with those characters which can be measured or, at any rate, expressed in numerical form. The collection of observed values of these characters gives rise, as we have seen, to frequency distributions, the shape of which is defined by the *proportions* of the observed values falling between various limits but does not depend on the total number of observations. Thus the shape could be defined by the relative frequencies where

$$\text{Relative frequency} = \frac{\text{Observed frequency in a given range}}{\text{Total number of observations}}.$$

For example, the shape of the distribution shown in column (2) of Table 6·1 is the shape of the distribution of relative frequencies shown in column (3) of the same table.*

TABLE 6·1

Medical grades assigned to 2,425,184 *men of military age*

(1 Nov. 1917–31 Oct. 1918)

Grade (1)	Number (2)	Relative frequency (3)
I	871,769	·360
II	546,276	·225
III	756,859	·312
IV	250,280	·103
Total number	2,425,184	1·000

* *J.I.A.* Vol. LII, p. 180.

Generally if a set of N observations divided among k groups contains:

n_1 observations falling in the		1st group	
n_2	,,	,,	2nd ,,
n_3	,,	,,	3rd ,,
....			
n_k	,,	,,	kth ,,

then the relative frequency in the jth group is n_j/N.

In the problem of sampling we are led to consider how the observed values might vary in repeated sampling. For instance, one important question is: By how much is the arithmetic mean of the observed values likely to differ from the arithmetic mean of the whole population? To answer this question we need to know how the arithmetic mean may be expected to vary from sample to sample, and we might give an answer in the form of a statement of the proportion of times in which the difference between sample mean and population mean may be expected to exceed a given value. The theoretical background should be such that it provides a reasonable basis for calculating this proportion.

6·2. The theory which is to be developed must, therefore, be capable of dealing with relative frequencies. The reader will probably see many analogies between relative frequencies and the probabilities dealt with in *Mathematics for Actuarial Students*, Part II. Both quantities have a lower limit of zero and an upper limit of unity. There is, moreover, an implication in the probability theory that equal probability leads to equal frequency of occurrence in the long run. Other analogies will readily occur and will become increasingly clear as we continue the study of the subject. The theory which is to be developed in the present book is, in fact, regarded as a theory of probability. It is, however, by no means the only one which has been propounded. We shall describe the better known of these other systems so that the reader may compare them with each other and with the system on which this book is based. It must be borne in mind that the theory which we shall develop is especially designed to deal with statistical questions. To this end it places special emphasis on frequency of occurrence and is sometimes called a *statistical probability theory*.

6·3. Theories of probability may be graded, very roughly, according to the relative importance which they ascribe to subjective elements and to objective elements. We use the word 'subjective' to describe those theories which emphasize the degree of belief in a person's mind and regard probability as a measure of this degree of belief. We use the word 'objective' to describe those theories which are concerned more with what is likely to happen, irrespective of our feelings in the matter. It should be borne in mind that these words are used in a different sense by philosophers and others and their rather special meanings in the present context should not be forgotten. By 'subjective' we do not confine ourselves to theories involving *individual* judgements but extend it to include those theories which endeavour to make probability a logical relation between a proposition and certain given evidence. By 'objective' we intend to convey the idea of a number in a theoretical model corresponding (or intended to correspond) with an external physical system. Evidently no theory can be either purely subjective or purely objective. The most subjective theory must take into consideration data external to the person assessing a probability, while the most objective theory must have been propounded, and is used, by human beings and to that extent is subjective. There is, however, a wide disparity in the relative importance which the various theories ascribe to the subjective and objective elements. The view has been put forward that there are, in fact, at least two distinct concepts involved. These are the subjective degree of belief, and the objective chance of occurrence. The former of these concepts seems to belong to the sphere of psychology and we shall not attempt to study it at all deeply. Statistical method is, however, essentially concerned with what happens in the long run and we shall, in future, concentrate on this concept.

6·4. Subjective theories.

It follows that the more subjective theories are not likely to be of great value for our purposes. This does not mean, of course, that such theories are fallacious but merely that they are not generally so well suited to our requirements. Under special conditions, indeed, concepts involved in the more subjective theories can prove very valuable.

A common characteristic of subjective theories is the assumption that the person dealing with a volume of data has already ideas concerning properties of the situation to which the data relate. It is further supposed that he has certain degrees of belief in these ideas and probabilities are used as measures of these degrees of belief. The theory is then concerned with the way in which the data will modify these '*a priori* probabilities' as they are often called. The resultant modified probabilities are called '*a posteriori* probabilities'. Usually Bayes' Theorem (see § 6·17) provides the connecting link whereby the *a posteriori* probabilities are calculated but as a general rule there is no relation specified between probabilities (either *a priori* or *a posteriori*) and relative frequencies. The connexion between *a priori* probability and the concept 'degree of belief' is easily appreciated. The subjective nature of the theory is also apparent in the dependence of *a priori* probability on the previous experience of the person dealing with the data. Bayes' Theorem is of great value in theories based on *a priori* probability as it provides a link between *a priori* and *a posteriori* probabilities.

6·5. Theory of arrangements.

The early writers on probability based their definitions on the concept of 'equally likely cases'. The values which an observation can take are split up into a number M of such cases. The number of these in which a specified condition is satisfied is then ascertained and if this number is m the probability of the specified condition being satisfied is defined as m/M. For example, suppose that two dice are thrown and the total number of dots on the two upper faces is observed. The combinations of any one face of one die with any one face of the other give a total of $6 \times 6 = 36$ cases. These are taken to be 'equally likely' so that $M = 36$. The total number of dots on the upper faces will be exactly three in two of these 36 equally likely cases. Hence $m = 2$, and by definition the probability that the total is three is $\frac{2}{36} = \frac{1}{18}$.

The enumeration of the possible 'equally likely cases' leads to consideration of the possible different combinations of results obtainable. For this reason the theory is sometimes referred to as the 'theory of (equally likely) arrangements'. The criticisms of the theory have been for the most part aimed at the assumption of 'equally likely' cases. This, indeed, is the point at which subjective judgement is needed in the theory of arrangements. Since, as has already been remarked, subjective elements can never be completely removed, this is not in itself a valid objection to the theory. It is, however, often difficult to decide which cases are 'equally likely', or even to discover any fundamental 'equally likely cases'. This difficulty arises in most statistical problems. The theory has no immediate connexion with frequency of occurrence or with any appeal to experiment.

6·6. The 'Kollektiv'.

The theory of probability put forward by R. von Mises has much in common with the frequency theory which we shall use. Von Mises' theory is based on the concept of the 'Kollektiv'. A 'Kollektiv' consists of an infinite series of alternatives such as 010010110 01... which satisfies certain conditions. These, briefly, amount to the requirements

(i) that the relative frequency of 0's in the first N members of the 'Kollektiv' tends to a limit p as N increases, and

(ii) that when an infinite sub-sequence is chosen from the 'Kollektiv' by a method such that the decision to choose or reject a given member does not depend on the actual value of that member, then the relative frequency of 0's in the first N members of the sub-sequence tends to the same limit p as N increases.

For this purpose a sub-sequence such as that formed by the observations immediately following a 1 would be regarded as satisfactory since the way in which it was constructed was not related to the values actually selected.

The common limit p is defined as the probability of occurrence of a 0.

Criticisms of the 'Kollektiv' theory are centred in the definition and possibility of existence of a 'Kollektiv'.

One great advantage of the theory is the way in which it links up with experimental results. There are, however, many statisticians who would not agree with Von Mises' dictum: 'A probability theory which does not introduce from the very beginning a connexion between probability and relative frequency is not able to contribute anything to the study of real phenomena.'

6·7. 'Mathematical theories.'

Some investigators have built up purely mathematical theories of probability. The underlying idea is to define mathematical functions having the properties usually ascribed to probabilities and then to pursue the study of these functions. Such a method of development increases the logical coherence of the theory by developing it from an axiomatic basis, in the same way as geometry may be developed. This gain in formal clarity is only attained by postponing the awkward questions arising in the application of the theory to observed data. The best known of the mathematical theories is that based on set theory developed by Kolmogoroff (see Bibliography).

6·8. Summary.

The frequency theory which we shall develop would be close to the 'Kollektiv' theory. It differs from the latter theory in its appeal to experience and a certain *naïveté* in presentation, which leads to simplicity of theory.

It may be mentioned that there are theories (e.g. that of Keynes) which do not admit the possibility of assigning a numerical value to a probability except in certain special cases. These theories permit only inequalities and equalities between probabilities.

The reader, having obtained an idea of the principles of the various theories which have been described, should not allow his knowledge to confuse him in the development of the frequency theory which follows. The different theories have much in common in their formal development, and the results which will be obtained later in this chapter are formally valid in them all.

6·9. Frequency theory.

Frequency theory is, in some ways, a parasite among probability theories. The theoretical assumptions of other theories may be, and often are, used to provide a framework within which the data may be examined. The distinctive characteristic of frequency theory is, however, quite fundamental, as it lies in its definition of probability. This definition is based on, but is not completely verifiable by, observation. It is in fact an abstraction in the same way as the definition of a point in geometry as 'having no length, breadth or thickness' is an abstraction based on observation of approximations to points. A somewhat different example is provided by the Newtonian definition of the acceleration due to gravity which is an abstraction derived from observation of certain experiments. These definitions are not completely verifiable by observation but prove useful in practical work.

The definition of probability which we shall use is based on the behaviour of relative frequencies, an outstanding feature of which is an increase in stability with an increase in the number of observations. Special experiments, involving as many as 10,000 trials, have been carried out to investigate this phenomenon. They have usually taken the form of the repeated tossings of a die or coin, or repeated drawings from a mixture of labelled balls or disks. In the coin-tossing experiments the number of times n out of N tosses in which the coin falls with a specified face (e.g. 'heads') uppermost is noted for various values of N and the relative frequency n/N is plotted against N. In other types of experiment, a particular result is called a success and n represents the number of successes out of N trials.

Fig. 6·1 is typical of the diagrams obtained by plotting the relative frequency (n/N) against the number (N) of trials.

These experiments all have two important features. The trials are all carried out under similar conditions so that the results are comparable, and a random element is usually present. Thus, in throwing a die, the same die should be used throughout and should be thrown by the same investigator in the same way as far as is possible. It is possible to imagine a delicate machine constructed in such a manner that if the die were inserted in it in the same way on every occasion it would throw it in *exactly* the same way on to the same spot on the table. In such circumstances the same result would always be obtained (subject to wear and tear) and probability theory would not be required, except in a trivial sense.

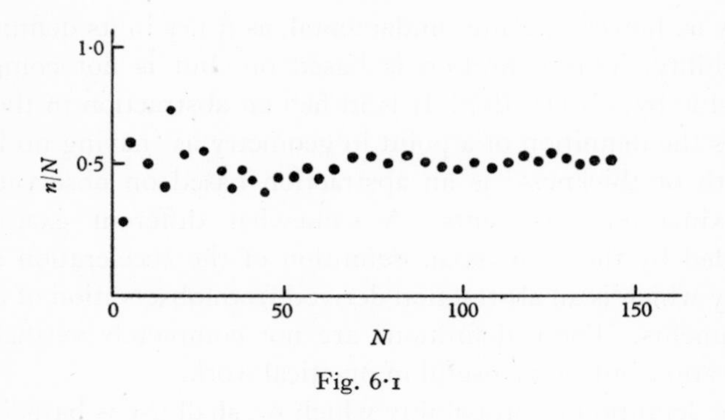

Fig. 6·1

Experiments of this nature are admittedly artificial, but not more so than experiments designed to illustrate some particular law in other sciences. Laboratory experiments in physics provide many such examples of special control of conditions for the purpose of isolating a particular phenomenon for study. The experiments on relative frequency are of the same nature. Just as the application of physical laws in a practical problem is more complex than in planned experiments so the application of probability theory becomes more complex in practical statistical problems.

Unfortunately the literature on experimental work in probability is limited, but reference may be made to a book of J. E. Kerrich (see Bibliography). Although the superstructure of the theory may tend to obscure the importance of experimental work the fact that the theory is fundamentally based on experiment should always be kept in mind. The classical theory of dynamics is an analogous case, an elaborate theory being developed on the basis of the few experimental results summarized and idealized in Newton's Laws of Motion.

6·10. Frequency theory. Definition of probability.

Instead of a single set of N trials we now imagine that we have a great number of sets each of N trials and that we plot the relative frequency (n/N) of successes for each.

We shall find that the values are scattered between 0 and 1 but that they tend to cluster together in a particular region. If N is not large this feature will not be very noticeable but as N increases the size of the cluster tends to diminish while its general position remains substantially the same. This position of the cluster gives us a measure of the probability p of a success. Clearly before we can give a formal definition of probability these general ideas based on a mass of experimental evidence must be given more precision.

When we speak of values tending 'to cluster', we mean that, although there might be a few outlying values, the vast majority of the relative frequencies would be found to lie within fairly narrow limits. To express this more precisely we must give a numerical measure to 'the vast majority' and we shall follow J. E. Kerrich in adopting (quite arbitrarily) the value 99%. We say therefore that 99% of the values of the relative frequency lie between limits $p+\alpha$ and $p-\beta$ say.* As N increases α and β tend to zero while p remains constant. We are thus led to the formal hypothesis, based on experimental evidence:

For a given value of N, positive numbers p, α and β exist such that about 99% of the observed values of the relative frequency (n/N) lie between the limits $p+\alpha$ and $p-\beta$. As N increases without limit α and β both tend to zero, p remaining constant at a value between 0 and 1.

p is defined as the probability of the event considered. If we wish to specify the event E we usually use the notation Pr. $\{E\}$ instead of p.

6·11. Some remarks on the definition.

It should be borne in mind that the formal statement in the previous paragraph leading up to the definition is a hypothesis, i.e.

* If we had chosen some other proportion such as 99·9% the limits $p+\alpha$ and $p-\beta$ would be altered to $p+\alpha'$ and $p-\beta'$ say.

it cannot be proved although there is a mass of experimental evidence to support it. It deals with mass phenomena and relates to only 99 % of observed values; it thus expressly allows for the fact that some results will be outside the limits $p+\alpha$ and $p-\beta$. As N increases the proportion 99 % remains unchanged, it is only α and β which change.

The reader may ask how the value of p is to be found in any given case. In fact it is only possible to assume a value for p. The value so assumed forms part of a theoretical model and the appropriateness of the latter depends to a great extent on how well the probabilities contained in it have been chosen. To illustrate the ways in which this choice is made we shall consider briefly three common types of problem. The first is the mathematical type of question with which the reader is already familiar, dealing with such problems as throwing dice, or drawing coloured balls from urns. We usually have no experimental evidence of any sort and therefore have to estimate the probabilities from considerations of physical shape, etc. Thus we argue that if a die is thrown there is no reason to assume one face more likely to appear uppermost than another and we take the probability of throwing a given number as 1/6th. Although this type of problem is of great value in teaching students to manipulate probabilities in what we may term the 'algebra' of the subject, we shall not usually be concerned with it in this book.

In the second type of problem we have only experimental evidence in the form of n successes out of N trials. We then usually assume that $p=n/N$. In by far the commonest type of case we have certain experimental results and also other information which may be the result of considerable experience.

The values of p assumed will usually be based on all our knowledge. Thus in dealing with mortality investigations actuaries may find from actual observations that out of N men aged x, n die before reaching age $x+1$, but the probability of death which they assume is not usually n/N but also takes into account the mortality at other ages and previous knowledge of mortality.

As a general rule the number of probabilities, the values of which are assigned arbitrarily, is kept as small as possible. The framework of the theoretical model should be such as to enable the other probabilities involved to be deduced from the few which have arbitrarily assigned values.

6·12. Events.

The word *event* is used technically to signify an observation* satisfying some specified condition or conditions. Consider a bag containing one hundred balls, twenty of each of the colours white, yellow, red, blue and black. If it is noted that a ball has colour red this is described as an *event*; if such a ball is drawn from the bag the event is said to occur. If the balls are also numbered the number on a ball may be used to define an event. Suppose the white balls are numbered 1–20, the yellow 11–30, the red 21–40, the blue 31–50 and the black 41–60. Then the event 'ball has number 23' will occur if either the red or the yellow ball with that number is drawn.

Different events may be combined to form *compound events*. Thus the events 'ball has colour black' and 'ball has number 43' may be combined to form the compound event 'ball has colour black *and* number 43'. This is known as the *logical product* of the two events. If one event be represented symbolically by E_1, and another by E_2, then the logical product is written $E_1 E_2$ and means 'both E_1 and E_2'.

Another type of compound event is defined by such statements as 'ball has colour black and/or number 43'. This is termed the *logical sum* of two events. In symbols it is written $E_1 + E_2$, meaning 'either E_1 or E_2 (or both)'.

The logical product of the two events 'ball has colour white' and 'ball has number 35' is 'ball has colour white and number 35' but this event cannot occur because the white balls are numbered 1–20. That is, the two events cannot occur together. Two such events are said to be *mutually exclusive*. Another, obvious, example of mutually exclusive events is 'ball has colour yellow' and 'ball has colour red'. The idea of event is of general application. Thus for a life chosen at random from those on an assurance company's books we can speak of the events 'age between 35 and 40'; 'premium between £50 and £60 p.a.' and of the logical sum and logical product of these events.

* And, in theoretical models, a concept corresponding to such an observation.

6·13. Some elementary consequences of the definition.

As we have seen any probability Pr. $\{E\}$ lies between 0 and 1. It can, in fact, take the extreme values 0 or 1 in the following rather artificial circumstances.

If an event E always occurs, i.e. if it is *certain*, $n=N$ and from the definition we are led to assume

$$\text{Pr.}\{E\}=1. \tag{6·1}$$

If the event E never occurs, i.e. if it is *impossible*, n is always equal to zero and

$$\text{Pr.}\{E\}=0. \tag{6·2}$$

It should be noted, however, that although Pr. $\{E\}$ is zero if E is impossible the converse is not true, i.e. Pr. $\{E\}$ may be zero even if E does occur. An example of such a zero probability will be found in §7·4.

Similarly Pr. $\{E\}$ may be unity even if sometimes E does not occur.

If $\bar{E}$ denotes the event 'not E' the relative frequency of occurrence of $\bar{E}$ is of the form $(N-n)/N=1-n/N$. It follows from the fundamental hypothesis that about 99% of the values of $1-n/N$ lie between $(1-p)-\alpha$ and $(1-p)+\beta$ and as N increases without limit α and β tend to zero while p remains constant.

Hence Pr. $\{\bar{E}\}=1-p=1-\text{Pr.}\{E\}$, or

$$\text{Pr.}\{E\}+\text{Pr.}\{\bar{E}\}=1. \tag{6·3}$$

6·14. The addition and multiplication theorems.

Suppose that in N observations the event E_1 occurs n_1 times in all, the event E_2, n_2 times in all and the compound event E_1E_2, $n_{1,2}$ times in all. Evidently the $n_{1,2}$ times E_1E_2 occurs are included in the n_1 times E_1 occurs, and E_1 occurs without E_1E_2 for $n_1-n_{1,2}$ of the N observations. Similarly E_2 occurs without E_1E_2 for $n_2-n_{1,2}$ of the N observations.

The event E_1+E_2 occurs $n_1+n_2-n_{1,2}$ times in the N observations. This may be appreciated by considering it as (the number of times E_1 occurs) + (the number of times E_2 occurs without E_1), i.e. $n_1+(n_2-n_{1,2})$. We shall assume that we may associate the probabilities Pr. $\{E_1\}$, Pr. $\{E_2\}$ and Pr. $\{E_1E_2\}$ with the events E_1, E_2 and E_1E_2 respectively. By the fundamental hypothesis, the relative frequency $(n_1+n_2-n_{1,2})/N$ about ninety-nine times out of every hundred will lie between limits

$$\text{Pr.}\{E_1+E_2\}+\alpha \quad \text{and} \quad \text{Pr.}\{E_1+E_2\}-\beta.$$

But the relative frequencies n_1/N, n_2/N and $n_{1,2}/N$ will tend in the same way to cluster round the values Pr. $\{E_1\}$, Pr. $\{E_2\}$ and Pr. $\{E_1E_2\}$. Hence the values of $(n_1+n_2-n_{12})/N$ will tend to cluster round the value

$$\text{Pr.}\{E_1\}+\text{Pr.}\{E_2\}-\text{Pr.}\{E_1E_2\},$$

i.e.
$$\text{Pr.}\{E_1+E_2\}=\text{Pr.}\{E_1\}+\text{Pr.}\{E_2\}-\text{Pr.}\{E_1E_2\}. \tag{6·4}$$

This is the *Addition Theorem* for probabilities. The proof just given is not rigorous but the reader will find it instructive to rewrite it introducing limits α and β for each relative frequency (different limits in each case) and thus eliminating the somewhat vague phrase 'cluster round'.

If the events E_1 and E_2 are mutually exclusive (i.e. if they cannot occur together) $n_{1,2}=0$ so that Pr. $\{E_1E_2\}=0$.

We thus have the simple relation for mutually exclusive events:

$$\text{Pr.}\{E_1+E_2\}=\text{Pr.}\{E_1\}+\text{Pr.}\{E_2\}. \tag{6·5}$$

By hypothesis, for a given value of N there exist positive numbers Pr. $\{E_1\}$, α and β such that about 99% of the observed values of n_1/N lie between the limits

$$\text{Pr.}\{E_1\}+\alpha \quad \text{and} \quad \text{Pr.}\{E_1\}-\beta.$$

Also there exist positive numbers Pr. $\{E_1E_2\}$, γ and δ such that about 99% of the observed values of $n_{1,2}/N$ lie between the limits

$$\text{Pr.}\{E_1E_2\}+\gamma \quad \text{and} \quad \text{Pr.}\{E_1E_2\}-\delta.$$

Moreover, as N increases without limit, α, β, γ and δ, all tend to zero, the quantities Pr. $\{E_1\}$ and Pr. $\{E_1E_2\}$ remaining constant.

Now
$$\frac{n_{1,2}}{n_1}=\frac{n_{1,2}/N}{n_1/N}. \tag{6·6}$$

Hence nearly all values of $\frac{n_{1,2}}{n_1}$ will lie between the limits

$$\frac{\text{Pr.}\{E_1E_2\}+\gamma}{\text{Pr.}\{E_1\}-\beta} \quad \text{and} \quad \frac{\text{Pr.}\{E_1E_2\}-\delta}{\text{Pr.}\{E_1\}+\alpha}. \tag{6·7}$$

Using the relative frequency $n_{1,2}/n_1$ in the same way as n/N in §6·10 we are led to the definition of the probability that E_2 occurs given that E_1 occurs. This is called a *conditional* probability and is written $\text{Pr.}\{E_2 \mid E_1\}$.

It follows from (6·7) that

$$\text{Pr.}\{E_2 \mid E_1\} = \text{Pr.}\{E_1 E_2\}/\text{Pr.}\{E_1\},$$

i.e.

$$\text{Pr.}\{E_1 E_2\} = \text{Pr.}\{E_1\}\,\text{Pr.}\{E_2 \mid E_1\} \qquad (6\cdot 8)$$

(equals similarly $\text{Pr.}\{E_2\}\,\text{Pr.}\{E_1 \mid E_2\}$.)

This is the *Multiplication Theorem* for probabilities. It is easily shown that the equations also hold if either $\text{Pr.}\{E_1\}$ or $\text{Pr.}\{E_2\}$ is zero.

It may be noted that in the symbol $\text{Pr.}\{E_2 \mid E_1\}$ for a conditional probability the 'E_1' following the vertical stroke specifies the conditions under which the probability of E_2 occurring is to be evaluated. Strictly speaking, other conditions should be included—method of choice, nature of observations, and so on. From the same strict point of view there should be a vertical bar followed by conditions, even in a simple probability such as $\text{Pr.}\{E_1\}$. It is the usual practice to omit these conditions from the symbols, but the fact that the probability does depend on the conditions under which the observations are obtained must not be forgotten. Consider, for instance, the tossing of a coin. Under usual conditions it is reasonable to assume a probability of between ·4 and ·6 for the event 'uppermost face is "heads"'. If, however, a special tossing machine is used it may be possible to arrange that the probability of this same event shall be nearly unity. The event 'uppermost face is "heads"' is unchanged, but the conditions of tossing, not usually expressed explicitly in the symbols, have altered, giving a different numerical value of the probability of occurrence of the event.

6·15. Independence.

In the theory of probability the event E_2 is said to be independent of the event E_1 if the probability of the occurrence of E_2 is the same whether the event E_1 occurs or not. It follows that if E_2 is independent of E_1 the conditional probability of E_2, given that E_1

occurs, is equal to the probability of E_2 calculated without reference to E_1. Expressed in symbols we have

$$\Pr.\{E_2 \mid E_1\} = \Pr.\{E_2 \mid \bar{E}_1\} = \Pr.\{E_2\}$$

if E_2 is independent of E_1.

Replacing $\Pr.\{E_2 \mid E_1\}$ by $\Pr.\{E_2\}$ in the Multiplication Theorem (equations 6·8) we have

$$\Pr.\{E_1 E_2\} = \Pr.\{E_1\} \Pr.\{E_2\} \tag{6·9}$$

if E_2 is independent of E_1.

If E_2 is independent of E_1 we have

$$\Pr.\{E_1\} \Pr.\{E_2\} = \Pr.\{E_1 E_2\} = \Pr.\{E_2\} \Pr.\{E_1 \mid E_2\}.$$

Hence $\Pr.\{E_1\} = \Pr.\{E_1 \mid E_2\}$ provided $\Pr.\{E_2\} \neq 0$. Thus, excluding events with probability zero, the statement that E_2 is independent of E_1 implies that E_1 is independent of E_2. Independence is therefore a mutual property and E_1 and E_2 may be called *independent events*; so may $\bar{E}_1$ and $\bar{E}_2$. For independent events the Multiplication Theorem takes the symmetrical form of equation (6·9) above.

6·16. Generalization.

The results obtained above for compounds of two events may be extended to compound events formed from an arbitrary number, k, of simple events. $E_1, E_2, \ldots, E_k$. Three useful and simple results follow.

(i) If $E_1, E_2, \ldots, E_k$ are mutually exclusive, i.e. only one of these k events can occur for any one observation; and if one of them must occur for each observation, then

$$\Pr.\{E_1\} + \Pr.\{E_2\} + \ldots + \Pr.\{E_k\} = 1,$$

i.e.

$$\sum_{j=1}^{k} \Pr.\{E_j\} = 1. \tag{6·10}$$

This is a generalization of equation (6·3). As an example consider the throw of a six-sided die. Let E be the event 'uppermost face has j spots' ($j = 1 \ldots 6$). Then the E_j's are mutually exclusive since only one face can be uppermost as a result of any one throw, and one of the E_j's must occur at any one throw since one face must be uppermost. Then

$$\Pr.\{E_1\} + \Pr.\{E_2\} + \Pr.\{E_3\} + \Pr.\{E_4\} + \Pr.\{E_5\} + \Pr.\{E_6\} = 1.$$

If further it is assumed that each face is equally likely to appear (borrowing an idea from the 'theory of equally likely arrangements') it follows that

$$\text{Pr.}\{E_j\}=\tfrac{1}{6} \quad [j=1, 2, 3, 4, 5, 6].$$

(ii) If the events $E_1, E_2, \ldots, E_k$ are mutually exclusive then

$$\text{Pr.}\{E_1+E_2+\ldots+E_k\}=\text{Pr.}\{E_1\}+\text{Pr.}\{E_2\}+\ldots+\text{Pr.}\{E_k\},$$

i.e.
$$\text{Pr.}\left\{\sum_{j=1}^{k} E_j\right\}=\sum_{j=1}^{k}\text{Pr.}\{E_j\}. \tag{6·11}$$

Equation (6·5) is a particular case of this result.

(iii) The events $E_1, E_2, \ldots, E_k$ are a mutually independent set, if any event E_{a_1} or any compound event $E_{a_1}E_{a_2}\ldots E_{a_s}$ is independent of any event E_{b_1} or any compound event $E_{b_1}E_{b_2}\ldots E_{b_r}$ where the a's and b's are integers between 1 and k inclusive and no two of the integers $a_1, \ldots, a_s$, $b_1, \ldots, b_r$ are equal. (Often $E_1, \ldots, E_k$ are a mutually independent set if any two of the events $E_1, \ldots, E_k$ are independent, but this is not always the case. See Exercise 6·12.)

If the events $E_1, \ldots, E_k$ are a mutually independent set

$$\text{Pr.}\{E_1E_2\ldots E_k\}=\text{Pr.}\{E_1\}\,\text{Pr.}\{E_2\}\,\text{Pr.}\{E_3\}\ldots\text{Pr.}\{E_k\},$$

i.e.
$$\text{Pr.}\left\{\prod_{j=1}^{k} E_j\right\}=\prod_{j=1}^{k}\text{Pr.}\{E_j\}. \tag{6·12}$$

Equation (6·9) is a particular case of this result.
The event $E_1E_2\ldots E_k$ is the event 'each of $E_1, E_2, \ldots, E_k$ occurring together'.

Attention may now be drawn to the remarks at the end of § 6·8. The results we have obtained for probabilities of compound events are indeed common to other theories and in particular are valid in the theory of equally likely arrangements developed in *Mathematics for Actuarial Students*.

6·17. Bayes' Theorem.

Consider two sets of events $E_1, E_2, \ldots, E_k$ and $H_1, H_2, \ldots, H_r$. The E's are mutually exclusive and so are the H's; the E's include all possible cases, and so do the H's. Hence

$$\sum_{i=1}^{k}\text{Pr.}\{E_i\}=\sum_{j=1}^{r}\text{Pr.}\{H_j\}=1.$$

The problem now to be solved is: given $\Pr.\{H_j\}(j=1,\ldots,r)$ and $\Pr.\{E_i \mid H_j\}(j=1,\ldots,r;\ i=1,\ldots,k)$ how can $\Pr.\{H_j \mid E_i\}$ be expressed in terms of these known probabilities?

By the Multiplication Theorem

$$\Pr.\{H_j \mid E_i\}=\Pr.\{H_j E_i\}/\Pr.\{E_i\}.$$

Since one of the H's must occur the events E_i and

$$(H_1+\ldots+H_r)\,E_i$$

are equivalent. Therefore

$$\begin{aligned}\Pr.\{E_i\}&=\Pr.\{(H_1+\ldots+H_r)\,E_i\}\\ &=\sum_{j=1}^{r}\Pr.\{H_j E_i\} && \text{(by the Addition Theorem)}\\ &=\sum_{j=1}^{r}\Pr.\{E_i \mid H_j\}\Pr.\{H_j\} && \text{(by the Multiplication Theorem).}\end{aligned}$$

Hence using the Multiplication Theorem again

$$\Pr.\{H_j \mid E_i\}=\frac{\Pr.\{E_i \mid H_j\}\Pr.\{H_j\}}{\sum_{j=1}^{r}\Pr.\{E_i \mid H_j\}\Pr.\{H_j\}}. \qquad (6\cdot 13)$$

This result is Bayes' Theorem. It is valid in all the four systems of probability we have considered. In particular, if $\Pr.\{H_j\}$ be regarded as an *a priori* probability in the sense of § 6·4, $\Pr.\{H_j \mid E_i\}$ is the *a posteriori* probability of the same event after the event E_i has occurred. Bayes' Theorem thus provides a formula for the calculation of *a posteriori* probabilities.

Its sphere of application is restricted in most systems by the difficulty of assigning values to the *a priori* probabilities $\Pr.\{H_j\}$.

Example 6·1.

Three bags A, B and C are indistinguishable in outward appearance. Each bag contains 10 balls. A contains 2 black balls, B contains 3 black balls and C contains 6 black balls. The remaining balls are not black. A bag is chosen at random and a ball drawn from it. What are the posterior probabilities that the bag chosen is A, B or C respectively if the ball chosen is (i) black, (ii) not black?

The symbol E_1 will represent the event 'chosen ball is black'; E_2 the event 'chosen ball is not black'. H_1, H_2, H_3 will represent the events 'chosen bag is A', 'chosen bag is B', 'chosen bag is C' respectively.

Since the bags are chosen at random, the *a priori* probabilities are

$$\text{Pr.}\{H_1\}=\text{Pr.}\{H_2\}=\text{Pr.}\{H_3\}=\tfrac{1}{3}.$$

Also since two balls out of ten in bag A are black

$$\text{Pr.}\{E_1 \mid H_1\}=\tfrac{2}{10}, \quad \text{Pr.}\{E_2 \mid H_1\}=\tfrac{8}{10}.$$

Similarly $$\text{Pr.}\{E_1 \mid H_2\}=\tfrac{3}{10}, \quad \text{Pr.}\{E_2 \mid H_2\}=\tfrac{7}{10};$$

and $$\text{Pr.}\{E_1 \mid H_3\}=\tfrac{6}{10}, \quad \text{Pr.}\{E_2 \mid H_3\}=\tfrac{4}{10}.$$

If the ball chosen is black the event E_1 has occurred. The *a posteriori* probability that the chosen bag is A is then $\text{Pr.}\{H_1 \mid E_1\}$. This probability may be evaluated by means of Bayes' Theorem and is

$$\text{Pr.}\{H_1 \mid E_1\}=\frac{\frac{2}{10}\cdot\frac{1}{3}}{\frac{2}{10}\cdot\frac{1}{3}+\frac{3}{10}\cdot\frac{1}{3}+\frac{6}{10}\cdot\frac{1}{3}}=\frac{2}{11}.$$

Similarly the other *a posteriori* probabilities are

$$\text{Pr.}\{H_2 \mid E_1\}=\frac{\frac{3}{10}\cdot\frac{1}{3}}{\frac{2}{10}\cdot\frac{1}{3}+\frac{3}{10}\cdot\frac{1}{3}+\frac{6}{10}\cdot\frac{1}{3}}=\frac{3}{11},$$

and $$\text{Pr.}\{H_3 \mid E_1\}=\frac{\frac{6}{10}\cdot\frac{1}{3}}{\frac{2}{10}\cdot\frac{1}{3}+\frac{3}{10}\cdot\frac{1}{3}+\frac{6}{10}\cdot\frac{1}{3}}=\frac{6}{11}.$$

Note that

$$\text{Pr.}\{H_1 \mid E_1\}+\text{Pr.}\{H_2 \mid E_1\}+\text{Pr.}\{H_3 \mid E_1\}=1$$

as should be the case.

The reader should obtain for himself the values

$$\text{Pr.}\{H_1 \mid E_2\}=\tfrac{8}{19},$$
$$\text{Pr.}\{H_2 \mid E_2\}=\tfrac{7}{19},$$
$$\text{Pr.}\{H_3 \mid E_2\}=\tfrac{4}{19}.$$

*6·18. *A priori* probabilities.

This section should not be read until the next chapter has been mastered. It is inserted here because it belongs logically to this chapter.

In some of the theories which we have described as 'subjective' the idea of equally likely alternatives (§6·5) has been taken a stage further back. When dealing with the results of a succession of trials as described in §7·1 such theories assign a distribution to the *a priori* probability ϖ. For example, we may, in the absence of any information to the contrary, decide to regard each possible value of

ϖ as equally likely. The distribution of *a priori* probability is then rectangular. The expected value of this distribution

$$\left(\text{i.e.} \int_0^1 \varpi\, d\varpi = \tfrac{1}{2}\right)$$

is then the *a priori* probability of success in the first trial. By the application of Bayes' Theorem the distribution of probabilities can be modified successively as we add to our number of trials, thus obtaining a succession of *a posteriori* probability distributions with their respective expected values as *a posteriori* probabilities. These are, in turn, the *a priori* probabilities of success in the next trial.

If ϖ is supposed to be a continuous variable it is necessary to use a modified form of Bayes' Theorem. It is easily seen that, if $p_1(\varpi)$ be the *a priori* probability density function, the *a posteriori* probability density function will be

$$p_2(\varpi \mid E_i) = \frac{\Pr.\{E_i \mid \varpi\}\, p_1(\varpi)}{\int_0^1 \Pr.\{E_i \mid \varpi\}\, p_1(\varpi)\, d\varpi}.$$

If n trials are made the possible events may be classified as $E_0, E_1, \ldots, E_n$, where E_i stands for 'i successes' and if all values of ϖ between 0 and 1 are assumed to be equally likely

$$p_1(\varpi) = 1 \quad (0 < \varpi < 1).$$

Hence, if the event E_i be observed, the *a posteriori* probability distribution is

$$p_2(\varpi \mid E_i) = \binom{n}{i} \varpi^i (1-\varpi)^{n-i} \quad (0 < \varpi < 1). \tag{6·14}$$

The *a posteriori* probability is the expected value $(i+1)/(n+1)$. If n and i are large this is very nearly equal to the relative frequency of successes, i/n. It may be noted that $p_2(\varpi \mid E_i)$ has a maximum at $\varpi = i/n$, and as n increases (i/n remaining constant), the distribution becomes more and more concentrated about the relative frequency. This may be interpreted as an indication of the way in which the subjective elements present in the *a priori* probability distribution recede in importance as the sample size grows, leaving finally an estimate based on relative frequency.

One difficulty in these theories is that if it be assumed that some function $y = f(\varpi)$ (instead of ϖ itself), is uniformly distributed different results are obtained yet there seems to be no reason for choosing ϖ rather than y as the variable suitable for a uniform distribution. Attempts have been made in recent years by H. Jeffreys and by W. Perks to overcome this difficulty but from our point of view the lack of clear-cut frequency interpretation of the *a posteriori* probabilities remains a disadvantage.

When there are reasons for favouring some values of ϖ rather than others it is, of course, possible in principle to modify the distribution of *a priori* probability to take account of this preference. This is not very often done and it can be shown that the *a posteriori* probability will again be close to the relative frequency when a large number of trials are carried out even in this more general case.

EXERCISES 6

6·1 In a lottery there have been sold 2500 £1 tickets numbered 0001 to 2500 and 5000 10*s*. tickets numbered 2501 to 7500, and it is arranged to draw £500 worth of tickets, the holders of which will receive 10 times the face value of their tickets. The following method of drawing the winning tickets has been suggested. Ten counters marked with the numbers 0 to 9 respectively are to be placed in a bag. A counter is to be taken at random from the bag and replaced; this is to be done four times, and the figures obtained are to be written down in the order in which they are drawn to form a four-figure number. Drawings are to be carried out in this way, the tickets bearing the numbers so drawn to participate in the prize, until £500 worth of tickets have been drawn, subject to the provision that any drawing giving a number to which there is no corresponding ticket or a number which has already been drawn or a number which would cause more than £500 worth of tickets to be drawn is to be ignored.

The following criticisms of the suggested method have been made:

(i) The holders of the 10*s*. tickets have an advantage over the holders of the £1 tickets, since although the 10*s*. tickets cost only half as much as the £1 tickets, they have the same chance of being drawn.

(ii) The system by which it is possible for a number to be drawn to which there is no corresponding undrawn ticket produces inequalities in the chances of the various ticket-holders.

(iii) The system of making the drawings is inequitable, as it does not ensure that the correct proportions of £1 and 10*s*. tickets will participate in the prize.

You are asked briefly to consider these criticisms and to advise whether the method is fair in all its aspects. (Institute of Actuaries Examinations, May 1937.)

6·2 *A* put 10 white and 10 black balls in a bag, handed the bag to *B* without letting him know how many balls there were of each colour, and asked him to make 1000 drawings, replacing each ball drawn after noting its colour.

Without the knowledge of *A* or *B*, *C* examined the contents and substituted another black ball for one of the white balls before the drawings commenced. The result of the 1000 drawings was

White	470
Black	530

A then says the probability of drawing a white ball from the bag is 1/2 and that the actual result was an accidental error. *B* says that the probability is 47/100, *C* says that it is 9/20 and that the result was an accidental error. Discuss these three statements. Who is right and why? (Institute of Actuaries Examinations, May 1933.)

6·3 Criticize the following argument. 'The chance of a male candidate passing a certain examination is 4/7; the chance of a female is 3/7. The chance of a (male or female) candidate passing is therefore $4/7+3/7=1$.'

6·4 Criticize the following, attempting to elucidate the implicit definitions of probability used:

(*a*) The probability of an integer being even is $\frac{1}{2}$.

(*b*) The probability of an integer being 'quadratfrei', i.e. having no repeated factors, is

$$\left(1-\frac{1}{2^2}\right)\left(1-\frac{1}{3^2}\right)\left(1-\frac{1}{5^2}\right)\left(1-\frac{1}{7^2}\right)\left(1-\frac{1}{11^2}\right)\cdots$$
$$=\left(1+\frac{1}{2^2}+\frac{1}{3^2}+\frac{1}{4^2}+\frac{1}{5^2}+\frac{1}{6^2}+\cdots\right)^{-1}$$
$$=6/\pi^2.$$

6·5 *A* speaks the truth 9 times out of 10 and *B* 7 times out of 8. A ball was drawn from a bag containing 5 white balls and 20 black balls and *A* and *B* both stated that a white ball was drawn. What is the chance that the ball drawn was white? (Faculty of Actuaries Examinations, Oct. 1923.)

6·6 A bag contains three balls, one white, one black, and the other either white or black. A ball is drawn and found to be white; find the probability that the third ball is white. (Faculty of Actuaries Examinations, April 1925.)

6·7 Four machines *A*, *B*, *C*, *D* are producing large numbers of small articles. It is known that the average proportions of defective articles produced by the machines are

$$A=1\%,\quad B=1\tfrac{1}{2}\%,\quad C=1\tfrac{1}{2}\%,\quad D=2\tfrac{1}{2}\%.$$

In a group of 20 articles known to have been produced by the same machine, one defective article is found. What is the probability that this group was produced by machine *D*?

State carefully any assumptions which you make.

6·8 X, Y and Z are three brothers who were aged x, y and z respectively on 1st January 1946. Given that just one of the brothers died in the year 1946, use Bayes' Theorem to find the probability that the brother who died was X. How would you interpret this probability? (Use q_x, q_y, q_z to denote the probabilities of X, Y and Z respectively dying during 1946.)

6·9 (i) Define 'statistical probability'.

(ii) Explain carefully the conditions under which you would expect to be able to apply a theory based on your definition, using practical illustrations taken from either (*a*) life assurance work, (*b*) agricultural experiments, (*c*) laboratory routine work, or (*d*) the statistics of economics.

6·10. If $E=E_1+E_2+\ldots+E_k$ and $E_1, E_2, \ldots, E_k$ are mutually exclusive, show that

$$\text{Pr.}\,\{E_0E\}=\sum_{j=1}^{k}\text{Pr.}\,\{E_0E_j\}.$$

Hence show that Pr. $\{E_0\}$ can be expressed as a weighted sum of conditional probabilities. (These are known as 'decomposition formulae'.)

6·11 Distinguish between the conditions in which the probability of an event may be considered as (*a*) the product or (*b*) the sum of the probabilities of two or more separate events. Give examples to illustrate your meaning.

Two throws are made, the first with three dice and the second with two. What is the probability both that the first throw is not less than 11 and that the second throw is not less than 8? (Institute of Actuaries Examinations, May 1930.)

6·12 There are four balls in a bag, one coloured red, one white, one black, and one red, white and black. A ball is drawn at random from the bag. The appearance of colour red on the ball drawn will be called the event E_1, the appearance of white E_2, and the appearance of black E_3. Show that, while any two of these events are independent, the event E_1 is not independent of the compound event E_2E_3.

6·13 According to a certain theory of probability, the probability of an event E is defined as

$$\lim_{N\to\infty}(n/N),$$

where n is the number of times E occurs in N trials.

How would you define conditional probability in this system?

Show that the fundamental theorems of probability apply to this system and give a critical appraisal of the merits and demerits of the theory.

BIBLIOGRAPHY

For an exposition of the main theories of probability see:

For Frequency Theory:

VENN. *Logic of Chance.* Macmillan, London, 1866.

For Inverse Probability:

H. JEFFREYS. *Theory of Probability.* Oxford, Clarendon Press, 1939.

W. PERKS. Some Observations on Inverse Probability including a New Indifference Rule. *J. Inst. Actu.* vol. 73, 1947.

For 'Kollektiv' Theory:

R. VON MISES. *Probability, Statistics and Truth.* 1939.

For Set Theory:

A. KOLMOGOROFF. *Grundbegriffe der Wahrscheinlichkeitsrechnung.* 1933.

For a general discussion:

F. URBAN. *Grundlagen der Theorie der Wahrscheinlichkeitsrechnung und der Theorie der Beobachtungsfehler.* Teubner, 1923.

I. TODHUNTER. *History of the Theory of Probability* (up to Laplace). Cambridge, 1865.

H. LEVY AND L. ROTH. *Elements of Probability* (Chapter 2). Oxford, Clarendon Press, 1936.

J. H. BAPTISTE. *Analyse des Probabilités.* 1947.

W. F. SHEPPARD. The Relation between Probability and Statistics. *Tran. Fac. Actu.* vol. 12.

J. E. KERRICH. *An Introduction to the Theory of Probability.* Munksgaard, Copenhagen, 1946.

M. G. KENDALL. On the Reconciliation of Theories of Probability. *Biometrika*, vol. 36, 1949.

H. CRAMÉR. *Mathematical Methods of Statistics.* Hugo Gebers Forlag, Upsala, 1945. Univ. Press, Princeton, 1946. (Chapters 13–14.)

CHAPTER 7

PROBABILITY: RANDOM VARIABLES

7·1. Random variables.

Statistical data consist of values obtained by measurements of a certain character or characters, of a number of individuals. The observed values of a given character are not usually all the same so that they give rise to the observed distributions studied in earlier chapters. We have now to define a theoretical concept to correspond to these observations. In many cases it is found that as the number of observations is increased the proportion of observations less than a fixed number X, say, becomes more and more stable. From the viewpoint of the frequency theory of probability the sequence of proportions may be regarded as the initial part of a sequence defining the probability that the observed value of the character falls below the number X.

The theoretical concept which we use to correspond with 'observed values' is the *random variable*. x is said to be a random variable if for any number X there is a probability $F(X)$ that x is less than or equal to X.

Symbolically

$$\text{Pr.}\{x \leqslant X\} = F(X). \tag{7·1}$$

The expression obtained by replacing X by x in $F(X)$ is called the *cumulative distribution function* of x. This may be written $F(X)_{x=X}$, or, provided there is no risk of confusion, $F(x)$. The analogy between the cumulative distribution function of a random variable and the cumulative chart of an observed distribution (§ 2·6) should be immediately apparent.

Example 7·1.

Assuming each face of a die equally likely to fall uppermost, what is the cumulative distribution function of x, the number of dots on the uppermost face?

Evidently:

$$\text{Pr.}\{x < 1\} = 0, \quad \text{and so} \quad F(x) = 0 \quad \text{for} \quad x < 1;$$

$\Pr.\{x<2\}=\Pr.\{x=1\}=\frac{1}{6}$, and so $F(x)=\frac{1}{6}$ for $1\leqslant x<2$;

$\Pr.\{x<3\}=\Pr.\{(x=1)+(x=2)\}=\Pr.\{x=1\}+\Pr.\{x=2\}$

since the events $(x=1)$, $(x=2)$ are mutually exclusive,

$=\frac{1}{6}+\frac{1}{6}=\frac{1}{3}$, and so $F(x)=\frac{1}{3}$ for $2\leqslant x<3$.

Similar arguments lead to the results:

$$F(x)=\tfrac{3}{6}=\tfrac{1}{2} \quad \text{for} \quad 3\leqslant x<4;$$
$$F(x)=\tfrac{4}{6}=\tfrac{2}{3} \quad \text{for} \quad 4\leqslant x<5;$$
$$F(x)=\tfrac{5}{6} \quad \text{for} \quad 5\leqslant x<6;$$
$$F(x)=1 \quad \text{for} \quad x\geqslant 6.$$

$F(x)$ may be represented graphically as in Fig. 7·1.

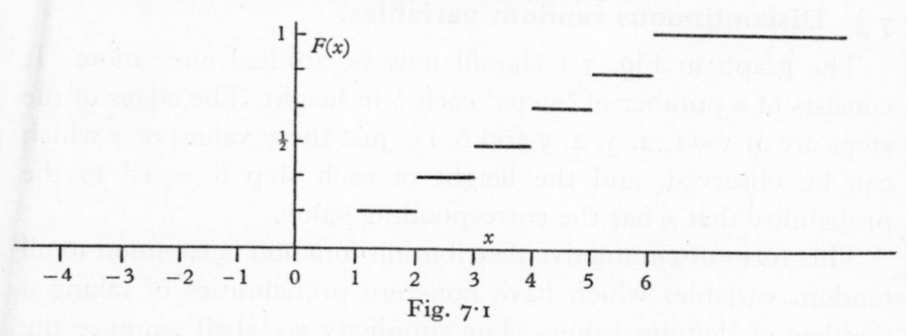

Fig. 7·1

7·2. Properties of cumulative distribution functions.

Since the value of a probability, according to our definition, must not be less than zero or greater than unity it follows that

$$0\leqslant F(x)\leqslant 1. \tag{7·2}$$

If $x_1<x_2$

$$\Pr.\{x\leqslant x_2\}=\Pr.\{(x\leqslant x_1)+(x_1<x\leqslant x_2)\}=\Pr.\{x\leqslant x_1\}+\Pr.\{x_1<x\leqslant x_2\}.$$

Since $\Pr.\{x_1<x\leqslant x_2\}\geqslant 0$ it follows that

$$\Pr.\{x\leqslant x_2\}\geqslant \Pr.\{x\leqslant x_1\}, \quad \text{i.e.} \quad F(x)_{x=x_2}\geqslant F(x)_{x=x_1}.$$

This result may be expressed more conveniently as follows:

If
$$x_1<x_2, \quad \text{then} \quad F(x_1)\leqslant F(x_2). \tag{7·3}$$

The properties expressed in (7·2) and (7·3) are common to all cumulative distribution functions. Hence all cumulative distribution functions are

(i) not less than zero nor greater than unity;
(ii) non-decreasing functions of x.

It will be noted that the function shown in Fig. 7·1 satisfies these conditions. This function also satisfies the further conditions

$$\lim_{x \to -\infty} F(x) = 0. \tag{7·4}$$

$$\lim_{x \to +\infty} F(x) = 1. \tag{7·5}$$

The cumulative relative frequencies of *observed* values also satisfy these conditions in practice. We shall complete our definition of cumulative distribution functions by requiring them to satisfy (7·4) and (7·5).

7·3. Discontinuous random variables.

The graph in Fig. 7·1 should now be studied once more. It consists of a number of 'steps' each $\frac{1}{6}$ in height. The edges of the steps are at $x = 1, 2, 3, 4, 5$ and 6, i.e. just those values of x which can be observed, and the height of each step is equal to the probability that x has the corresponding value.

This form of cumulative distribution function is common to all random variables which have non-zero probabilities of taking a number of definite values. For simplicity we shall suppose the definite values to be finite in number. Let there be k of them $x_1 < x_2 < \ldots < x_k$ and let the probabilities of x taking these values be $p_1, p_2, \ldots, p_k$ respectively, i.e.

$$\text{Pr.}\{x = x_i\} = p_i \quad (i = 1, 2, \ldots, k).$$

Then if $x_{i-1} \leqslant x < x_i$

$$\begin{aligned} F(x) &= \text{Pr.}\{x \leqslant x_{i-1}\} \\ &= p_1 + p_2 + \ldots + p_{i-1}, \end{aligned}$$

while if $x_i \leqslant x < x_{i+1}$

$$F(x) = p_1 + p_2 + \ldots + p_{i-1} + p_i \quad (i = 2, 3, \ldots, k-1).$$

Hence, the form of the graph of $F(x)$ in the neighbourhood of x_i is of the form shown in Fig. 7·2. There is a step of height p_i at x_i. It is easy to see that there is an initial step of height p_1 at x_1 and a final step of height p_k at x_k. The case where the number of possible values is not finite gives similar results.

Since x must have one of the values $x_1, x_2, \ldots, x_k$ and the events $(x=x_i)$ $(i=1, 2, \ldots, k)$ are mutually exclusive it follows that

$$\sum_{i=1}^{k} p_i = 1.$$

This shows that $F(x)$ satisfies the condition $\lim_{x\to\infty} F(x)=1$. The reader should satisfy himself that $\lim_{x\to-\infty} F(x)=0$.

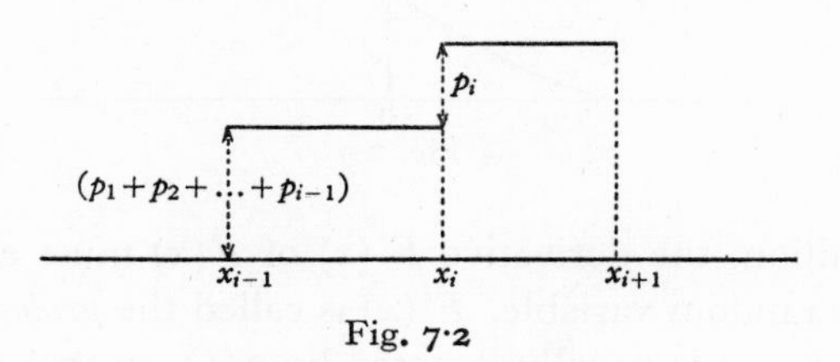

Fig. 7·2

Random variables of the type considered above are termed *discontinuous*; they can take only isolated values. Thus values lying between x_i and x_{i+1} in the above example are not possible. Their cumulative distribution functions are step-functions—the steps occurring at the possible values and the heights of the steps being equal to the corresponding probabilities. A discontinuous random variable may have an infinity of possible discrete values

$$\ldots x_{-2}, x_{-1}, x_0, x_1, x_2, \ldots.$$

If p_i be the probability of such a variable taking the value x_i then the conditions $p_i \geqslant 0$, $\sum_{-\infty}^{+\infty} p_i = 1$ must be satisfied.

7·4. Continuous random variables.

While the discontinuous random variable seems to be an adequate theoretical concept to correspond to certain measurable characters such as number of children in family, there are other characters such as age which are conveniently represented by a random variable which may take *any* real value between certain limits. Such a random variable is said to be *continuous* and is defined by the condition that its cumulative distribution function is continuous and differentiable for all values of x. The graph of such a cumulative distribution function will be of the general form shown in Fig. 7·3. It should be noted that the cumulative distribution function of a continuous random variable must satisfy conditions (7·2), (7·3), (7·4) and (7·5).

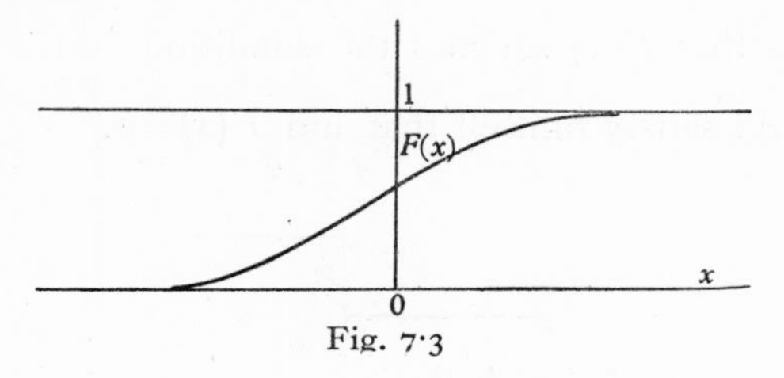

Fig. 7·3

By definition, the derivative $F'(x)$ of $F(x)$ must exist if x is a continuous random variable. $F'(x)$ is called the *probability density function* of x and is usually denoted by $p(x)$, so that $p(x)=F'(x)$.

$$\int_{\alpha}^{\beta} p(x)\,dx=\int_{\alpha}^{\beta} F'(x)\,dx=[F(x)]_{\alpha}^{\beta}=F(\beta)-F(\alpha)$$
$$=\text{Pr.}\{\alpha<x\leqslant\beta\}. \tag{7·6}$$

We see that as $\beta\to\alpha$
$$\text{Pr.}\{\alpha<x\leqslant\beta\}\to 0,$$
i.e.
$$\text{Pr.}\{x=\alpha\}=0.$$

We must express this by saying that the probability of a continuous random variable taking any particular value is zero. This is a distinctive property of continuous random variables as compared with the discontinuous type. Reference has already been made in § 6·13 to the possibility of occurrence of events which have zero probability. For continuous variables it is immaterial whether we write $\text{Pr.}\{\alpha<x<\beta\}$ or $\text{Pr.}\{\alpha<x\leqslant\beta\}$.

Since $\lim\limits_{x\to-\infty} F(x)=0$ and $\lim\limits_{x\to+\infty} F(x)=1$, it follows from equation (7·6) that
$$\int_{-\infty}^{+\infty} p(x)\,dx=1. \tag{7·7}$$

This property of a probability density function is analogous to the property $\Sigma p_i=1$ which holds for the elementary probabilities associated with a discontinuous random variable.

The property corresponding to $p_i \geqslant 0$ is obtained as follows: Let δ be small and positive, then

$$\text{Pr.}\{X-\tfrac{1}{2}\delta < x < X+\tfrac{1}{2}\delta\} = \int_{X-\frac{1}{2}\delta}^{X+\frac{1}{2}\delta} p(x)\,dx \doteq p(X)\,\delta.$$

But $$\text{Pr.}\{X-\tfrac{1}{2}\delta < x < X+\tfrac{1}{2}\delta\} \geqslant 0.$$

Since X may have any value, it follows that

$$p(x) \geqslant 0. \tag{7·8}$$

The relation

$$\text{Pr.}\{X-\tfrac{1}{2}\delta < x < X+\tfrac{1}{2}\delta\} \doteq p(X)\,\delta$$

also indicates the reason for the term 'probability density function'. $p(x)$ is, in fact, approximately, the 'probability per unit interval' in the immediate neighbourhood of x.

Although an unlimited variety of types of random variable may be defined, the two classes, discontinuous and continuous, are sufficient to provide an adequate theory for most practical problems. It should, however, be borne in mind that they do not exhaust the possibilities.

7·5. Expected values.

Suppose that we are in possession of N observations each of which may have any one of a finite number of values $x_1, x_2, \ldots, x_k$. Suppose, further, that n_1 of these observations have the value x_1, n_2 have the value x_2 and, in general, there are n_i observations with the value x_i.

Evidently $\sum_{i=1}^{k} n_i = N$ and the arithmetic mean of these observations is

$$\bar{x} = \frac{1}{N}(n_1x_1 + n_2x_2 + \ldots + n_kx_k) = \frac{1}{N}\sum_{i=1}^{k} n_ix_i = \sum_{i=1}^{k} x_i\left(\frac{n_i}{N}\right).$$

If x is a discontinuous random variable which takes the possible values $x_1, x_2, \ldots, x_k$ with probabilities $p_1, p_2, \ldots, p_k$ respectively, then, on our definition of probability, n_i/N will, in about 99% of cases, lie between limits $p_i+\alpha_i$ and $p_i-\beta_i$ $(i=1, 2, \ldots, k)$ where α_i and β_i will tend to zero as N tends to infinity.

Hence $\sum_{i=1}^{k} x_i(n_i/N)$ will nearly always lie between limits

$$\sum_{i=1}^{k} x_i p_i + \sum_{i=1}^{k} \alpha_i x_i \quad \text{and} \quad \sum_{i=1}^{k} x_i p_i - \sum_{i=1}^{k} \beta_i x_i$$

which have the common limit $\sum_{i=1}^{k} x_i p_i$ as $N \to \infty$.

The quantity $\sum_{i=1}^{k} x_i p_i$ is called the *expected value* of the discontinuous random variable x which takes the possible values $x_1, x_2, \ldots, x_k$ with probabilities $p_1, p_2, \ldots, p_k$ respectively. The expected value of a random variable is denoted by the symbol $\mathscr{E}(x)$.

Hence for the discontinuous random variable x

$$\mathscr{E}(x) = \sum_{i=1}^{k} x_i p_i. \tag{7·9}$$

It should be borne in mind that $\mathscr{E}$ is an operator and $\mathscr{E}(x)$ is not a function of x in the usual mathematical sense.

Evidently the expected value is a theoretical parameter analogous to the observed sample mean. In fact, under certain conditions the expected value may be regarded as the population mean, as we shall see in Chapter 9.

The definition may be extended immediately to discontinuous random variables with an infinite number of possible values

$$\ldots x_{-2}, x_{-1}, x_0, x_1, x_2, \ldots,$$

associated with probabilities $\ldots p_{-2}, p_{-1}, p_0, p_1, p_2, \ldots$. The expected value in this case is

$$\mathscr{E}(x) = \sum_{i=-\infty}^{+\infty} x_i p_i. \tag{7·10}$$

We approach the definition of the expected value of a continuous random variable by first replacing the continuous random variable by an approximately equivalent discontinuous one. It has already been shown that if δ be small and positive

$$\text{Pr.}\{X - \tfrac{1}{2}\delta < x < X + \tfrac{1}{2}\delta\} \doteqdot p(X)\delta.$$

Hence the discontinuous random variable taking the values

$$\ldots -2\delta, -\delta, 0, \delta, 2\delta, \ldots,$$

with probabilities $\ldots p(-2\delta)\delta, p(-\delta)\delta, p(0)\delta, p(\delta)\delta, p(2\delta)\delta, \ldots,$

is approximately equivalent to x. This new variable has expected value

$$\sum_{i=-\infty}^{+\infty} i\delta \,.\, p(i\delta)\,\delta.$$

The smaller δ is, the more closely will the discontinuous and continuous random variables correspond. The expected value of the continuous random variable x is therefore defined as

$$\mathscr{E}(x) = \lim_{\delta\to 0} \sum_{i=-\infty}^{+\infty} i\delta \,.\, p(i\delta)\,\delta = \int_{-\infty}^{+\infty} x \,.\, p(x)\,dx. \qquad (7\cdot 11)$$

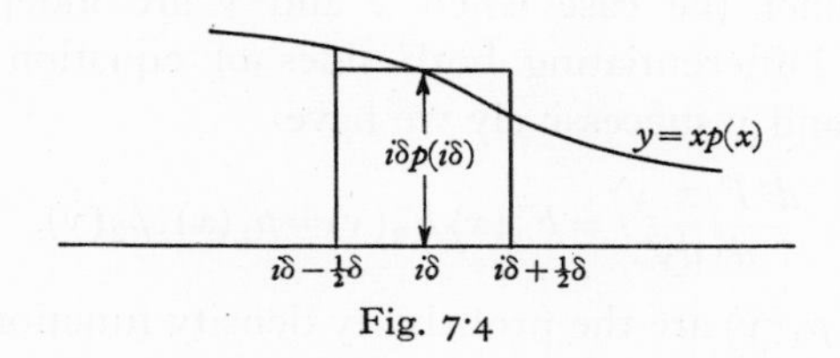

Fig. 7·4

Fig. 7·4 may help the reader to appreciate the meaning of equation (7·11). The true probability is represented by the area bounded by the curve, the axis of x and the two ordinates δ apart while the approximate value used is represented by the area of the rectangle.

Any function of a random variable x, $f(x)$ say, is also a random variable. Hence $f(x)$ also has an expected value. Since it takes the value $f(x_i)$ when $x = x_i$ it follows that

$$\left.\begin{aligned} &\mathscr{E}[f(x)] = \Sigma f(x_i)\,p_i \quad \text{if } x \text{ be a discontinuous random variable.} \\ &\mathscr{E}[f(x)] = \int_{-\infty}^{+\infty} f(x)\,p(x)\,dx \quad \text{if } x \text{ be a continuous random variable.} \end{aligned}\right\} \qquad (7\cdot 12)$$

7·6. Independence.

The random variables x and y are said to be *independent* if the events $(x \leqslant X)$ and $(y \leqslant Y)$ are independent for all values of X and Y.

If we define the *joint cumulative distribution function* of two random variables x and y as

$$F(X, Y) = \text{Pr.}\{x \leqslant X \text{ and } y \leqslant Y\},$$

then if x and y are independent it follows from the definition that

$$\text{Pr.}\{x \leqslant X \text{ and } y \leqslant Y\} = \text{Pr.}\{x \leqslant X\}\,\text{Pr.}\{y \leqslant Y\},$$

and so $$F(X, Y) = F(X)F(Y),$$

i.e. $$F(x, y) = F_1(x) F_2(y), \qquad (7\cdot13)$$

where $F_1(x)$, $F_2(y)$ are the cumulative distribution functions of x and y respectively.

If x and y are independent discontinuous random variables $(x \leqslant X)$ and $(y \leqslant Y)$ and hence $(x = x_i)$, $(y = y_j)$ are independent events. In these conditions therefore

$$\text{Pr.}\{x = x_i \text{ and } y = y_j\} = \text{Pr.}\{x = x_i\}\,\text{Pr.}\{y = y_j\}.$$

Now consider the case when x and y are independent and continuous. Differentiating both sides of equation (7·13) with respect to x and y successively we have

$$\frac{d^2F(x, y)}{dx\,dy} = F_1'(x) F_2'(y) = p_1(x).p_2(y),$$

where $p_1(x)$, $p_2(y)$ are the probability density functions of x and y respectively.

$\dfrac{d^2F(x, y)}{dx\,dy}$ is defined to be the joint probability density function of x and y and may be denoted by $p(x, y)$. Hence, if x and y are independent

$$p(x, y) = p_1(x).p_2(y).$$

The joint probability density function $p(x, y)$ has properties similar to the simple probability density function $p_1(x)$. It can easily be proved that for any two continuous variables x and y, independent or not independent,

(i) $p(x, y) \geqslant 0$. $\qquad$ (7·14)

(ii) $\text{Pr.}\{\alpha < x < \beta;\ \alpha' < y < \beta'\} = \displaystyle\int_{\alpha'}^{\beta'}\int_{\alpha}^{\beta} p(x, y)\,dx\,dy.$ $\qquad$ (7·15)

(iii) $\displaystyle\int_{-\infty}^{+\infty}\int_{-\infty}^{+\infty} p(x, y)\,dx\,dy = 1.$ $\qquad$ (7·16)

Since

$$\int_{\alpha}^{\beta} p_1(x)\,dx = \text{Pr.}\{\alpha < x < \beta\} = \text{Pr.}\{\alpha < x < \beta;\ -\infty < y < +\infty\}$$

$$= \int_{\alpha}^{\beta}\int_{-\infty}^{+\infty} p(x, y)\,dy\,dx \quad \text{by } (7\cdot15)$$

$$= \int_{\alpha}^{\beta}\left\{\int_{-\infty}^{+\infty} p(x, y)\,dy\right\} dx$$

we have the further result

(iv) $$\int_{-\infty}^{+\infty} p(x,y)\,dy = p_1(x) \qquad (7\cdot17)$$

and by symmetry $$\int_{-\infty}^{+\infty} p(x,y)\,dx = p_2(y).$$

The expected value of a function $f(x,y)$ is defined as

$$\mathscr{E}[f(x,y)] = \int_{-\infty}^{+\infty}\int_{-\infty}^{+\infty} f(x,y)\,p(x,y)\,dx\,dy. \qquad (7\cdot18)$$

Joint probability density functions will be studied in more detail in Chapter 11 in the second volume.

7·7. Fundamental theorems on expected values.

We shall first state two simple preliminary results. These are: if A be a constant and x a random variable then

$$\text{(i)}\ \mathscr{E}(A) = A; \quad \text{(ii)}\ \mathscr{E}(Ax) = A\mathscr{E}(x).$$

These results are so obvious that no proof is given. The reader should check their validity for himself.

Theorem A. Let x and y be two discontinuous random variables. Then

$$\mathscr{E}(x+y) = \mathscr{E}(x) + \mathscr{E}(y),$$

i.e. the sum of the expected values equals the expected value of the sum.

Proof. Let

Pr. $\{x = x_i\} = p_i$; Pr. $\{y = y_j\} = p'_j$; Pr. $\{x = x_i$ and $y = y_j\} = P_{ij}$.

Then $$\mathscr{E}(x) = \sum_i x_i p_i, \quad \mathscr{E}(y) = \sum_j y_j p'_j,$$

the summation extending over all possible values.

$(x+y)$ may be regarded as a random variable taking the values $(x_i + y_j)$ with probabilities P_{ij} for all combinations of values of i and j. Hence

$$\begin{aligned}\mathscr{E}(x+y) &= \sum_i\sum_j (x_i + y_j) P_{ij} \\ &= \sum_i\sum_j x_i P_{ij} + \sum_i\sum_j y_j P_{ij}.\end{aligned}$$

Now $$\sum_i\sum_j x_i P_{ij} = \sum_i x_i \sum_j P_{ij}$$

and $$\sum_j P_{ij} = \sum_j \text{Pr.}\{x = x_i \text{ and } y = y_j\} = \text{Pr.}\{x = x_i\} = p_i$$

(since all possible values of y are included in $\sum_j$).

Hence $$\sum_i \sum_j x_i P_{ij} = \sum_i x_i p_i = \mathscr{E}(x),$$

and similarly $$\sum_i \sum_j y_j P_{ij} = \mathscr{E}(y).$$

Thus $$\mathscr{E}(x+y) = \mathscr{E}(x) + \mathscr{E}(y).$$

(Similarly $$\mathscr{E}(x-y) = \mathscr{E}(x) - \mathscr{E}(y).)$$

Theorem B. Let x and y be two independent discontinuous random variables. Then

$$\mathscr{E}(xy) = \mathscr{E}(x)\mathscr{E}(y),$$

i.e. the product of the expected values equals the expected value of the product provided that the variables are independent.

Proof. Using the same notation as in theorem A, since x and y are independent

$$\text{Pr.}\{x = x_i \text{ and } y = y_j\} = \text{Pr.}\{x = x_i\}\,\text{Pr.}\{y = y_j\}$$

that is $$P_{ij} = p_i p'_j.$$

Regarding xy as a random variable which assumes the values $x_i y_j$ with probabilities P_{ij} we have

$$\mathscr{E}(xy) = \sum_i \sum_j x_i y_j P_{ij} = \sum_i \sum_j x_i y_j p_i p'_j = \sum_i x_i p_i \sum_j y_j p'_j.$$
$$= \mathscr{E}(x) . \mathscr{E}(y).$$

It should be noted that theorem A is valid even if the variables x and y are not independent. The two theorems should now be compared with the two fundamental theorems on probabilities of compound events (§6·14). Since a continuous random variable may be regarded as an approximation to a discontinuous random variable for which the possible values are closely packed, we might expect the two theorems to be valid also for continuous random variables. This is, in fact, the case as is indicated by the following brief proofs.

Theorem A.

$$\mathscr{E}(x+y) = \int_{-\infty}^{+\infty} \int_{-\infty}^{+\infty} (x+y)\, p(x,y)\, dx\, dy$$
$$= \int_{-\infty}^{+\infty} \int_{-\infty}^{+\infty} x p(x,y)\, dx\, dy + \int_{-\infty}^{+\infty} \int_{-\infty}^{+\infty} y p(x,y)\, dx\, dy.$$

$$\int_{-\infty}^{+\infty} \int_{-\infty}^{+\infty} x p(x,y)\, dx\, dy = \int_{-\infty}^{+\infty} x \int_{-\infty}^{+\infty} p(x,y)\, dy\, dx$$
$$= \int_{-\infty}^{+\infty} x p_1(x)\, dx = \mathscr{E}(x).$$

Similarly $$\int_{-\infty}^{+\infty}\int_{-\infty}^{+\infty} yp(x,y)\,dx\,dy = \mathscr{E}(y),$$

and the result follows.

Theorem B.

$$\begin{aligned}\mathscr{E}(xy) &= \int_{-\infty}^{+\infty}\int_{-\infty}^{+\infty} xyp(x,y)\,dx\,dy \\ &= \int_{-\infty}^{+\infty}\int_{-\infty}^{+\infty} xyp_1(x)p_2(y)\,dx\,dy \quad \text{since } x \text{ and } y \text{ are independent} \\ &= \left[\int_{-\infty}^{+\infty} xp_1(x)\,dx\right]\left[\int_{-\infty}^{+\infty} yp_2(y)\,dy\right] \\ &= \mathscr{E}(x)\mathscr{E}(y).\end{aligned}$$

A further useful concept is the *conditional expected value.* This is the expected value of a random variable x when another random variable y has a given value. The conditional expected value is written $\mathscr{E}(x \mid y)$. It can be shown that

$$\mathscr{E}(xy) = \mathscr{E}\{x\mathscr{E}(y \mid x)\} = \mathscr{E}\{y\mathscr{E}(x \mid y)\}$$

for any two random variables x and y.

Example 7·2.

If the joint distribution of x and y is that shown in Table 7·1 find $\mathscr{E}(x)$, $\mathscr{E}(y)$, $\mathscr{E}(x+y)$ and $\mathscr{E}(xy)$.

TABLE 7·1

Hypothetical distribution of two random variables

$y=$ \\ $x=$	1	2	3	4	5	6
1	1/36	1/18	—	—	1/36	1/12
2	1/36	—	1/18	—	—	1/18
3	1/36	1/18	—	—	1/18	—
4	1/36	—	1/18	1/6	1/18	1/36
5	1/36	1/18	—	—	—	—
6	1/36	—	1/18	—	1/36	—

By summing rows and columns the elementary probabilities of the distributions of x and y are obtained.

We have

$$\text{Pr.}\{x=1\}=\text{Pr.}\{x=2\}=\ldots=\text{Pr.}\{x=6\}=\tfrac{1}{6};$$

$$\text{Pr.}\{y=1\}=\tfrac{7}{36};\quad \text{Pr.}\{y=2\}=\tfrac{5}{36};\quad \text{Pr.}\{y=3\}=\tfrac{5}{36};$$

$$\text{Pr.}\{y=4\}=\tfrac{12}{36}=\tfrac{1}{3};\quad \text{Pr.}\{y=5\}=\tfrac{3}{36}=\tfrac{1}{12};\quad \text{Pr.}\{y=6\}=\tfrac{4}{36}=\tfrac{1}{9}.$$

Hence

$$\mathscr{E}(x)=1\times\tfrac{1}{6}+2\times\tfrac{1}{6}+\ldots+6\times\tfrac{1}{6}=3\tfrac{1}{2},$$

$$\mathscr{E}(y)=1\times\tfrac{7}{36}+2\times\tfrac{5}{36}+3\times\tfrac{5}{36}+4\times\tfrac{1}{3}+5\times\tfrac{1}{12}+6\times\tfrac{1}{9}=3\tfrac{11}{36}.$$

Using theorem A, $\mathscr{E}(x+y)=\mathscr{E}(x)+\mathscr{E}(y)=6\tfrac{29}{36}$.

Clearly x and y are not independent and theorem B cannot be used. Using conditional expectations we have:

$$\mathscr{E}(y\,|\,x=1)=\frac{1\times\frac{1}{36}+2\times\frac{1}{36}+3\times\frac{1}{36}+4\times\frac{1}{36}+5\times\frac{1}{36}+6\times\frac{1}{36}}{\frac{1}{36}+\frac{1}{36}+\frac{1}{36}+\frac{1}{36}+\frac{1}{36}+\frac{1}{36}}=3\tfrac{1}{2}.$$

Similarly

$$\mathscr{E}(y\,|\,x=2)=3;\quad \mathscr{E}(y\,|\,x=3)=4;\quad \mathscr{E}(y\,|\,x=4)=4;$$

$$\mathscr{E}(y\,|\,x=5)=3\tfrac{1}{2};\quad \mathscr{E}(y\,|\,x=6)=1\tfrac{5}{6}.$$

Hence $\quad \mathscr{E}(xy)=\tfrac{1}{6}[1\times3\tfrac{1}{2}+2\times3+3\times4+4\times4+5\times3\tfrac{1}{2}+6\times1\tfrac{5}{6}]$

$$=11.$$

It will be noted that $\mathscr{E}(x)\mathscr{E}(y)=3\tfrac{1}{2}\times3\tfrac{11}{36}=11\tfrac{41}{72}$ which is not equal to $\mathscr{E}(xy)$. The similarity between Table 7·1 and a correlation table such as Table 4·2 should be noted.

The reader should now construct a dice experiment for which the above example might provide an appropriate theoretical model.

7·8. Standard deviation of a random variable.

The standard deviation of the random variable x is defined as the square-root of the expected value of the square of the difference between x and its expected value. If σ_x be the standard deviation

$$\sigma_x=\sqrt{[\mathscr{E}[\{x-\mathscr{E}(x)\}^2]]}. \qquad (7\cdot19)$$

Squaring in both sides of equation (7·19)

$$\begin{aligned}\sigma_x^2&=\mathscr{E}[\{x-\mathscr{E}(x)\}^2]\\ &=\mathscr{E}[x^2-2x\mathscr{E}(x)+\{\mathscr{E}(x)\}^2]\\ &=\mathscr{E}(x^2)-\mathscr{E}[2x\mathscr{E}(x)]+\mathscr{E}[\{\mathscr{E}(x)\}^2]\quad\text{by theorem A.}\end{aligned}$$

It should be realized that $\mathscr{E}(x)$ is a constant and not a variable function of x. Using the results of §7·7 we have:

$$\sigma_x^2 = \mathscr{E}(x^2) - 2\mathscr{E}(x)\mathscr{E}(x) + \{\mathscr{E}(x)\}^2$$
$$= \mathscr{E}(x^2) - \{\mathscr{E}(x)\}^2. \qquad (7\cdot 20)$$

Formula (7·20) is important and incidentally shows that

$$\mathscr{E}(x^2) \geq \{\mathscr{E}(x)\}^2.$$

The analogy between (7·20) and formula (3·23)

$$s_x^2 = \frac{1}{n}\sum_{i=1}^{n} x_i^2 - \bar{x}^2$$

should be noted. σ_x^2 is indeed the theoretical counterpart of s_x^2 and as we shall see in Chapter 9 may sometimes be regarded as a population standard deviation in the sense of §5·2.

As an example let us calculate the standard deviations of the variables x and y of example 7·2.

$$\text{Pr.}\{x^2 = 1^2\} = \text{Pr.}\{x = 1\} = \tfrac{1}{6}.$$

Similarly

$$\text{Pr.}\{x^2 = 4\} = \text{Pr.}\{x^2 = 9\} = \text{Pr.}\{x^2 = 16\} = \text{Pr.}\{x^2 = 25\}$$
$$= \text{Pr.}\{x^2 = 36\} = \tfrac{1}{6}.$$

Hence $\qquad \mathscr{E}(x^2) = \frac{1}{6}(1 + 4 + 9 + 16 + 25 + 36) = \frac{91}{6},$

and so $\qquad \sigma_x^2 = \frac{91}{6} - \left(\frac{7}{2}\right)^2 = \frac{35}{12},$

$$\sigma_x = \sqrt{\tfrac{35}{12}} = 1\cdot 7078 \quad \text{to four places of decimals.}$$

Similarly

$$\mathscr{E}(y^2) = \tfrac{1}{36}(7 \times 1^2 + 5 \times 2^2 + 5 \times 3^2 + 12 \times 4^2 + 3 \times 5^2 + 4 \times 6^2) = \tfrac{483}{36}.$$

Hence $\qquad \sigma_y^2 = \frac{483}{36} - \left(\frac{119}{36}\right)^2 = \frac{3227}{1296},$

therefore

$$\sigma_y = \sqrt{\tfrac{3227}{1296}} = 1\cdot 5780 \quad \text{to four places of decimals.}$$

7·9. Correlation coefficient for two random variables.

Analogously to the definition of the correlation coefficient between two sets of observed variables (§4·4), the *correlation coefficient* between the random variables x and y is defined as

$$\rho_{xy} = \frac{\mathscr{E}[\{x - \mathscr{E}(x)\}\{y - \mathscr{E}(y)\}]}{\sigma_x \sigma_y}. \qquad (7\cdot 21)$$

Formulae for σ_x and σ_y have already been obtained. The numerator of the expression for ρ_{xy} may be simplified by expansion of the product

$$\{x-\mathscr{E}(x)\}\{y-\mathscr{E}(y)\}.$$

We have

$$\mathscr{E}[\{x-\mathscr{E}(x)\}\{y-\mathscr{E}(y)\}]=\mathscr{E}[xy-x\mathscr{E}(y)-y\mathscr{E}(x)+\mathscr{E}(x)\mathscr{E}(y)]$$
$$=\mathscr{E}(xy)-\mathscr{E}[x\mathscr{E}(y)]-\mathscr{E}[y\mathscr{E}(x)]+\mathscr{E}[\mathscr{E}(x)\mathscr{E}(y)].$$

Remembering that $\mathscr{E}(x)$ and $\mathscr{E}(y)$ are constants we have therefore

$$\mathscr{E}[\{x-\mathscr{E}(x)\}\{y-\mathscr{E}(y)\}]=\mathscr{E}(xy)-\mathscr{E}(x)\mathscr{E}(y)$$
$$-\mathscr{E}(y)\mathscr{E}(x)+\mathscr{E}(x)\mathscr{E}(y)$$
$$=\mathscr{E}(xy)-\mathscr{E}(x)\mathscr{E}(y) \qquad (7\cdot22)$$

(compare with (4·16)).

As an example let us calculate the correlation coefficient of the variables x and y of example 7·2.

We have already found that $\mathscr{E}(xy)=11$; $\mathscr{E}(x)=3\frac{1}{2}$; $\mathscr{E}(y)=3\frac{11}{36}$.

Hence $\mathscr{E}[\{x-\mathscr{E}(x)\}\{y-\mathscr{E}(y)\}]=11-\frac{7}{2}.\frac{119}{36}=-\frac{41}{72}=-\cdot5694,$

and $$\rho_{xy}=-\frac{\cdot5694}{1\cdot7078\times1\cdot5780}=-\cdot211 \text{ approx.}$$

We shall now show that $\rho_{xy}^2\leqslant 1$. Consider the new random variable

$$u=[y-\mathscr{E}(y)]\,\sigma_x-[x-\mathscr{E}(x)]\,\rho_{xy}\,\sigma_y;$$
$$\mathscr{E}(u)=\sigma_x\mathscr{E}[y-\mathscr{E}(y)]-\rho_{xy}\,\sigma_y\mathscr{E}[x-\mathscr{E}(x)]=0$$

since $$\mathscr{E}[y-\mathscr{E}(y)]=\mathscr{E}[x-\mathscr{E}(x)]=0;$$

$$\mathscr{E}(u^2)=\sigma_x^2\mathscr{E}[\{y-\mathscr{E}(y)\}^2]-2\rho_{xy}\,\sigma_x\,\sigma_y\mathscr{E}[\{x-\mathscr{E}(x)\}\{y-\mathscr{E}(y)\}]$$
$$+\rho_{xy}^2\,\sigma_y^2\mathscr{E}[\{x-\mathscr{E}(x)\}^2]$$
$$=\sigma_x^2\,\sigma_y^2-2\rho_{xy}\,\sigma_x\,\sigma_y\rho_{xy}\,\sigma_x\,\sigma_y+\rho_{xy}^2\,\sigma_y^2\,\sigma_x^2$$
$$=\sigma_x^2\,\sigma_y^2(1-\rho_{xy}^2).$$

Hence $$\sigma_u^2=\mathscr{E}(u^2)-\{\mathscr{E}(u)\}^2=\sigma_x^2\,\sigma_y^2(1-\rho_{xy}^2).$$

But $$\sigma_u^2\geqslant 0,\quad \sigma_x^2\geqslant 0\quad\text{and}\quad \sigma_y^2\geqslant 0.$$

Hence $$1-\rho_{xy}^2\geqslant 0;\quad\text{that is}\quad \rho_{xy}^2\leqslant 1.$$

The reader should now refer to §4·5 and note the parallelism between the method used in that section and the present one.

If $\rho_{xy} = \pm 1, \sigma_u^2 = 0$; hence the probability is unity that $u = \mathscr{E}(u) = 0$. In other words if $\rho_{xy} = \pm 1$ the relationship

$$[y - \mathscr{E}(y)]\,\sigma_x = \pm [x - \mathscr{E}(x)]\,\sigma_y$$

holds effectively always. It will be remembered that in § 6·13 it was pointed out that, if the variable is continuous, zero probability does not imply an impossible event. Conversely probability unity does not imply certainty and it is for this reason that the words 'effectively always' are used above.

When $\rho_{xy} = \pm 1$ there is therefore effectively an exact linear relationship between x and y. The converse is obviously true.

We shall now show that when x and y are independent $\rho_{xy} = 0$.

If x and y are independent $\mathscr{E}(xy) = \mathscr{E}(x)\mathscr{E}(y)$ by theorem B. This means that $\mathscr{E}[\{x - \mathscr{E}(x)\}\{y - \mathscr{E}(y)\}] = 0$, and so $\rho_{xy} = 0$.

We have now shown (i) that exact linear relationship between two variables corresponds to a correlation coefficient of ± 1 and that the converse holds, and (ii) that a correlation coefficient of zero arises if the two variables are entirely independent. As we shall show in Example 7·3, however, the converse of the latter statement is not necessarily true—two dependent variables may have a zero correlation coefficient. A zero correlation coefficient is not an indication of lack of dependence, but of lack of a particular form of dependence —*linear* dependence. For this reason the correlation coefficient is sometimes called the linear correlation coefficient, emphasizing the special connexion of the coefficient with linear correlation.

Example 7·3.

Two coins are tossed and a die is thrown. If both coins show the same face (either heads or tails) twice the number shown by the die is taken, otherwise the number itself is taken. Investigate the relationship to be expected between number of heads and number obtained from the throw of the die.

We shall consider only the first steps in the solution of this problem, i.e. the construction of a theoretical model and its examination.

Let x be a random variable corresponding to the number of heads. Assuming each coin to have a probability of $\frac{1}{2}$ of falling heads, we have Pr. $\{x=2\} = \frac{1}{2} . \frac{1}{2} = \frac{1}{4}$; Pr. $\{x=0\} = \frac{1}{4}$ (by the multiplication theorem for probabilities).

Hence Pr. $\{x=1\} = \frac{1}{2}$ since x can take values 0, 1, 2 only. If y be the random variable corresponding to the number arising from the throw of the die, then assuming each face of the die equally likely to fall uppermost

$$\Pr.\{y=2k \mid x=0\} = \Pr.\{y=2k \mid x=2\} = \tfrac{1}{6}; \quad (k=1 \ldots 6);$$
$$\Pr.\{y=k \mid x=1\} = \tfrac{1}{6} \quad (k=1 \ldots 6).$$

Using the multiplication theorem for probabilities we obtain Table 7·2 showing the joint distribution of x and y.

From this table

$$\Pr.\{y=1\} = \Pr.\{y=3\} = \Pr.\{y=5\} = \tfrac{1}{12};$$
$$\Pr.\{y=2\} = \Pr.\{y=4\} = \Pr.\{y=6\} = \tfrac{1}{6};$$
$$\Pr.\{y=8\} = \Pr.\{y=10\} = \Pr.\{y=12\} = \tfrac{1}{12}.$$

TABLE 7·2

$y=$ \ $x=$	0	1	2
1	—	1/12	—
2	1/24	1/12	1/24
3	—	1/12	—
4	1/24	1/12	1/24
5	—	1/12	—
6	1/24	1/12	1/24
8	1/24	—	1/24
10	1/24	—	1/24
12	1/24	—	1/24

$$\mathscr{E}(x) = 0 \times \tfrac{1}{4} + 1 \times \tfrac{1}{2} + 2 \times \tfrac{1}{4} = 1;$$
$$\mathscr{E}(y) = (1+3+5)\tfrac{1}{12} + (2+4+6)\tfrac{1}{6} + (8+10+12)\tfrac{1}{12} = 5\tfrac{1}{4};$$
$$\mathscr{E}(y \mid x=0) = 7 = \mathscr{E}(y \mid x=2); \quad \mathscr{E}(y \mid x=1) = 3\tfrac{1}{2};$$
$$\mathscr{E}(xy) = 0 \times 7 \times \tfrac{1}{4} + 1 \times 3\tfrac{1}{2} \times \tfrac{1}{2} + 2 \times 7 \times \tfrac{1}{4} = 1\tfrac{3}{4} + 3\tfrac{1}{2} = 5\tfrac{1}{4}.$$

Hence $\mathscr{E}(xy) = \mathscr{E}(x)\mathscr{E}(y)$ and so $\rho_{xy} = 0$.

Although $\rho_{xy} = 0$, x and y are clearly not independent since, for example, $\Pr.\{y>6 \mid x=0\} = \tfrac{1}{2}$ while $\Pr.\{y>6 \mid x=1\} = 0$.

7·10. Linear functions of random variables.

A new system of notation will now be employed. $x_1, x_2, \ldots, x_n$ will denote n random variables. This use of these symbols should not be confused with their use in the earlier parts of this chapter to denote particular values of a discontinuous random variable x.

For convenience we shall replace σ_{xi} by σ_i, and $\rho_{x_i x_j}$ by ρ_{ij} and denote $\mathscr{E}(x_i)$ by ξ_i.

Consider the random variable

$$y = a_1 x_1 + a_2 x_2 + \ldots + a_n x_n = \sum_{i=1}^{n} a_i x_i,$$

formed by a linear combination of the random variables $x_1, x_2, \ldots, x_n$ with constant coefficients a_i. The expected value of y is

$$\begin{aligned}\mathscr{E}(y) &= \mathscr{E}(a_1 x_1 + a_2 x_2 + \ldots + a_n x_n)\\ &= \mathscr{E}(a_1 x_1) + \mathscr{E}(a_2 x_2) + \ldots + \mathscr{E}(a_n x_n)\\ &= a_1 \xi_1 + a_2 \xi_2 + \ldots + a_n \xi_n \quad (\text{since } \mathscr{E}(x_i) = \xi_i).\end{aligned}$$

Therefore

$$\mathscr{E}(y) = \sum_{i=1}^{n} a_i \xi_i. \qquad (7{\cdot}23)$$

Also,

$$\begin{aligned}\sigma_y^2 &= \mathscr{E}[\{y - \mathscr{E}(y)\}^2]\\ &= \mathscr{E}[\{a_1 x_1 + a_2 x_2 + \ldots + a_n x_n - (a_1 \xi_1 + a_2 \xi_2 + \ldots + a_n \xi_n)\}^2]\\ &= \mathscr{E}[\{a_1 (x_1 - \xi_1) + a_2 (x_2 - \xi_2) + \ldots + a_n (x_n - \xi_n)\}^2]\\ &= \mathscr{E}\left[\sum_{i=1}^{n} a_i^2 (x_i - \xi_i)^2 + 2 \sum_{i=1}^{n} \sum_{j=i+1}^{n} a_i a_j (x_i - \xi_i)(x_j - \xi_j)\right]\\ &= \sum_{i=1}^{n} a_i^2 \mathscr{E}[(x_i - \xi_i)^2] + 2 \sum_{i=1}^{n} \sum_{j=i+1}^{n} a_i a_j \mathscr{E}[(x_i - \xi_i)(x_j - \xi_j)].\end{aligned}$$

Remembering that $\mathscr{E}(x_i) = \xi_i$ we have

$$\mathscr{E}[(x_i - \xi_i)^2] = \sigma_i^2, \quad \mathscr{E}[(x_i - \xi_i)(x_j - \xi_j)] = \rho_{ij} \sigma_i \sigma_j.$$

Hence

$$\sigma_y^2 = \sum_{i=1}^{n} a_i^2 \sigma_i^2 + 2 \sum_{i=1}^{n} \sum_{j=i+1}^{n} a_i a_j \rho_{ij} \sigma_i \sigma_j. \qquad (7{\cdot}24)$$

Equations (7·23) and (7·24) are important general results. We now proceed to consider their application in special cases.

If the random variables $x_1, x_2, \ldots, x_n$ are mutually independent the correlation coefficients ρ_{ij} are all zero. Equation (7·23) is unaltered by this fact, but equation (7·24) takes the simpler form

$$\sigma_y^2 = \sum_{i=1}^{n} a_i^2 \sigma_i^2. \qquad (7{\cdot}25)$$

If we take $a_1 = a_2 = \ldots = a_n = \frac{1}{n}$,

$$y = \frac{1}{n}(x_1 + x_2 + \ldots + x_n).$$

y may be called the arithmetic mean of the x's and we shall write $\bar{x}$ in place of y. From equation (7·23)

$$\mathscr{E}(\bar{x}) = \frac{1}{n}\sum_{i=1}^{n}\xi_i = \bar{\xi} \quad \text{say,} \tag{7·26}$$

whether the x's are independent or not.

If all the x's have the same expected value ξ then

$$\mathscr{E}(\bar{x}) = \xi. \tag{7·27}$$

From equation (7·24)

$$\sigma_{\bar{x}}^2 = \frac{1}{n^2}\left[\sum_{i=1}^{n}\sigma_i^2 + 2\sum_{i=1}^{n}\sum_{j=i+1}^{n}\rho_{ij}\sigma_i\sigma_j\right], \tag{7·28}$$

while from equation (7·25)

$$\sigma_{\bar{x}}^2 = \frac{1}{n^2}\sum_{i=1}^{n}\sigma_i^2 \quad \text{if the } x\text{'s are independent.} \tag{7·29}$$

If, in this latter case, all the x's have the same standard deviation so that $\sigma_1 = \sigma_2 = \ldots = \sigma_n = \sigma$ say, then equation (7·29) becomes

$$\sigma_{\bar{x}}^2 = \frac{1}{n^2}n\sigma^2 = \frac{\sigma^2}{n},$$

i.e.

$$\sigma_{\bar{x}} = \frac{\sigma}{\sqrt{n}}. \tag{7·30}$$

This last result may be expressed as follows: if the random variables $x_1, x_2, \ldots, x_n$ are independent and have the same standard deviation σ then their arithmetic mean has standard deviation $\sigma/\sqrt{n}$.

This result is very important. It shows that, under the above conditions, the standard deviation of the arithmetic mean becomes smaller and smaller as the number of variables included in it increases. This leads us to regard the mean of a number of *observed* values, which can be supposed independent and of equal variability, as being the less variable the greater the number of observations. The theory which we are constructing has led to this conclusion, which is a preliminary example of the way in which theoretical results are applied to the study of observational data.

If we put $n=2$ in equation (7·24) we obtain

$$\sigma_y^2 = a_1^2\sigma_1^2 + 2a_1a_2\rho_{12}\sigma_1\sigma_2 + a_2^2\sigma_2^2,$$

where

$$y = a_1x_1 + a_2x_2.$$

Putting $a_1 = 1$, $a_2 = 1$ we have

$$\sigma^2_{x_1+x_2} = \sigma_1^2 + 2\rho_{12}\sigma_1\sigma_2 + \sigma_2^2. \tag{7·31}$$

Putting $a_1 = 1$, $a_2 = -1$ we have

$$\sigma^2_{x_1-x_2} = \sigma_1^2 - 2\rho_{12}\sigma_1\sigma_2 + \sigma_2^2. \tag{7·32}$$

These are the formulae for the standard deviation of the sum and difference respectively of two random variables. If x_1 and x_2 are independent then

$$\sigma^2_{x_1+x_2} = \sigma^2_{x_1-x_2} = \sigma_1^2 + \sigma_2^2. \tag{7·33}$$

If therefore $\bar{x}_1$ be the mean of n_1 random variables, each with standard deviation σ_1, $\bar{x}_2$ the mean of another n_2 random variables each with standard deviation σ_2 and all the random variables are mutually independent we may combine equations (7·30) and (7·33) to obtain the formula for the standard deviation of the difference between two independent means

$$\sigma^2_{\bar{x}_1-\bar{x}_2} = \frac{\sigma_1^2}{n_1} + \frac{\sigma_2^2}{n_2}. \tag{7·34}$$

7·11. Expected value of the mean square deviation.

As a further example of evaluation of expected values we shall consider the important *mean square deviation* or *squared standard deviation*

$$s^2 = \frac{1}{n}\sum_{i=1}^{n}(x_i - \bar{x})^2.$$

$\bar{x}$ is the arithmetic mean of the n random variables $x_1, x_2, \ldots, x_n$. The random variable s is evidently the analogue in the theoretical system of the sample standard deviation.

We suppose the x's are mutually independent random variables and that

$$\mathscr{E}(x_i) = \xi. \quad \mathscr{E}[(x_i - \xi)^2] = \sigma^2 \quad (i = 1, 2, \ldots, n).$$

Let $y_i = x_i - \xi$ $(i = 1, 2, \ldots, n)$, so that

$$\mathscr{E}(y_i) = 0 \quad \text{and} \quad \mathscr{E}(y_i^2) = \sigma^2.$$

We have already shown that if

$$\bar{y} = \frac{1}{n}\sum_{i=1}^{n} y_i = \bar{x} - \xi \tag{7·35}$$

then $$\mathscr{E}(\bar{y}^2)=\sigma^2/n \quad \text{(see (7·30))}.$$

Now $$s^2=\frac{1}{n}\sum_{i=1}^{n}[(x_i-\xi)-(\bar{x}-\xi)]^2=\frac{1}{n}\sum_{i=1}^{n}(y_i-\bar{y})^2$$

$$=\frac{1}{n}\sum_{i=1}^{n}y_i^2-\bar{y}^2. \qquad (7·36)$$

Hence $$\mathscr{E}(s^2)=\frac{1}{n}\sum_{i=1}^{n}\mathscr{E}(y_i^2)-\mathscr{E}(\bar{y}^2)$$

$$=\frac{1}{n}.n\sigma^2-\frac{\sigma^2}{n}$$

$$=\frac{n-1}{n}\sigma^2. \qquad (7·37)$$

We note therefore that the expected value of the random variable corresponding to the square of the sample standard deviation differs slightly from the quantity corresponding to the square of the population standard deviation. This should be compared with the result, obtained in §7·10, on the expected value of the arithmetic mean.

Several important results which may be obtained by the methods of this section are given as exercises for the reader in Exercises 7·9–7·11.

7·12. Approximate methods.

(i) Consider the random variable y defined as the ratio of the independent random variables x_1, x_2, i.e.

$$y=\frac{x_1}{x_2}.$$

The problem of finding the expected value and standard deviation of y is difficult to solve rigorously but a useful approximation is possible provided it may be assumed that the difference of x_2 from its expected value ξ_2 is small compared with ξ_2.

Let
$$\delta x_1=x_1-\xi_1, \quad \delta x_2=x_2-\xi_2.$$

We shall assume $\dfrac{\delta x_2}{\xi_2}$ to be small.

Then

$$y=\frac{\xi_1+\delta x_1}{\xi_2+\delta x_2}=\frac{\xi_1}{\xi_2}\left(1+\frac{\delta x_1}{\xi_1}\right)\left(1+\frac{\delta x_2}{\xi_2}\right)^{-1}$$

$$\doteqdot\frac{\xi_1}{\xi_2}\left(1+\frac{\delta x_1}{\xi_1}\right)\left\{1-\frac{\delta x_2}{\xi_2}+\left(\frac{\delta x_2}{\xi_2}\right)^2\right\},\quad \text{since } \frac{\delta x_2}{\xi_2} \text{ is small}$$

$$\doteqdot\frac{\xi_1}{\xi_2}\left[1+\frac{\delta x_1}{\xi_1}-\frac{\delta x_2}{\xi_2}-\frac{\delta x_1\,\delta x_2}{\xi_1\xi_2}+\left(\frac{\delta x_2}{\xi_2}\right)^2+\frac{\delta x_1}{\xi_1}\left(\frac{\delta x_2}{\xi_2}\right)^2\right].$$

Now $\mathscr{E}(\delta x_1)=\mathscr{E}(\delta x_2)=0$;

$$\mathscr{E}[(\delta x_1)^2]=\sigma_1^2;\quad \mathscr{E}[(\delta x_2)^2]=\sigma_2^2;\quad \mathscr{E}(\delta x_1\,\delta x_2)=\mathscr{E}[\delta x_1(\delta x_2)^2]=0$$

since x_1 and x_2 are independent.

Therefore

$$\mathscr{E}(y)\doteqdot\mathscr{E}\left[\frac{\xi_1}{\xi_2}\left\{1+\frac{\delta x_1}{\xi_1}-\frac{\delta x_2}{\xi_2}-\frac{\delta x_1\,\delta x_2}{\xi_1\xi_2}+\left(\frac{\delta x_2}{\xi_2}\right)^2+\frac{\delta x_1}{\xi_1}\left(\frac{\delta x_2}{\xi_2}\right)^2\right\}\right]$$

$$\doteqdot\frac{\xi_1}{\xi_2}\left(1+\frac{\sigma_2^2}{\xi_2^2}\right) \tag{7·38}$$

and

$$\mathscr{E}(y^2)\doteqdot\mathscr{E}\left[\frac{\xi_1^2}{\xi_2^2}\left\{1+3\left(\frac{\delta x_2}{\xi_2}\right)^2+\left(\frac{\delta x_1}{\xi_1}\right)^2+3\left(\frac{\delta x_1}{\xi_1}\right)^2\left(\frac{\delta x_2}{\xi_2}\right)^2\right\}\right]$$

omitting terms with expected value zero or of third and higher powers in $\delta x_2/\xi_2$; therefore

$$\mathscr{E}(y^2)\doteqdot\frac{\xi_1^2}{\xi_2^2}\left(1+3\frac{\sigma_2^2}{\xi_2^2}+\frac{\sigma_1^2}{\xi_1^2}+3\frac{\sigma_1^2\sigma_2^2}{\xi_1^2\xi_2^2}\right).$$

Hence

$$\sigma_y^2\doteqdot\frac{\xi_1^2}{\xi_2^2}\left(\frac{\sigma_1^2}{\xi_1^2}+\frac{\sigma_2^2}{\xi_2^2}+3\frac{\sigma_1^2\sigma_2^2}{\xi_1^2\xi_2^2}\right), \tag{7·39}$$

omitting terms of the third and higher powers in σ_2/ξ_2.

The ratio of two random variables is, of course, a theoretical concept which might be applied to observed index numbers.

(ii) Consider the random variable y defined as a monotonic function $f(x)$ of the random variable x. A monotonic function of x is one which always increases (or always decreases) as x increases. The problem of finding the expected value and standard deviation of y, given the expected value ξ and standard deviation σ_x of x, may be solved, approximately, by the following method.

With a notation analogous to that used in (i) of this section we write

$$\delta x=x-\xi;\quad \delta y=y-\mathscr{E}(y).$$

Expanding $f(x)$ by Taylor's series

$$y=f(\xi)+\frac{\delta x}{1\,!}f^{\text{i}}(\xi)+\frac{(\delta x)^2}{2\,!}f^{\text{ii}}(\xi)+\dots$$

Taking expected values of both sides of this equation we have:

$$\mathscr{E}(y)\doteqdot f(\xi)+\frac{\sigma_x^2}{2\,!}f^{\text{ii}}(\xi)\quad\text{since}\quad\mathscr{E}[(\delta x)^2]=\sigma_x^2.$$

Hence $\quad \delta y=y-\mathscr{E}(y)\doteqdot\delta x\,.\,f^{\text{i}}(\xi)+\tfrac{1}{2}[(\delta x)^2-\sigma_x^2]f^{\text{ii}}(\xi).$

Therefore

$$(\delta y)^2=(\delta x)^2[\{f^{\text{i}}(\xi)\}^2-\tfrac{1}{2}\sigma_x^2\{f^{\text{ii}}(\xi)\}^2]-\sigma_x^2\delta x\,.\,f^{\text{i}}(\xi)f^{\text{ii}}(\xi)$$
$$+\tfrac{1}{4}\sigma_x^4\{f^{\text{ii}}(\xi)\}^2+\text{terms}$$

involving the third and higher powers of δx.

Taking expected values of both sides of this equation we have

$$\sigma_y^2\doteqdot\sigma_x^2\{f^{\text{i}}(\xi)\}^2,\quad\sigma_y\doteqdot\sigma_x f^{\text{i}}(\xi),\tag{7·40}$$

if σ_x is so small that fourth and higher powers can be ignored. (7·40) may be written in the suggestive form

$$\frac{\sigma_y}{\sigma_x}\doteqdot\left|\frac{dy}{dx}\right|_{x=\xi}.$$

This approximation is especially useful in deducing the approximate standard deviation of the square-root of a random variable with a known standard deviation, e.g. in deducing σ_s from σ_{s^2}.

The two methods outlined above often provide valuable approximate solutions of what are otherwise difficult problems.

7·13. Moments.

Again proceeding by analogy with our treatment of observed distributions we define the rth moment of the random variable x about A (A being a constant) as

$${}_A\mu_r=\mathscr{E}[(x-A)^r].\tag{7·41}$$

If $A=0$ we have the *rth moment about zero*

$$\mu_r'={}_0\mu_r=\mathscr{E}(x^r).\tag{7·42}$$

If $A=\mathscr{E}(x)$ we have the *rth central moment*

$$\mu_r={}_{\mathscr{E}(x)}\mu_r=\mathscr{E}[\{x-\mathscr{E}(x)\}^r].\tag{7·43}$$

The relations $\mu_2 = \mu_2' - \mu_1'^2$, (7·44)

$$\mu_3 = \mu_3' - 3\mu_1'\mu_2' + 2\mu_1'^3, \qquad (7\cdot45)$$

and $$\mu_4 = \mu_4' - 4\mu_1'\mu_3' + 6\mu_1'^2\mu_2' - 3\mu_1'^4, \qquad (7\cdot46)$$

which are analogous to equations (3·30), (3·36) and (3·37) are easily proved.

Evidently $\quad {}_A\mu_0 = 1, \quad \mu_1' = \mathscr{E}(x) \quad$ and $\quad \mu_2 = \sigma_x^2$.

The *rth absolute moment* of x about A is defined as

$${}_A\nu_r = \mathscr{E}[|x - A|^r].$$

The *rth absolute moment about zero* is $\nu_r' = {}_0\nu_r = \mathscr{E}(|x|^r)$.

The *rth absolute central moment* is $\nu_r = {}_{\mathscr{E}(x)}\nu_r = \mathscr{E}[|x - \mathscr{E}(x)|^r]$.

Evidently, if r be even, ${}_A\mu_r = {}_A\nu_r$.

If $r = 1$; $\mu_1 = 0$ while ν_1 is called the *mean deviation* of x.

The moment ratios α_j are defined by the equations

$$\alpha_j = \frac{\mu_j}{\mu_2^{\frac{1}{2}j}} \quad (j = 3, 4, \ldots).$$

$$\alpha_3 = \frac{\mu_3}{\mu_2^{\frac{3}{2}}} \text{ is often referred to as } \sqrt{\beta_1};$$

$$\alpha_4 = \frac{\mu_4}{\mu_2^2} \text{ is often referred to as } \beta_2.$$

The analogy of $\sqrt{\beta_1}$ and β_2 to $\sqrt{b_1}$ and b_2 will be at once apparent.

Example 7·4.

Find the expected value, standard deviation and general moment ratio of the continuous variable x which has the probability density function $p(x) = 1/2d$ for $\xi - d \leqslant x \leqslant \xi + d$

$$= 0 \text{ elsewhere.}$$

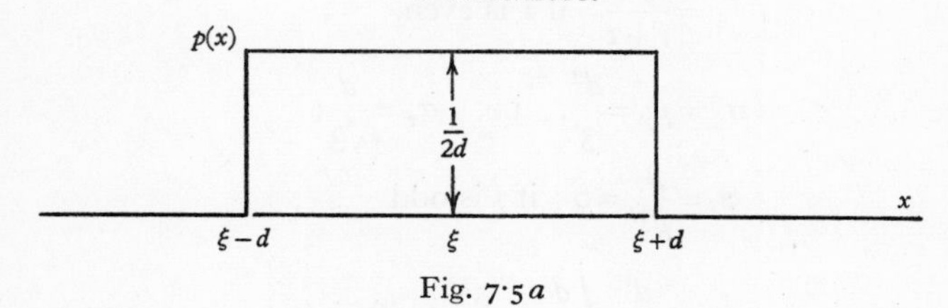

Fig. 7·5 *a*

Fig. 7·5 *a* shows the graph of $p(x)$ and Fig. 7·5 *b* shows the graph of the corresponding cumulative distribution function $F(x)$. The distribution defined by $p(x)$ is called the *rectangular distribution*.

We may first check whether $p(x)$ as defined above satisfies the conditions required of a probability density function. Since $p(x) \geqslant 0$ and

$$\int_{-\infty}^{\infty} p(x)\,dx = \int_{-\infty}^{\xi-d} 0\,.\,dx + \int_{\xi-d}^{\xi+d} \frac{1}{2d}\,dx + \int_{\xi+d}^{\infty} 0\,.\,dx = 1,$$

$p(x)$ does satisfy these conditions.

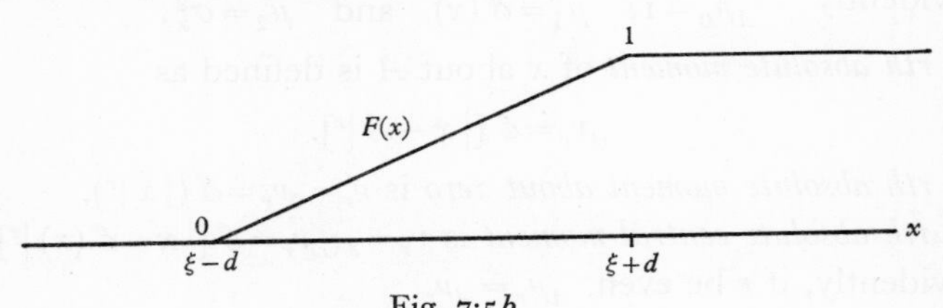

Fig. 7·5*b*

$$\mathscr{E}(x) = \int_{-\infty}^{+\infty} x\,p(x)\,dx = \int_{\xi-d}^{\xi+d} x\,.\,\frac{1}{2d}\,dx$$

$$= \frac{1}{4d}\left[x^2\right]_{\xi-d}^{\xi+d} = \xi,$$

$$\mu_r = \mathscr{E}\left[(x-\xi)^r\right] = \int_{-\infty}^{+\infty} (x-\xi)^r\,p(x)\,dx = \int_{\xi-d}^{\xi+d} (x-\xi)^r\,p(x)\,dx.$$

Substituting $x - \xi = t$ this becomes

$$\int_{-d}^{d} t^r \frac{1}{2d}\,dt = \frac{1}{2(r+1)\,d}\left[t^{r+1}\right]_{-d}^{d};$$

therefore $\mu_r = 0$ if r is odd

$$= \frac{d^r}{r+1} \quad \text{if } r \text{ is even.}$$

Hence $\sigma_x^2 = \mu_2 = \dfrac{d^2}{3}$, i.e. $\sigma_x = \dfrac{d}{\sqrt{3}}$;

$$\alpha_j = \frac{\mu_j}{\mu_2^{\frac{1}{2}j}} = 0 \quad \text{if } j \text{ is odd}$$

$$= \frac{d^j}{j+1}\Big/\frac{d^j}{3^{\frac{1}{2}j}} = \frac{3^{\frac{1}{2}j}}{j+1} \quad \text{if } j \text{ is even.}$$

In particular $\sqrt{\beta_1} = \alpha_3 = 0$, $\beta_2 = \alpha_4 = \dfrac{3^2}{5} = 1\cdot 8.$

The random variable x might be an appropriate theoretical model for the rounding off error in tabulated values of a function. If there be, say, four decimal places given in the table we should take $\xi=0$ and $d=5\times 10^{-5}$.

7·14. Standardization.

From a random variable x with a finite expected value ξ and standard deviation σ_x there may be constructed a random variable x' with expected value zero and standard deviation unity, having the same moment-ratios as x. The random variable x' is known as the *standardized* variable corresponding to x. x and x' are related by the equation

$$x'=\frac{x-\xi}{\sigma_x}. \tag{7·47}$$

Evidently $$\mathscr{E}(x')=\frac{1}{\sigma_x}\mathscr{E}(x-\xi)=0,$$

$$\sigma^2_{x'}=\mathscr{E}(x'^2)=\frac{1}{\sigma^2_x}\mathscr{E}[(x-\xi)^2]=\frac{1}{\sigma^2_x}\sigma^2_x=1.$$

The jth moment ratio of x' is

$$\alpha_j(x')=\frac{\mathscr{E}(x'^j)}{1^{\frac{1}{2}j}}=\frac{1}{\sigma_x{}^j}\mathscr{E}[(x-\xi)^j]=\alpha_j(x), \tag{7·48}$$

so that the moment-ratios of x' equal those of x, as required.

If $\mathscr{E}(y)=\eta$, and $y'=\dfrac{y-\eta}{\sigma_y}$ is the standardized variable corresponding to y, then

$$\mathscr{E}(x'y')=\mathscr{E}\left[\frac{x-\xi}{\sigma_x}.\frac{y-\eta}{\sigma_y}\right]=\frac{1}{\sigma_x\sigma_y}\mathscr{E}[(x-\xi)(y-\eta)]=\rho_{xy}.$$

But $$\rho_{x'y'}=\frac{1}{\sigma_{x'}\sigma_{y'}}[\mathscr{E}(x'y')-\mathscr{E}(x')\mathscr{E}(y')]=\frac{1}{1\times 1}(\rho_{xy}-0).$$

Therefore $$\rho_{x'y'}=\rho_{xy}. \tag{7·49}$$

Thus the correlation coefficient is unchanged by standardization. More generally the correlation coefficient of any linear function of x and any linear function of y is equal to the correlation coefficient of x and y.

7·15. Tchebyshev's inequalities.

It is clear that the smaller the standard deviation of a random variable the less often it should take values differing by a great deal from its expected value. The results to be obtained in this section give more precise shape to this general idea and are applicable to *any distribution*. The proof will be given for the case of a continuous random variable only, the discontinuous case being left to the reader.

Let $p(y)$ be the probability density function of a random variable y which cannot take negative values.

Then

$$\mathscr{E}(y^r) = \int_0^\infty y^r p(y)\, dy = \int_0^A y^r p(y)\, dy + \int_A^\infty y^r p(y)\, dy,$$

where A is an arbitrary constant

$$\int_A^\infty y^r p(y)\, dy \geqslant A^r \int_A^\infty p(y)\, dy = A^r \text{ Pr.}\{y > A\}.$$

Also
$$\int_0^A y^r p(y)\, dy \geqslant 0.$$

Therefore
$$\mathscr{E}(y^r) \geqslant A^r \text{ Pr.}\{y > A\}. \tag{7·50}$$

Now put $y = |x - \mathscr{E}(x)|$ which is, of course, positive or zero. Then (7·50) becomes

$$\mathscr{E}(|x - \mathscr{E}(x)|^r) \geqslant A^r \text{ Pr.}\{|x - \mathscr{E}(x)| > A\}$$

or
$$\nu_r \geqslant A^r \text{ Pr.}\{|x - \mathscr{E}(x)| > A\}.$$

Putting
$$A = t\nu_r^{\frac{1}{r}}$$

we have
$$\text{Pr.}\{|x - \mathscr{E}(x)| > t\nu_r^{\frac{1}{r}}\} \leqslant \frac{1}{t^r}. \tag{7·51}$$

The special case corresponding to $r = 2$ is usually called Tchebyshev's inequality although its discovery was anticipated by Bienaimé. In this case the inequality becomes

$$\text{Pr.}\{|x - \mathscr{E}(x)| > t\sigma_x\} \leqslant \frac{1}{t^2}, \tag{7·52}$$

or
$$\text{Pr.}\left\{\left|\frac{x - \mathscr{E}(x)}{\sigma_x}\right| > t\right\} \leqslant \frac{1}{t^2}, \tag{7·53}$$

which gives an upper limit to the frequency with which in the long run x may be expected to differ from its expected value by t times its standard deviation or more. (7·53) is in a convenient form for standardized variates.

As formula (7·52) is of very wide application to all random variables we should expect the actual probabilities of a deviation of $t\sigma_x$ or more from the expected value to be considerably less than $1/t^2$ in many cases. Thus if x be distributed rectangularly as in Example 7·4 and we take $t=\frac{3\sqrt{3}}{4}$, (7·52) gives

$$\text{Pr.}\left\{|x-\mathscr{E}(x)|>\frac{3\sqrt{3}}{4}\sigma_x\right\}\leqslant\tfrac{16}{27}=\cdot 59 \text{ approx.}$$

Actually $\sigma_x=\frac{d}{\sqrt{3}}$ in the notation of the example and $\frac{3\sqrt{3}}{4}\sigma_x$ is therefore $\frac{3d}{4}$.

Hence
$$\text{Pr.}\left\{|x-\mathscr{E}(x)|>\frac{3\sqrt{3}}{4}\sigma_x\right\}=\cdot 25.$$

If (7·52) be applied to the random variable $\bar{x}$ which is the arithmetic mean of n independent random variables each with expected value ξ and standard deviation σ then

$$\mathscr{E}(\bar{x})=\xi \quad\text{and}\quad \sigma_{\bar{x}}=\frac{\sigma}{\sqrt{n}}.$$

We therefore obtain

$$\text{Pr.}\left\{|\bar{x}-\xi|>\frac{t\sigma}{\sqrt{n}}\right\}\leqslant\frac{1}{t^2},$$

or putting

$$t'=\frac{t}{\sqrt{n}},$$

$$\text{Pr.}\{|\bar{x}-\xi|>t'\sigma\}\leqslant\frac{1}{nt'^2}. \tag{7·54}$$

From (7·54) we see that

$$\lim_{n\to\infty}\text{Pr.}\{|\bar{x}-\xi|>t'\sigma\}=0.$$

Since t' may have any value this means that as n increases the difference between $\bar{x}$ and ξ exceeds any pre-assigned value (however small) with diminishing frequency and finally extremely rarely.

This type of limit is probably new to the reader but it is important in probability theory. We have not shown that $|\bar{x}-\xi|$ will tend to zero; however big n may be the difference $|\bar{x}-\xi|$ may be quite large but the *probability* of obtaining a large value will be small. Suppose, for instance, that the pre-assigned value is ·001 so that we are considering the probability that $|\bar{x}-\xi|$ will exceed the one-thousandth part of the standard deviation σ. However large n may be $|\bar{x}-\xi|$ (calculated for n values) *may* exceed $\cdot 001\,\sigma$ but the theorem enunciated above tells us that the probability that it will do so becomes smaller as n increases and tends to zero as n tends to infinity.

*7·16. Gauss' inequality.

The inequality (7·53) usually overestimates the probability by a considerable amount. No lower estimate based on the standard deviation alone would, however, be of such universal validity. That this is the case may be seen by considering distributions of the type $\Pr.\{x=0\}=\Pr.\{x=2\}=p$; $\Pr.\{x=1\}=1-2p$. The expected value of such a distribution is 1 and its standard deviation is $\sqrt{(2p)}$.

$\Pr.\left\{\left|\dfrac{x-\mathscr{E}(x)}{\sqrt{(2p)}}\right|>t\right\}$ is equal to $2p$ for all values of t less than $(\sqrt{(2p)})^{-1}$, while $t^{-2}=2p$ if $t=(\sqrt{(2p)})^{-1}$, showing that no lower limit is possible in this case.

If, however, the distribution of the random variable x is not known precisely, certain of its properties may be known with fair certitude. These properties may, without completely defining the distribution, so restrict the possible forms which it can take that considerable improvement on Tchebyshev's inequality is possible. This is to be expected, since the case of partially restrictive conditions is intermediate between the case of unrestricted conditions in which Tchebyshev's inequality holds, and the case of completely defined distributions when the relevant probabilities may be determined exactly.

In this section an inequality called *Gauss' inequality* will be developed. While not possessing the universal validity of Tchebyshev's inequality, it is yet applicable in many practical cases. The inequality applies to both discontinuous and continuous random variables, with appropriate rewording of the restrictive condition. We shall consider here the case of a continuous random variable, x.

It will be convenient to deal not with x directly but with the random variable y defined by the equation

$$y=\left|\frac{x-\mathscr{E}(x)}{\sigma_x}\right|. \tag{7·55}$$

Evidently
$$\mathscr{E}(y^2)=\int_0^\infty y^2 p(y)\,dy=1, \tag{7·56}$$

since
$$p(y)=0 \quad \text{if} \quad y<0.$$

As in §7·15 an upper limit for Pr. $\{y>t\}$ will be sought.

The restrictive condition will now be introduced; it is

$$p(y)\geqslant p(y)_{y=t} \quad \text{if} \quad y<t, \tag{7·57}$$

$$p(y)\leqslant p(y)_{y=t} \quad \text{if} \quad y>t. \tag{7·58}$$

If $p(y)$ decreases as y increases from 0 to ∞, this condition is satisfied for all values of t. It may hold for *some* values of t, even if this is not the case. The assumption that the condition holds is reasonable if it is felt that the probability of a deviation from the expected value is likely to decrease as the absolute magnitude of the deviation increases, except possibly when this absolute magnitude is fairly small.

In the following mathematical work we shall use p_t as a convenient abbreviation for $p(y)_{y=t}$.

We define l as a number such that

$$lp_t=\text{Pr.}\{y>t\}=\int_t^\infty p(y)\,dy. \tag{7·59}$$

Since
$$p(y)\geqslant p_t \quad \text{if} \quad y<t,$$

$$\int_0^t y^2 p(y)\,dy\geqslant p_t\int_0^t y^2\,dy. \tag{7·60}$$

$$\int_t^\infty y^2 p(y)\,dy=\int_t^{t+l} y^2 p(y)\,dy+\int_{t+l}^\infty y^2 p(y)\,dy$$

$$=\int_t^{t+l} y^2 p_t\,dy+\int_t^{t+l} y^2\{p(y)-p_t\}\,dy+\int_{t+l}^\infty y^2 p(y)\,dy. \tag{7·61}$$

We shall now prove that the right-hand side of this equation is greater than $\int_t^{t+l} y^2 p_t\,dy$.

From (7·59) $lp_t = \int_t^\infty p(y)\,dy = \int_t^{t+l} p(y)\,dy + \int_{t+l}^\infty p(y)\,dy.$

Also
$$lp_t = \int_t^{t+l} p_t\,dy.$$

Hence
$$\int_{t+l}^\infty p(y)\,dy = \int_t^{t+l} \{p_t - p(y)\}\,dy. \tag{7·62}$$

Throughout the range $t+l$ to ∞ y^2 is greater than at any point of the range t to $t+l$.

Therefore from (7·62)
$$\int_{t+l}^\infty y^2 p(y)\,dy \geqslant \int_t^{t+l} y^2\{p_t - p(y)\}\,dy. \tag{7·63}$$

Hence (7·61) becomes
$$\int_t^\infty y^2 p(y)\,dy \geqslant p_t \int_t^{t+l} y^2\,dy,$$

and adding corresponding sides of this equation and (7·60) we have
$$\int_0^\infty y^2 p(y)\,dy \geqslant p_t \int_0^{t+l} y^2\,dy. \tag{7·64}$$

Using (7·56) and (7·59) we can write this in the form:
$$1 \geqslant \text{Pr.}\{y > t\} \frac{(t+l)^3}{3l},$$

or
$$\text{Pr.}\{y > t\} \leqslant \frac{3l}{(t+l)^3}. \tag{7·65}$$

t is fixed and by differentiation it can be shown that the right-hand side has a maximum value when $l = \frac{1}{2}t$.

Hence
$$\text{Pr.}\{y > t\} \leqslant \frac{4}{9t^2}. \tag{7·66}$$

When t is less than 2/3 this inequality is useless since $\frac{4}{9}t^{-2}$ is then greater than 1. For such values of t another inequality
$$\text{Pr.}\{y > t\} \leqslant 1 - \frac{t}{\sqrt{3}} \tag{7·67}$$

may be used. The inequalities (7·66) and (7·67) are known as Gauss' inequalities; the second form is not proved in this book.

This proof is based (with changes of notation) on an interesting note by W. Perks in *J.S.S.* Vol. VII in which the following more general result is also obtained.

Using y^r instead of y^2 in the above we arrive at the result (corresponding to (7·64))

$$\nu'_r = \int_0^\infty y^r p(y)\, dy \geqslant p_t \int_t^{t+l} y^r\, dy,$$

where ν_r is the rth (absolute) moment of the distribution of y.

Proceeding as before we deduce that

$$\Pr.\{y > t\} \leqslant \frac{(r+1)\, l\nu'_r}{(t+l)^{r+1}},$$

and as the right-hand side has a maximum value when $l = t/r$,

$$\Pr.\{y > t\} \leqslant \frac{r^r \nu'_r}{(1+r)^r t^r}. \qquad (7{\cdot}68)$$

In §7·16 we considered the rectangular distribution as an example of the application of Tchebyshev's inequality which gave

$$\Pr.\left\{ | x - \mathscr{E}(x) | > \frac{3\sqrt{3}}{4} \sigma_x \right\} \leqslant \frac{16}{27}.$$

Putting $t = \dfrac{3\sqrt{3}}{4}$ in (7·66) we obtain an upper limit for this probability of $\frac{64}{243}$ which is a great improvement on Tchebyshev's limit and is nearly equal to the exact answer ·25. (Such a close approximation cannot be relied upon in all cases.)

EXERCISES 7

*7·1 Using standard life-table symbols, write down the cumulative distribution function of the random variables corresponding to

(i) age last birthday at death,
(ii) exact age at death,
(iii) number of persons dying in a year in a stationary population of size N.

7·2 A die has $(n+1)$ faces, numbered $0, \frac{1}{n}, \frac{2}{n}, \ldots, \frac{n-1}{n}, 1$ respectively. Assuming it is equally likely to fall with any one face uppermost, find the expected value and standard deviation of the random variable corresponding to the number on the uppermost face.

As n increases without limit show that the distribution of the random variable tends to a certain continuous distribution, and hence find the expected value and standard deviation of this distribution. To what situation would the continuous variable correspond?

7·3 Find the expected value, standard deviation and moment ratios of the exponential distribution

$$\left.\begin{aligned} p(x) &= \frac{1}{\theta} e^{-(x-\gamma)/\theta} \quad \text{if} \quad x \geqslant \gamma \\ &= 0 \qquad\qquad\quad \text{if} \quad x < \gamma \end{aligned}\right\} \quad (\theta > 0).$$

Obtain an expression for the corresponding cumulative distribution function and sketch it.

7·4 n members of a committee occupy chairs numbered 1 to n at random. Explain what this means and find the coefficient of correlation between the random variables corresponding to the numbers of the chairs occupied by any particular pair of committee members.

7·5 A sample of n different individuals is chosen at random from a population of N individuals. A character has values $u_1, u_2, \ldots, u_N$ respectively in the N individuals of the population, and the values $x_1, x_2, \ldots, x_n$ in the n individuals in the sample.

Show that

$$\sigma_{\bar{x}}^2 = \frac{N-n}{(N-1)\,n}\,\sigma^2,$$

where

$$\bar{x} = \frac{1}{n} \sum_{i=1}^{n} x_i$$

and

$$\sigma = \sqrt{\left\{\frac{1}{N} \sum_{i=1}^{N} (u_i - \bar{u})^2\right\}}.$$

7·6 If $x_1, x_2, \ldots, x_n$ are n independent random variables each having the same standard deviation σ, under what conditions are the random variables

$$y_1 = a_{11}x_1 + a_{12}x_2 + \ldots + a_{1n}x_n,$$
$$y_2 = a_{21}x_1 + a_{22}x_2 + \ldots + a_{2n}x_n$$

uncorrelated?

Show that the arithmetic mean $\bar{x}$ is uncorrelated with any deviation $(x_i - \bar{x})$ from the arithmetic mean.

7·7 Find an approximate expression for the standard deviation of $z = x/y$, where x and y are random variables with expected values ξ and η respectively, standard deviations σ_x and σ_y respectively, and correlation coefficient ρ_{xy}. State the conditions necessary for the usefulness of the approximation.

Apply your result to the case where

$$x = ku_1 + u_2, \quad y = u_1,$$

k being a positive constant, and u_1 and u_2 independent random variables such that

$$\mathscr{E}(u_1) = \omega, \qquad \mathscr{E}(u_2) = 0,$$
$$\sigma(u_1) = \sigma_1, \quad \sigma(u_2) = \sigma_2.$$

Suggest a practical question to which this result might possibly apply.

7·8 The coefficient of variation of a positive random variable, x, is small and the value of $\sqrt{\beta_1}$ for the distribution of x is positive. Under what conditions is the value of $\sqrt{\beta_1}$ likely to be smaller for the distribution of $\sqrt{x}$ than for the distribution of x?

In Exercises 7·9–7·11 $x_1, x_2, \ldots, x_n$ are independent random variables each with the same standard deviation σ, and the same first and second moment ratios $\sqrt{\beta_1}$, β_2.

7·9 Show that

$$\text{(i)}\ \sqrt{\beta_1(\bar{x})} = \sqrt{\beta_1}/\sqrt{n}, \quad \text{where } \bar{x} = \frac{1}{n}\sum_{i=1}^{n} x_i,$$

$$\text{(ii)}\ \beta_2(\bar{x}) = 3 + (\beta_2 - 3)/n.$$

(Note that $\lim_{n\to\infty} \sqrt{\beta_1(\bar{x})} = 0$; $\lim_{n\to\infty} \beta_2(\bar{x}) = 3$.)

7·10 If

$$s^2 = \frac{1}{n}\sum_{i=1}^{n} (x_i - \bar{x})^2,$$

show that

$$s^4 = \frac{(n-1)^2}{n^4}\sum_{i=1}^{n} x_i^4 + \left[\frac{2(n-1)^2}{n^4} + \frac{4}{n^4}\right]\sum_{i=1}^{n}\sum_{j=1}^{i-1} x_i^2 x_j^2 + \text{terms containing odd}$$

powers of the x_i's,
and hence that

$$\mathscr{E}(s^4) = \frac{(n-1)^2}{n^3}\beta_2\sigma^4 + \frac{(n-1)(n^2-2n+3)}{n^3}\sigma^4.$$

Deduce that
$$\sigma_{s^2} = \frac{(n-1)\sigma^2}{n}\sqrt{\left\{\frac{1}{n}\left(\beta_2 - \frac{n-3}{n-1}\right)\right\}}.$$

7·11 If n is large and $\beta_2 = 3$ show that

$$\sigma_{s^2} \doteqdot \sigma^2\sqrt{\frac{2}{n}}, \quad \sigma_s \doteqdot \sigma\sqrt{\frac{1}{2n}}.$$

and
$$\mathscr{E}(s) \doteqdot \sigma\left(1 - \frac{3}{4n}\right).$$

7·12 By considering the quantity

$$\int_{-\infty}^{\infty} (x^2 + ax + b)^2\, p(x)\, dx$$

or otherwise, prove that the β_1 and β_2 of any continuous distribution satisfy the inequality

$$\beta_2 \geqslant \beta_1 + 1.$$

Extend the proof to discontinuous distributions.

7·13 x and y are random variables with joint probability density function

$$p(x, y) = \frac{5x^2 e^{-yx^2}}{(1+|x|)^{11}} \quad \begin{pmatrix} 0 < y < \infty \\ -\infty < x < +\infty \end{pmatrix}$$

$$= 0 \text{ elsewhere.}$$

Show that x and y are uncorrelated but not independent.

*7·14 It has been suggested that the proportion of female births tends to decrease as the birth-rate decreases. What kind of data would you require to investigate this statement?

Discuss:

(i) the construction of an appropriate theoretical framework for your analysis of the data;

(ii) how you would make allowances for random fluctuations. (If necessary use approximate methods.)

7·15 $x_1, x_2, \ldots, x_n$ are random variables each with the same expected value, ξ, and the same standard deviation σ. The correlation between any two of the x's is ρ. Show that

(i) $\{\sigma(\bar{x})\}^2 = (\sigma^2/n) + (1 - 1/n)\,\rho, \sigma^2$

(ii) $\mathscr{E}\left[\sum_{i=1}^{n} (x_i - \bar{x})^2\right] = (n-1)(1-\rho)\,\sigma^2,$

(iii) $\rho > -\dfrac{1}{n-1}.$

7·16 Describe how you would use a table of random numbers to make an experimental investigation of the theoretical result of § 7·11.

Attempt such an experimental investigation yourself, using materials at your disposal.

7·17 Cards are dealt one by one from a well-shuffled pack until an ace appears. Show that the probability that exactly n cards are dealt before the first ace is

$$\frac{(51-n)(50-n)(49-n)}{13.51.50.49}.$$

By a suitable transformation show that the frequency distribution of n follows approximately the curve:

$$y = x^3 - x,$$

and hence find approximate values for the mean and standard deviation of n.

7·18 If, in the previous question, cards continue to be dealt until a second ace appears, prove that the probability that exactly r cards are dealt in all before the second ace is

$$\frac{r(51-r)(50-r)}{13.17.50.49}.$$

Find the approximate values of the mean and standard deviation of r.

(The last two questions are based on an interesting Note by W. H. Carter, B.A., I.C.S., in *J. Inst. Actu.* vol. 64.)

BIBLIOGRAPHY

J. V. Uspensky. *An Introduction to Mathematical Probability* (Chapters 1–3, 9). McGraw Hill, New York and London, 1937.

H. Levy and L. Roth. *Elements of Probability* (Chapter 7). Oxford, Clarendon Press, 1936.

C. E. Weatherburn. *A First Course in Mathematical Statistics* (Chapter 2). Cambridge University Press, 1946.

F. N. David. *Probability Theory for Statistical Methods* (Chapters 10–11). Cambridge University Press, 1949.

CHAPTER 8

PROBABILITY: SOME IMPORTANT DISTRIBUTIONS

8·1. The binomial distribution.

Suppose we have n independent trials for each of which the probability of a 'success' is p and the probability of a 'failure' $1-p$ or q. By the Multiplication Theorem (6·9) we find the probability of exactly r successes and $(n-r)$ failures occurring *in a given order* to be

$$p \times p \times p \times \ldots (r \text{ factors}) \ldots \times q \times q \times q \times \ldots ((n-r) \text{ factors}) = p^r q^{n-r}.$$

There are $\binom{n}{r}$ different orders in which the r successes and $n-r$ failures can occur, where $\binom{n}{r}$ denotes the binomial coefficient ${}^nC_r$, and if we include all these, the probability for all orders combined becomes, by the Addition Theorem,

$$\binom{n}{r} p^r q^{n-r},$$

i.e. the probabilities of $0, 1, 2, \ldots, r, \ldots, n$ successes are respectively

$$q^n, \quad \binom{n}{1} pq^{n-1}, \quad \binom{n}{2} p^2 q^{n-2}, \quad \ldots, \quad \binom{n}{r} p^r q^{n-r}, \quad \ldots, \quad p^n.$$

These probabilities are, of course, the successive terms of the expansion of $(q+p)^n$.

If u be a random variable and

$$\text{Pr.}\{u=r\} = \binom{n}{r} p^r q^{n-r} \quad (r = 0, 1, 2, \ldots, n)$$

where n is an integer and $0 \leqslant p \leqslant 1$, then the distribution of u is called a *binomial distribution* with parameters n and p, and u is called a *binomial variable*.

Example 8·1.

The concept of a binomial distribution is likely to provide a useful model whenever we are dealing with a series of n observations which we may assume to be independent and in each of which we expect a certain event to have the same chance (p) of occurring. As a simple case consider the probability of throwing exactly 0, 1, 2, etc., aces in fifteen throws with an ordinary die. If we assume the chance of throwing an ace is $\frac{1}{6}$ for each throw, and further, that each throw is independent of all other throws then the number of aces appearing in fifteen throws would have a binomial distribution with parameters $n=15$ and $p=\frac{1}{6}$. The probability of throwing an ace exactly r times would be $\binom{15}{r}\left(\frac{1}{6}\right)^r\left(\frac{5}{6}\right)^{15-r}$, i.e. in a long sequence of sets of 15 throws we should expect about this proportion of sets to contain exactly r aces.

8·2. Moments of the binomial distribution.

The sth moment about the origin is given by:

$$\begin{aligned}\mu_s' &= 0^s.q^n + 1^s\binom{n}{1}pq^{n-1} + 2^s\binom{n}{2}p^2q^{n-2} + \ldots + n^s.p^n \\ &= \left\{q^n + \binom{n}{1}pq^{n-1}E + \binom{n}{2}p^2q^{n-2}E^2 + \ldots + p^nE^n\right\}0^s, \qquad (8\cdot1)\end{aligned}$$

where E is the operator used in Finite Differences and 0^s is used conventionally in the sense that $E^t0^s = t^s$.

$$\begin{aligned}\mu_s' &= (q+pE)^n\,0^s = (1+\Delta p)^n\,0^s \quad [\text{since } E \equiv 1+\Delta] \\ &= 0^s + \binom{n}{1}p\Delta 0^s + \binom{n}{2}p^2\Delta^2 0^s + \binom{n}{3}p^3\Delta^3 0^s + \ldots + p^n\Delta^n 0^s. \qquad (8\cdot2)\end{aligned}$$

$\Delta 0^s$, $\Delta^2 0^s$, etc., are the so-called 'differences of zero' (see *Mathematics for Actuarial Students*, Pt. II, Chap. VII) and their numerical values are readily obtained. Substituting these values we have successively

$$\left.\begin{aligned}\mu_1' &= np, \\ \mu_2' &= np + n(n-1)p^2, \\ \mu_3' &= np + 3n(n-1)p^2 + n(n-1)(n-2)p^3, \\ \mu_4' &= np + 7n(n-1)p^2 + 6n(n-1)(n-2)p^3 \\ &\qquad + n(n-1)(n-2)(n-3)p^4.\end{aligned}\right\} \qquad (8\cdot3)$$

Using the relationships (7·44) to (7·46) we obtain the central moments

$$\mu_2 = np - np^2 = npq, \qquad (8\cdot4)$$

$$\mu_3 = np - 3np^2 + 2np^3 = npq(q-p), \qquad (8\cdot5)$$

$$\mu_4 = np + n(3n-7)p^2 - 6n(n-2)p^3 + 3n(n-2)p^4$$
$$= 3n^2p^2q^2 + npq(1-6pq). \tag{8·6}$$

Hence $\sqrt{\beta_1} = \mu_3\mu_2^{-\frac{3}{2}} = (q-p)(npq)^{-\frac{1}{2}}$ (8·7)

and $\beta_2 = \mu_4\mu_2^{-2} = 3 + (1-6pq)(npq)^{-1}$. (8·8)

8·3. Bernoulli's theorem.

Tchebyshev's inequality (§7·15) is of quite general application. Whatever may be the distribution of a random variable, it must satisfy this inequality; in particular the binomial distribution must do so.

If, then, x be a binomial variable, with parameters n and p, so that $\mathscr{E}(x) = np$, and $\sigma_x = \sqrt{(npq)}$, Tchebyshev's inequality is

$$\text{Pr.}\{|x - np| > t\sqrt{(npq)}\} \leqslant t^{-2}.$$

The event $|x - np| > t\sqrt{(npq)}$ is the same as the event

$$\left|\frac{x}{n} - p\right| > t\sqrt{\frac{pq}{n}}.$$

Hence
$$\text{Pr.}\left\{\left|\frac{x}{n} - p\right| > t\sqrt{\frac{pq}{n}}\right\} \leqslant \frac{1}{t^2}. \tag{8·9}$$

This symbolic relation has a very interesting interpretation. The binomial distribution is often used in theoretical models as the distribution of a random variable corresponding to the number of times an event occurs in n independent trials, the probability of occurrence of the event in any single trial being p. In such a model x/n represents the relative frequency of occurrence of the event.

Relation (8·9) is a statement about the probability of this relative frequency differing from p by more than a certain amount. Taking $t = 10$ say, we see that if n be large enough the chance of a deviation greater than any given small quantity will still be less than 1 in 100. That is to say when n is large the relative frequency is not likely to differ greatly from the probability p.

This general deduction is expressed more formally in:

Bernoulli's theorem. If (i) $f_n = x/n$ where x is a binomial variable with parameters n and p, (ii) η and ϵ are any two positive numbers, then there is a number $n_0(\eta, \epsilon)$ depending on η and ϵ such that

$$\text{Pr.}\{|f_n - p| > \eta\} < \epsilon \quad \text{if} \quad n > n_0(\eta, \epsilon),$$

however small may be η and ϵ.

Proof. Since x is a binomial variable, relation (8·9) holds and hence

$$\text{Pr.}\left\{|f_n - p| > t\sqrt{\frac{pq}{n}}\right\} \leqslant t^{-2}.$$

Putting $t = \epsilon^{-\frac{1}{2}}$ we have

$$\text{Pr.}\left\{|f_n - p| > \sqrt{\frac{pq}{n\epsilon}}\right\} \leqslant \epsilon.$$

Now $\text{Pr.}\{|f_n - p| > \eta\} < \text{Pr.}\left\{|f_n - p| > \sqrt{\frac{pq}{n\epsilon}}\right\}$ if $\eta > \sqrt{\frac{pq}{n\epsilon}}$,

i.e. if $$n > \frac{pq}{\eta^2 \epsilon}.$$

Since $0 \leqslant pq \leqslant \frac{1}{4}$ we may take $n_0(\eta, \epsilon) = \frac{1}{4}\eta^{-2}\epsilon^{-1}$. Then if

$$n > \tfrac{1}{4}\eta^{-2}\epsilon^{-1}, \quad \text{Pr.}\{|f_n - p| > \eta\} < \epsilon. \tag{8·10}$$

Bernoulli's theorem is true in all the numerical theories of probability considered in Chapter 6 but there are, naturally, differences of interpretation between the theories. While the result is not unexpected in the theory which we have developed it is more remarkable in, for example, the theory based on equally likely arrangements. It cannot, however, be regarded as a link between frequency theory and other theories since it gives only an inequality for the probability of a certain event. The fact that this concerns the relative frequency of an event does not affect the nature of the probability concerned. For example it does not follow that the theory of arrangements implies that f_n usually tends to p, since probability in this theory is not associated with frequency of occurrence.

In any numerical theory of probability, if u_n be a random variable with distribution depending on n, and U be a constant such that for any positive values of η and ϵ

$$\text{Pr.}\{|u_n - U| > \eta\} < \epsilon \quad \text{if} \quad n > n_0(\eta, \epsilon)$$

u_n is said to *converge in probability* to U as n tends to infinity.

Thus Bernoulli's theorem shows that f_n converges in probability to p as n tends to infinity.

8·4. The Poisson distribution.

Although the binomial distribution provides a mathematical model which is appropriate for many sets of observed data, it involves rather heavy arithmetical work unless n is small and use is often made of other distributions which are more easily handled but give a reasonable approximation to the binomial in suitable circumstances.

One of these is the Poisson distribution which is used if n is large and p small. We shall in fact assume that n tends to infinity but that p simultaneously tends to zero in such a way that

$$np = m \quad \text{(a constant)}.$$

The general term of the binomial distribution may then be written

$$\frac{n!}{r!\,(n-r)!}\left(\frac{m}{n}\right)^r\left(1-\frac{m}{n}\right)^{n-r}$$

$$=\frac{m^r}{r!}\left(1-\frac{m}{n}\right)^n\left[\frac{n!}{(n-r)!\,n^r\left(1-\frac{m}{n}\right)^r}\right]. \qquad (8\cdot 11)$$

Using Stirling's approximation for factorials (see Appendix 2) the term in square brackets becomes

$$\frac{\sqrt{(2\pi)}\,n^{n+\frac{1}{2}}\,e^{-n}}{\sqrt{(2\pi)}\,(n-r)^{n-r+\frac{1}{2}}\,e^{-(n-r)}\,n^r\left(1-\frac{m}{n}\right)^r}=\frac{1}{\left(1-\frac{r}{n}\right)^{n-r+\frac{1}{2}}e^r\left(1-\frac{m}{n}\right)^r}.$$

$$(8\cdot 12)$$

As $\quad n\to\infty, \quad \left(1-\frac{r}{n}\right)^{n-r+\frac{1}{2}}\to e^{-r}$ and $\left(1-\frac{m}{n}\right)^r\to 1.$

Hence expression (8·12) tends to unity as n tends to infinity and at the same time the factor $(1-m/n)^n$ in (8·11) tends to e^{-m}.

Hence the general term of the binomial tends to the value $e^{-m}\dfrac{m^r}{r!}$.

In other words if u is a binomial variable such that

$$\text{Pr.}\{u=r\}=\binom{n}{r}p^r q^{n-r},$$

then $\lim\limits_{\substack{n\to\infty\\ np=m}} \text{Pr.}\{u=r\}=\dfrac{m^r}{r!}e^{-m}$. We note that $\sum\limits_{r=0}^{\infty}\dfrac{m^r}{r!}e^{-m}=1$, so that

$$\text{Pr.}\{u=r\}=\frac{m^r}{r!}e^{-m} \quad (r=0, 1, 2, \ldots)$$

defines a possible distribution function of the random variable u.

If u is a random variable for which

$$\Pr.\{u=r\}=\frac{m^r}{r!}e^{-m}\quad (r=0, 1, \ldots)\,(m>0)$$

then the distribution of u is called a *Poisson distribution* and u is called a *Poisson variable*.

Example 8·2.

Suppose that the probability of death within a year for a person aged exactly x is q_x. If there are n_x persons aged exactly x, what is the probability that r of these persons will die before reaching exact age $(x+1)$? Assuming that deaths occur independently (of course, this assumption may involve too great an error for the resultant model to be useful) the probability that the number of deaths* θ_x is equal to r will be

$$\Pr.\{\theta_x=r\}=\binom{n_x}{r}q_x^r p_x^{n_x-r},\quad \text{where}\quad p_x=1-q_x.$$

It should be noted that the parameters of the distribution of θ_x are n_x and q_x.

Unless x is an advanced age, q_x will be small (e.g. $q_{40}=\cdot 00562$, according to English Life Table No. 10, Males). If n_x be large (e.g. $n_x \geqslant 100$) then it is reasonable to suppose θ_x to be a *Poisson variable* and we have

$$\Pr.\{\theta_x=r\}=\frac{(n_x q_x)^r}{r!}e^{-(n_x q_x)}\quad (r=0, 1, \ldots)$$

where $n_x q_x$ is the expected number of deaths, i.e. $\mathscr{E}(\theta_x)=n_x q_x$.

Another instance where the assumption of a Poisson variable is often appropriate involves industrial injuries. Usually the probability (q) that a specified workman will be injured in a given year is very small but the number of workmen employed (n) is so large that the 'expected' number of accidents $m=nq$ is quite appreciable.

If we assume the number of accidents A to be a Poisson variable we have

$$\Pr.\{A=r\}=\frac{m^r}{r!}e^{-m}\quad (r=0, 1, \ldots).$$

In this type of data substantial deviations from the Poisson form of distribution are sometimes observed. These have been attributed to the inadequacy of the assumption of independence implied in the binomial distribution and therefore in the Poisson approximation.

* It would perhaps be more consistent with our notation to use y_x for the variable and θ_x for its expected value $n_x q_x$ but we have conformed with established actuarial practice, using θ_x for actual deaths at age x.

Example 8·3.

A very interesting example involving a Poisson distribution is given by R. D. Clarke in *J.I.A.* Vol. LXXII, p. 481.

An investigation was made to test whether the points of impact of flying-bombs in London tended to be grouped in clusters. An area of 144 sq.km. in south London was divided into 576 squares of $\frac{1}{4}$ sq.km. each and a count was made of the numbers of squares within which 0, 1, 2, ..., flying-bombs fell. These figures are given in the third column of the table following.

As 537 bombs in all fell within the total area it was assumed that the m of the Poisson distribution was $\frac{537}{576}$ (i.e. the average number of bombs per square).

The 'expected' numbers of squares within which r bombs fell were then calculated from the formula $576\frac{m^r}{r!}e^{-m}$ $(r=0, 1, 2, \ldots)$ where

$$m=\tfrac{537}{576}.$$

These numbers are shown in the second column and it will be seen that they conform very well with the actual numbers observed.

No. of flying-bombs per square	Expected no. of squares (Poisson)	Actual no. of squares
0	226·74	229
1	211·39	211
2	98·54	93
3	30·62	35
4	7·14	7
5 and over	1·57	1
Total	576·00	576

8·5. Moments of the Poisson distribution.

The sth moment about the origin may be written

$$\mu_s'=e^{-m}\left\{0^s+\frac{m}{1!}.1^s+\frac{m^2}{2!}.2^s+\ldots+\frac{m^r}{r!}.r^s+\ldots\right\}$$

$$=e^{-m}\left\{1+\frac{m}{1!}E+\frac{m^2}{2!}E^2+\ldots+\frac{m^r}{r!}E^r+\ldots\right\}0^s$$

in the notation of § 8·2

$$=e^{-m}\,e^{mE}\,0^s=e^{m\Delta}\,0^s \quad [\text{on putting } E\equiv 1+\Delta]$$

$$=\left\{1+m\Delta+\frac{m^2}{2!}\Delta^2+\ldots+\frac{m^r}{r!}\Delta^r+\ldots\right\}0^s.$$

Substituting the known values of the differences of zero we have successively

$$\left.\begin{aligned} \mu_1' &= m, \\ \mu_2' &= m + m^2, \\ \mu_3' &= m + 3m^2 + m^3, \\ \mu_4' &= m + 7m^2 + 6m^3 + m^4. \end{aligned}\right\} \qquad (8 \cdot 13)$$

From these we obtain the central moments

$$\mu_2 = m, \qquad (8 \cdot 14)$$

$$\mu_3 = m, \qquad (8 \cdot 15)$$

$$\mu_4 = m + 3m^2. \qquad (8 \cdot 16)$$

Hence

$$\sqrt{\beta_1} = m^{-\frac{1}{2}} \qquad (8 \cdot 17)$$

and

$$\beta_2 = 3 + m^{-1}. \qquad (8 \cdot 18)$$

It will be noticed that whereas the definition of the binomial distribution involves two 'parameters', n and p (or q), the Poisson distribution is fully defined by the single parameter m.

8·6. The Normal distribution.

Both the distributions considered hitherto, being distributions of discontinuous variables, consist of a number of isolated terms. We now consider a continuous distribution which is of great importance in statistical theory, since, as we shall see later, it provides an adequate theoretical model in very many cases.

Consider the probability density function

$$p(x) = y_0 \exp\left[-\frac{1}{2a^2}(x-\xi)^2\right] \quad -\infty < x < +\infty.$$

The curve $y = p(x)$ is symmetrical about the line $x = \xi$ since a change in the sign of $(x-\xi)$ does not affect $p(x)$. By differentiation we find that $p(x)$ has a maximum at $x = \xi$, points of inflexion at $x = \xi \pm a$, and tends asymptotically to zero as x tends to $\pm\infty$. The distribution can in fact be represented by a curve of the general shape shown in Fig. 8·1.

To determine y_0 we use equation (7·7) which in the present case becomes

$$y_0 \int_{-\infty}^{+\infty} \exp\left[-\frac{1}{2a^2}(x-\xi)^2\right] dx = 1.$$

Putting $(x-\xi)^2 = 2a^2 t$, we obtain

$$\sqrt{2}\, ay_0 \int_0^\infty t^{-\frac{1}{2}} e^{-t}\, dt = 1 \quad \left[\text{since} \int_{-\infty}^{+\infty} e^{-\frac{1}{2}y^2}\, dy = 2\int_0^\infty e^{-\frac{1}{2}y^2}\, dy\right],$$

i.e.

$$\sqrt{(2\pi)}\, ay_0 = 1.$$

[A proof that $\Gamma(\frac{1}{2}) = \int_0^\infty t^{-\frac{1}{2}} e^{-t} dt = \sqrt{\pi}$ will be given in Vol. II of this book.]

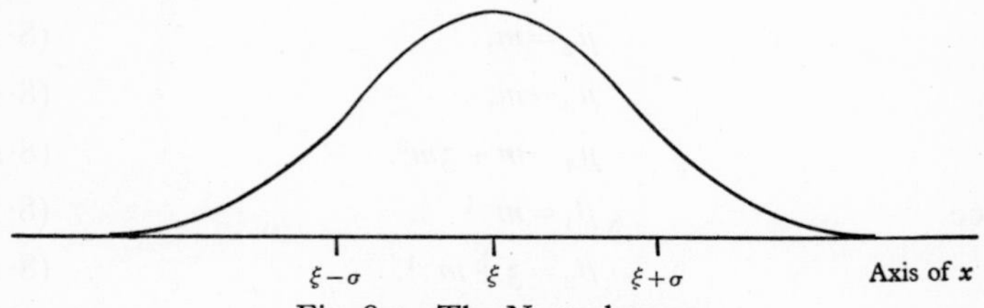

Fig. 8·1. The Normal curve.

Hence

$$y_0 = (\sqrt{(2\pi)}\, a)^{-1}$$

and

$$p(x) = \frac{1}{\sqrt{(2\pi)}\, a} \exp\left[-\frac{1}{2a^2}(x-\xi)^2\right]. \tag{8·19}$$

Since the distribution is symmetrical about $x = \xi$, $\mathscr{E}(x) = \xi$ and the square of the standard deviation of x is

$$\sigma^2 = \frac{1}{\sqrt{(2\pi)}\, a}\int_{-\infty}^{+\infty} (x-\xi)^2 \exp\left[-\frac{1}{2a^2}(x-\xi)^2\right] dx.$$

Substituting $(x-\xi)^2 = 2a^2 t$,

$$\sigma^2 = \frac{2a^2}{\sqrt{\pi}}\int_0^\infty t^{\frac{1}{2}} e^{-t}\, dt = \frac{2a^2}{\sqrt{\pi}}\,\Gamma\left(\frac{3}{2}\right) = \frac{2a^2}{\sqrt{\pi}}\,\tfrac{1}{2}\Gamma(\tfrac{1}{2}) = a^2, \tag{8·20}$$

since $\Gamma(\frac{1}{2}) = \sqrt{\pi}$.

Hence we may write $\sigma = a$, and

$$p(x) = \frac{1}{\sqrt{(2\pi)}\, \sigma} \exp\left[-\frac{1}{2\sigma^2}(x-\xi)^2\right]. \tag{8·21}$$

It will sometimes be convenient to take $\xi = 0$. Evidently this will not alter any of the central moments or moment-ratios of x. We can therefore use the simpler form

$$p(x) = \frac{1}{\sqrt{(2\pi)}\, \sigma} e^{-x^2/2\sigma^2} \tag{8·22}$$

when dealing with central moments.

If further $\sigma = 1$, x is called a *unit Normal variable* and its distribution is called a *unit Normal distribution*. It may be noted in passing that if any Normal variable be standardized as described in § 7·14, the standardized variable is a unit Normal variable. Extensive tables of various functions associated with the unit Normal distribution have been prepared. A short set of tables of this type is given in Appendix 4. These tables show values of

(i) the ordinate of the density function curve $z = \frac{1}{\sqrt{(2\pi)}} e^{-\frac{1}{2}x^2}$ for a few values of x,

(ii) the cumulative distribution function

$$F(x) = \frac{1}{\sqrt{(2\pi)}} \int_{-\infty}^{x} e^{-\frac{1}{2}t^2}\, dt$$

for the same values, and

(iii) values of x for which $F(x)$ has certain values.

Another function sometimes tabulated is α_x (not to be confused with the moment-ratios defined in § 7·13), the area bounded by the curve, the x-axis and the ordinates at $\pm x$,

i.e.
$$\alpha_x = \frac{1}{\sqrt{(2\pi)}} \int_{-x}^{+x} e^{-\frac{1}{2}t^2}\, dt. \tag{8·23}$$

Clearly, since the total area under the curve $y = \frac{1}{\sqrt{(2\pi)}} e^{-\frac{1}{2}x^2}$ is unity and since the curve is symmetrical about $x = 0$,

$$F(x) = \tfrac{1}{2}(1 + \alpha_x) \tag{8·24}$$

so that either of $F(x)$ or α_x can readily be determined from the other.

The probability that any Normal variable, x, having expected value ξ and standard deviation σ, falls between given limits α and β can be expressed in terms of the cumulative distribution function of the unit Normal variable.

For $\quad \Pr.\{\alpha < x < \beta\} = \frac{1}{\sqrt{(2\pi)}\sigma} \int_{\alpha}^{\beta} \exp\left[-\frac{1}{2}\left(\frac{x-\xi}{\sigma}\right)^2\right] dx.$

Putting $\quad (x-\xi)/\sigma = x'$ we have

$$\Pr.\{\alpha < x < \beta\} = \frac{1}{\sqrt{(2\pi)}} \int_{(\alpha-\xi)/\sigma}^{(\beta-\xi)/\sigma} e^{-\frac{1}{2}x'^2}\, dx'$$

$$= F\left(\frac{\beta-\xi}{\sigma}\right) - F\left(\frac{\alpha-\xi}{\sigma}\right).$$

8·7. Constants of the Normal distribution.

Since the distribution is symmetrical all its odd central moments are zero.

We have seen above that its second central moment is σ^2. Its fourth central moment is

$$\mu_4 = \frac{1}{\sqrt{(2\pi)}\,\sigma}\int_{-\infty}^{+\infty} x^4\, e^{-x^2/2\sigma^2}\, dx.$$

Making the substitution $x^2 = 2\sigma^2 t$ we have

$$\mu_4 = \frac{4\sigma^4}{\sqrt{\pi}}\int_0^\infty t^{\frac{3}{2}}\, e^{-t}\, dt$$

$$= \frac{4\sigma^4}{\sqrt{\pi}}\,\Gamma\left(\tfrac{5}{2}\right)$$

$$= \frac{4\sigma^4}{\sqrt{\pi}}\,.\,\tfrac{3}{2}\,.\,\tfrac{1}{2}\,.\,\Gamma\left(\tfrac{1}{2}\right)$$

$$= 3\sigma^4. \qquad (8·25)$$

Hence
$$\sqrt{\beta_1} = 0 \qquad (8·26)$$
and
$$\beta_2 = 3. \qquad (8·27)$$

In general

$$\mu_{2k} = \frac{1}{\sqrt{(2\pi)}\,\sigma}\int_{-\infty}^{+\infty} x^{2k}\, e^{-x^2/2\sigma^2}\, dx = \frac{\sqrt{2}}{\sqrt{\pi}\,\sigma}\int_0^\infty x^{2k}\, e^{-x^2/2\sigma^2}\, dx.$$

Making the substitution $x^2 = 2\sigma^2 t$ we have

$$\mu_{2k} = \frac{2^k\,\sigma^{2k}}{\sqrt{\pi}}\int_0^\infty t^{\frac{1}{2}(2k-1)}\, e^{-t}\, dt$$

$$= \frac{2^k\,\sigma^{2k}}{\sqrt{\pi}}\,\Gamma\left(\frac{2k+1}{2}\right)$$

$$= \frac{2^k\,\sigma^{2k}}{\sqrt{\pi}}\,.\,\frac{2k-1}{2}\,.\,\frac{2k-3}{2}\,\ldots\ldots\,\tfrac{3}{2}\,.\,\tfrac{1}{2}\sqrt{\pi}$$

$$= (2k-1)(2k-3)\ldots 3\,.\,1\,.\,\sigma^{2k}. \qquad (8·28)$$

Whence the moment ratio α_{2k} of the Normal distribution is

$$\alpha_{2k} = \frac{\mu_{2k}}{\sigma^{2k}} = (2k-1)(2k-3)\ldots 3\,.\,1. \qquad (8·29)$$

Also $$\nu_1 = 2\int_0^\infty xp(x)\,dx = \frac{\sqrt{2}}{\sigma\sqrt{\pi}}\int_0^\infty xe^{-x^2/2\sigma^2}\,dx$$

$$= \sqrt{\frac{2}{\pi}}\,\sigma\,[-e^{-x^2/2\sigma^2}]_0^\infty$$

$$= \cdot 7979\,\sigma \text{ approx.} \qquad (8\cdot30)$$

The upper quartile $M_{\cdot 75}$ is given by the formula $M_{\cdot 75} = \xi + m_{\cdot 75}\,\sigma$

where $$\frac{1}{\sqrt{(2\pi)}}\int_0^{m_{\cdot 75}} e^{-\frac{1}{2}t^2}\,dt = \cdot 25 \quad \text{or} \quad F(m_{\cdot 75}) = \cdot 75.$$

From Appendix 4 we see that the upper quartile is

$$\xi + \cdot 6745\,\sigma \qquad (8\cdot31)$$

and the lower quartile is, by symmetry, $\xi - \cdot 6745\,\sigma$. $\cdot 6745\,\sigma$ is the *probable error* of a Normal distribution having standard deviation σ.

8·8. The Normal approximation to the binomial distribution.

In §8·4 we showed that if p became small and n large and np remained fixed, the binomial distribution approximated to the Poisson form. By interchanging p and q we see that the same type of approximation will apply if p is nearly equal to unity except that in this case m will be equal to nq and not np.

When p and q are nearly equal or if n is large the binomial distribution approximates to the Normal distribution. In Appendix 3 it is shown that if $(p-q)/(npq)$ is small the probability of attaining a value differing from the expected value np by w is given approximately by

$$\frac{1}{\sqrt{(2\pi npq)}}\,e^{-w^2/2npq}.$$

In other words, instead of calculating the successive terms of the binomial $(q+p)^n$ we could find approximations by calculating the ordinates of a Normal curve for which the mean was at np and σ^2 was equal to npq.

This does not in itself take us very far since to answer such questions as 'What is the probability of more than 60 successes out of 100 trials for each of which $p = \cdot 4$?', we should still have to calculate 40 terms for the Normal curve instead of 40 terms of the binomial $(\cdot 6 + \cdot 4)^{100}$. A simple way of dealing with the problem is provided by Laplace's theorem which is dealt with in §A. 3·2 (Appendix 3). This theorem relates the sum of a series of binomial terms to the area of the unit Normal curve lying between appropriate limits. It states that if x' is the standardized variate

$$(x-np)(npq)^{-\frac{1}{2}}$$

then
$$\lim_{n\to\infty} \text{Pr.}\{\alpha < x' < \beta\} = \frac{1}{\sqrt{(2\pi)}}\int_{\alpha}^{\beta} e^{-\frac{1}{2}t^2}\,dt. \tag{8·32}$$

The following, more accurate, formula is obtained in Appendix 3

$$\text{Pr.}\{\alpha < x' < \beta\} = \frac{1}{\sqrt{(2\pi)}}\int_{\alpha_n}^{\beta_n} e^{-\frac{1}{2}t^2}\,dt + \frac{1}{2\sqrt{(2\pi npq)}}\{e^{-\frac{1}{2}\alpha_n^2} + e^{-\frac{1}{2}\beta_n^2}\} \tag{8·33}$$

where α_n is the smallest value which x' can take greater than α,
and β_n is the greatest value which x' can take less than β.

The corrective terms in this formula are sometimes allowed for by simply using the integral with slightly altered limits:

$$\alpha' = \alpha_n - \frac{1}{2\sqrt{(npq)}}; \quad \beta' = \beta_n + \frac{1}{2\sqrt{(npq)}}. \tag{8·34}$$

The quantities $\pm\dfrac{1}{2\sqrt{(npq)}}$ are known as *continuity corrections* and were first introduced by De Morgan (1806–71). Evidently if

$$(x_\beta - np)(npq)^{-\frac{1}{2}} = \beta_n \quad \text{and} \quad (x_\alpha - np)(npq)^{-\frac{1}{2}} = \alpha_n,$$

then
$$(x_\beta + \tfrac{1}{2} - np)(npq)^{-\frac{1}{2}} = \beta' \quad \text{and} \quad (x_\alpha - \tfrac{1}{2} - np)(npq)^{-\frac{1}{2}} = \alpha', \tag{8·35}$$

so that the continuity corrections to the original variable x are $\pm\frac{1}{2}$.

We are, in effect, using the integral of the Normal curve to approximate to the sum of ordinates of the same curve at points $(r-np)/(npq)^{\frac{1}{2}}$, r taking a series of integral values. If this is appreciated the need for the continuity correction may be seen from geometrical considerations.

Example 8·4.

What is the chance of more than one-quarter of a group of one hundred men aged 85 exactly, dying in the course of the next year, the rate of mortality being ·21085?

To avoid confusion put $q_{85} = \cdot 21085 = p$ in the above notation. We require

$$\text{Pr.}\{26 \leqslant \text{Number of deaths} \leqslant 100\}.$$

Using the formulae (8·35) with $p = \cdot 21085$; $n = 100$, we have

$$\begin{aligned}
\alpha' &= (26 - \tfrac{1}{2} - 100 \times \cdot 21085)/(100 \times \cdot 21085 \times \cdot 78915)^{\frac{1}{2}} \\
&= \frac{4 \cdot 415}{4 \cdot 079} \\
&= 1 \cdot 082; \\
\beta' &= (100 + \tfrac{1}{2} - 100 \times \cdot 21085)/(100 \times \cdot 21085 \times \cdot 78915)^{\frac{1}{2}} \\
&= \frac{79 \cdot 415}{4 \cdot 079} \\
&= 19 \cdot 469.
\end{aligned}$$

The approximate formula for the probability is then

$$\frac{1}{\sqrt{(2\pi)}} \int_{1 \cdot 082}^{19 \cdot 469} e^{-\frac{1}{2}t^2} = \frac{1}{\sqrt{(2\pi)}} \int_{1 \cdot 082}^{\infty} e^{-\frac{1}{2}t^2}\, dt \quad \text{effectively}$$

$$= \cdot 1398 \quad \text{from the table in Appendix 4.}$$

The exact value is $\cdot 1402$.

If the continuity correction had not been used we should have had

$$\alpha = \frac{4 \cdot 915}{4 \cdot 079} = 1 \cdot 205; \quad \beta = \frac{78 \cdot 915}{4 \cdot 079} = 19 \cdot 347,$$

and our estimate of the probability would have been

$$\frac{1}{\sqrt{(2\pi)}} \int_{1 \cdot 205}^{19 \cdot 347} e^{-\frac{1}{2}t^2}\, dt = \frac{1}{\sqrt{(2\pi)}} \int_{1 \cdot 205}^{\infty} e^{-\frac{1}{2}t^2}\, dt \quad \text{effectively}$$

$$= \cdot 1141.$$

The continuity correction therefore makes quite a substantial difference in this case.

It can be shown in a similar way that if x be a Poisson variable with parameter m,

i.e. $$\text{Pr.}\{x = r\} = \frac{m^r}{r!} e^{-m} \quad (r = 0, 1, \ldots),$$

and x' be the standardized Poisson variable

$$x' = \frac{x - m}{\sqrt{m}},$$

then $$\lim_{m \to \infty} \text{Pr.}\{\alpha < x' < \beta\} = \frac{1}{\sqrt{(2\pi)}} \int_{\alpha}^{\beta} e^{-\frac{1}{2}t^2}\, dt.$$

A similar continuity correction applies in this case provided m is large (about 50 or more), so that, to a close degree of approximation

$$\sum_{r=r_1}^{r_2} \text{Pr.}\{x=r\} = \sum_{r=r_1}^{r_2} \frac{m^r}{r!} e^{-m} \doteq \frac{1}{\sqrt{(2\pi)}} \int_{(r_1-\frac{1}{2}-m)m^{-\frac{1}{2}}}^{(r_2+\frac{1}{2}-m)m^{-\frac{1}{2}}} e^{-\frac{1}{2}t^2}\, dt,$$

r_1 and r_2 being non-negative integers, $r_1 < r_2$.

We shall see in Vol. II of this book that other distributions tend to the Normal form in certain circumstances and it should not be assumed from what has been said that the main importance of the Normal distribution is its approximation in certain circumstances to the binomial.

It is, in fact, difficult to overemphasize its importance in theoretical work, since we usually assume that the characteristic under consideration is Normally distributed in the populations involved. In practical work many sets of observational data approximate to the Normal form as will be seen from the examples given in earlier chapters.

*8·9. Normal approximation to the distribution of the arithmetic mean.

The Normal distribution is also of importance as an approximation to the distribution of the arithmetic mean. In §7·10, the definitions and notation of which we shall continue to use, we have already shown that the standard deviation of the arithmetic mean of n independent variables is $\sigma/\sqrt{n}$ if σ is the standard deviation of each of the n variables (see (7·30)). It can be shown that under the conditions of §7·10 the distribution of the standardized arithmetic mean tends to the unit Normal distribution, i.e.

$$\lim_{n\to\infty} \text{Pr.}\left\{\alpha < \frac{\sqrt{n}\,(\bar{x}-\xi)}{\sigma} < \beta\right\} = \frac{1}{\sqrt{2\pi}} \int_\alpha^\beta e^{-\frac{1}{2}t^2}\, dt,$$

but the proof is beyond the scope of this book. We shall, however, show that the moment-ratios of the distribution of the arithmetic mean tend to the values they have for the Normal curve as n increases, provided only that the moments of the common distribution of all the x's are all finite. Since change of origin does not affect the central moments we may, without loss of generality, take $\xi = 0$, i.e. $\mathscr{E}(x_i) = 0$; $\mathscr{E}(x_i^2) = \sigma^2$; $\mathscr{E}(x_i^3) = \sqrt{\beta_1}\,.\,\sigma^3$ $(i = 1, 2, \ldots, n)$. Then

$$\mathscr{E}(\bar{x}^r) = n^{-r}\mathscr{E}\left[\left(\sum_{i=1}^{n} x_i\right)^r\right]$$

and, provided n is large enough, it can be shown (see below) that when r is odd

$$\mathscr{E}(\bar{x}^r) = \left[\frac{r!}{(2!)^{\frac{1}{2}(r-3)}\,3!\left(\dfrac{r-3}{2}\right)!}\sqrt{\beta_1}\,.\,\sigma^r\right] n^{-\frac{1}{2}(r+1)} + (\text{terms in higher powers of } n^{-1})$$

and, when r is even,

$$\mathscr{E}(\bar{x}^r) = \left[\frac{r!}{(2!)^{\frac{1}{2}r}\left(\dfrac{r}{2}\right)!}\sigma^r\right] n^{-\frac{1}{2}r} + (\text{terms in higher powers of } n^{-1}).$$

Hence if $\alpha_r(\bar{x})$ be the rth moment-ratio of $\bar{x}$; $\alpha_r(\bar{x}) = n^{r/2}\sigma^{-r}\mathscr{E}(\bar{x}^r)$, and so

$$\alpha_r(\bar{x}) = \left[\frac{r!}{(2!)^{\frac{1}{2}(r-3)}\,3!\left(\dfrac{r-3}{2}\right)!}\sqrt{\beta_1}\right] n^{-\frac{1}{2}} + (\text{terms in higher powers of } n^{-1}) \text{ if } r \text{ is odd,}$$

$$\alpha_r(\bar{x}) = \left[\frac{r!}{(2!)^{\frac{1}{2}r}\left(\dfrac{r}{2}\right)!}\right] + (\text{terms in } n^{-\frac{1}{2}} \text{ and higher powers of } n^{-1}) \text{ if } r \text{ is even.}$$

Hence $\lim\limits_{n\to\infty} \alpha_r(\bar{x}) = 0$ if r is odd: $\lim\limits_{n\to\infty} \alpha_r(\bar{x}) = \dfrac{r!}{2^{\frac{1}{2}r}\left(\dfrac{r}{2}\right)!}$ if r is even.

Putting $r = 2k$ in the last equation we see by comparison with (8·29) that the moment-ratios of the arithmetic mean tend to the moment-ratios of the Normal distribution as n increases.

The proof of the approximate expressions for $\mathscr{E}(\bar{x}^r)$ given above is difficult, but the following brief outline indicates some of the main steps. It is not, however, a rigorous demonstration.

$$\mathscr{E}(\bar{x}^r) = n^{-r}\mathscr{E}\left[\left(\sum_{i=1}^{n} x_i\right)^r\right].$$

Now the expansion of $(x_1+x_2+\ldots+x_n)^r$ will consist of terms such as

$$x_1^{a_1}\,x_2^{a_2}\ldots x_t^{a_t},\quad \text{where}\quad a_1+a_2+\ldots+a_t=r,$$

and since n is to be large we may assume $n>r$. By the multinomial theorem the coefficient of this term is

$$\frac{r\,!}{a_1\,!\,a_2\,!\ldots a_t\,!},\quad \text{where}\quad a_1+a_2+\ldots+a_t=r,$$

and it can be shown that this expression increases as $a_1, a_2, \ldots, a_t$ diminish in size but increase in number. Thus the terms which occur most often involve only the first powers of r of the x's, but, since $\mathscr{E}(x_i)=0$, the expected values of all such terms (and indeed of all terms involving the first power of any of the x's) must be zero. The terms which occur most frequently after those involving only the first powers are of the form

$$x_1^2\,x_2^2\ldots x_t^2 \quad\text{or}\quad x_1^2\,x_2^2\ldots x_{t-1}^2\,x_t^3.$$

If r is even we shall have terms involving the squares of $\frac{1}{2}r$ different x's while if r is odd one x must occur with an odd index. As we have seen, the expected value is zero if the first power of an x is introduced and hence the most common term we need consider involves the second power of $\frac{1}{2}(r-3)$ x's and the third power of another.

r even. The $\frac{1}{2}r$ x's can be selected in $\binom{n}{\frac{1}{2}r}$ ways and the coefficient of a term such as $x_1^2\,x_2^2\ldots x_{\frac{1}{2}r}^2$ is $r\,!\,(2\,!)^{-\frac{1}{2}r}$.

Also $\mathscr{E}(x_i^2)=\sigma^2$ so that we have

$$\mathscr{E}(\bar{x}^r)=\binom{n}{\frac{1}{2}r}\frac{r\,!\,\sigma^r}{(2\,!)^{\frac{1}{2}r}\,n^r}+(\text{terms in higher powers of } n^{-1}).$$

If n is very large

$$\binom{n}{\frac{1}{2}r},\quad \text{i.e.}\quad n(n-1)\ldots(n-\tfrac{1}{2}r+1)/(\tfrac{1}{2}r)\,!$$

is approximately equal to $n^{\frac{1}{2}r}/(\frac{1}{2}r)\,!$ and we have

$$\mathscr{E}(\bar{x}^r)=\left[\frac{r\,!\,\sigma^r}{(2\,!)^{\frac{1}{2}r}\,(\frac{1}{2}r)\,!}\right]n^{-\frac{1}{2}r}+(\text{terms in higher powers of } n^{-1}).$$

r odd. $\frac{1}{2}(r-3)$ x's can be chosen in $\binom{n}{\frac{1}{2}(r-3)}$ ways and one further

x in $n-\frac{1}{2}(r-3)$ ways. The coefficient of a term involving the second powers of $\frac{1}{2}(r-3)$ x's and the third power of another x is

$$\frac{r!}{(2!)^{\frac{1}{2}(r-3)}3!}.$$

As before $\mathscr{E}(x_i^2)=\sigma^2$. Also $\mathscr{E}(x_i^3)=\sqrt{\beta_1}.\sigma^3$.

Hence

$\mathscr{E}(\bar{x}^r)=\binom{n}{\frac{1}{2}(r-3)}[n-\frac{1}{2}(r-3)]\dfrac{r!\sqrt{\beta_1}.\sigma^r}{(2!)^{\frac{1}{2}(r-3)}3!\,n^r}+$ (terms in higher powers of n^{-1}).

If n is very large $\binom{n}{\frac{1}{2}(r-3)}$ is approximately equal to

$$n^{\frac{1}{2}(r-3)}/(\tfrac{1}{2}[r-3])!$$

and

$\mathscr{E}(\bar{x}^r)=\left[\dfrac{r!}{(2!)^{\frac{1}{2}(r-3)}3!\left(\dfrac{r-3}{2}\right)!}\sqrt{\beta_1}.\sigma^r\right]n^{-\frac{1}{2}(r+1)}+$ (terms in higher powers of n^{-1}).

8·10. Pearsonian frequency curves.

Karl Pearson developed a whole family of curves suitable for use as probability density functions. For a detailed treatment the reader is referred to the books mentioned in the Bibliography. The following brief outline of the principal characteristics is sufficient for our purposes.

If we write the equation of the Normal curve in the form

$$y=\frac{1}{\sqrt{(2\pi)}\,\sigma}e^{-x^2/2\sigma^2}$$

we have on taking logarithms and differentiating:

$$\frac{1}{y}\frac{dy}{dx}=-\frac{x}{\sigma^2}.$$

This is a particular case of the more general equation

$$\frac{1}{y}\frac{dy}{dx}=\frac{x+k}{c_0+c_1x+c_2x^2}, \qquad (8{\cdot}36)$$

from which the Pearsonian curves are derived.

It will be noted that, in general, $\dfrac{dy}{dx}=0$ when $x=-k$. The mode, if any, of a Pearson curve does, in fact, correspond to this value of x. The range of values of x for which the formulae resulting from the solution of (8·36) may be used to represent probability density functions are limited by the following considerations:

(*a*) The values of y given by the formulae must be real and non-negative.

(*b*) It is also desirable that the range of values of x should be continuous; for example, it should not consist of two ranges separated by a gap.

Clearly the solution of equation (8·36) depends on the roots of the equation

$$c_0 + c_1 x + c_2 x^2 = 0. \tag{8·37}$$

The following results are listed here for reference purposes. Anyone familiar with the solution of elementary differential equations should have no difficulty in deducing them from equation (8·36) but in order to produce the precise forms given a change of origin is usually necessary.

Type I. If equation (8·37) has real roots of opposite sign we can split the right-hand side of (8·36) into partial fractions and the solution is easily obtained in the form

$$y = y_0 \left(1 + \frac{x}{a_1}\right)^{\lambda a_1} \left(1 - \frac{x}{a_2}\right)^{\lambda a_2}. \tag{8·38}$$

The range of values of x is from $-a_1$ to a_2. We have changed the origin to the mode and thereby reduced the number of parameters from four to three (λ, a_1 and a_2).

Type II. This is the same as Type I except that $a_1 = a_2$ and

$$y = y_0 \left(1 - \frac{x^2}{a^2}\right)^m. \tag{8·39}$$

The range of values of x is from $-a$ to a.

Type III. If $c_2 = 0$ we obtain this important type. Integrating both sides of equation (8·36) we have:

$$\log y = \int \frac{x + k}{c_0 + c_1 x} dx$$

$$= \frac{x}{c_1} + \left(k - \frac{c_0}{c_1}\right) \frac{1}{c_1} \log (c_0 + c_1 x) + \text{const.}$$

leading, after transferring the origin, to an equation of the form

$$y = y_0 e^{-\gamma x}\left(1+\frac{x}{\kappa}\right)^{\kappa\gamma}. \qquad (8\cdot40)$$

The range of values of x is from $-\kappa$ to ∞.

Type IV. If equation (8·37) has complex roots the denominator can be thrown into the form

$$c_2(X^2+a^2)$$

and the solution is of the form

$$y = y_0 e^{-\nu \tan^{-1} x/a}\left(1+\frac{x^2}{a^2}\right)^{-m}. \qquad (8\cdot41)$$

The range of values of x is unlimited.

Type V. If the roots are real and equal the solution is of the form

$$y = y_0 x^{-p} e^{-\gamma/x}. \qquad (8\cdot42)$$

The range of values of x is from 0 to ∞.

Type VI. If the roots are real but of the same sign the solution is no longer as in (8·38) above, but by using a different origin it can be expressed as

$$y = y_0 (x-a)^{m_1} x^{-m_2}. \qquad (8\cdot43)$$

The range of values of x is from a to ∞.

Type VII. If $c_1=0$ and c_0, c_2, are of the same sign the solution can be thrown into the form

$$y_1 = y_0\left(1+\frac{x^2}{a^2}\right)^{-m}. \qquad (8\cdot44)$$

The range of values of x is unlimited.

Consideration of the equations (8·38)–(8·44) enables the following general description to be given.

Types I and II are limited in range in both directions. Type III is limited in one direction only and is therefore skew. Types V and VI are similar in shape to Type III.

We now come to curves unrestricted at both ends, Types IV and VII. Type VII is symmetrical and leptokurtic ($\beta_2 > 3$) while Type IV is skew. The reader may sometimes find the Normal curve referred to as Type VII but it is more properly regarded as a limiting form of all the Types I–VII.

8·11. Some approximations to the binomial distribution.

We have seen that in suitable circumstances the Poisson and the Normal distributions are approximations to the binomial distribution. The Type III curve of equation (8·40) is also very useful in this connexion although the calculation of the constants γ and κ is rather laborious. We shall content ourselves therefore with setting out in the following tables the values of certain terms calculated from the binomial expansion $(p+q)^n$ and approximations to those terms calculated from Poisson, Normal and Type III distributions respectively. These tables are taken from an important paper by H. L. Seal on 'Tests of a Mortality Table Graduation' (*J.I.A.* Vol. LXXI) which goes more fully into the subject.

The values of q used are of the order of magnitude of rates of mortality and in the paper n is represented by E and r by θ. The binomial term in each case is $\binom{n}{r} q^r p^{n-r}$ and the corresponding Poisson term is $e^{-m}\frac{m^r}{r!}$ where $m=nq$.

It will be seen therefore that as the tables are set out m is the same for each pair, namely 10, and the same Poisson approximation therefore applies, for instance for $n=4000$, $q=\cdot 0025$, as for $n=2000$, $q=\cdot 005$. The Normal and Type III distributions relate to continuous variables and the approximations given replace the binomial terms by areas on unit base. The parameters of these distributions are chosen so as to make their lower order moments agree with the corresponding moments of the binomial distribution as far as possible.

It will be noticed that throughout Seal's paper p and q are interchanged in relation to their use in this book; this is because in general statistical work p is taken as the chance of a success while in actuarial work on mortality the chance of a death is q_x, the rate of mortality at age x.

TABLE 8·1

Comparison of binomial and other distributions

r	$q=\cdot 0025$ $n=4000$			$q=\cdot 005$ $n=2000$			Poisson	r
	Binomial	Normal	Type III	Binomial	Normal	Type III		
−3	—	·0000	—	—	·0000	—	—	−3
−2	—	·0001	—	—	·0001	—	—	−2
−1	—	·0003	·0000	—	·0003	·0000	—	−1
0	·0000	·0009	·0001	·0000	·0009	·0001	·0000	0
1	·0004	·0022	·0007	·0004	·0022	·0007	·0005	1
2	·0022	·0052	·0026	·0022	·0052	·0026	·0023	2
3	·0075	·0110	·0079	·0075	·0110	·0078	·0076	3
4	·0188	·0210	·0189	·0188	·0209	·0188	·0189	4
5	·0377	·0363	·0374	·0376	·0362	·0373	·0378	5
6	·0630	·0568	·0624	·0629	·0567	·0623	·0631	6
7	·0901	·0804	·0896	·0900	·0804	·0895	·0901	7
8	·1127	·1031	·1125	·1127	·1032	·1126	·1126	8
9	·1252	·1197	·1254	·1254	·1198	·1255	·1251	9
10	·1253	·1258	·1256	·1254	·1259	·1257	·1251	10
11	·1139	·1197	·1141	·1140	·1198	·1142	·1137	11
12	·0949	·1031	·0948	·0950	·1032	·0949	·0948	12
13	·0729	·0804	·0728	·0730	·0804	·0728	·0729	13
14	·0521	·0568	·0519	·0521	·0567	·0519	·0521	14
15	·0347	·0363	·0345	·0346	·0362	·0345	·0347	15
16	·0216	·0210	·0216	·0216	·0209	·0216	·0217	16
17	·0127	·0110	·0127	·0127	·0110	·0127	·0128	17
18	·0071	·0052	·0071	·0070	·0052	·0071	·0071	18
19	·0037	·0022	·0038	·0037	·0022	·0038	·0037	19
20	·0018	·0009	·0019	·0018	·0009	·0019	·0019	20
21	·0009	·0003	·0009	·0009	·0003	·0009	·0009	21
22	·0004	·0001	·0004	·0004	·0001	·0004	·0004	22
23	·0002	·0000	·0002	·0002	·0000	·0002	·0002	23
24	·0001	—	·0001	·0001	—	·0001	·0001	24
25	·0000	—	·0000	·0000	—	·0000	·0000	25

TABLE 8·1 (*cont.*)

r	$q=·01$ $n=1000$			$q=·03$ $n=333$			Poisson	r
	Binomial	Normal	Type III	Binomial	Normal	Type III		
−3	—	·0000	—	—	·0000	—	—	−3
−2	—	·0001	—	—	·0001	—	—	−2
−1	—	·0003	·0000	—	·0003	·0000	—	−1
0	·0000	·0009	·0001	·0000	·0008	·0001	·0000	0
1	·0004	·0022	·0007	·0004	·0020	·0006	·0005	1
2	·0022	·0051	·0026	·0021	·0048	·0024	·0023	2
3	·0074	·0108	·0077	·0071	·0104	·0074	·0076	3
4	·0186	·0208	·0187	·0181	·0202	·0180	·0189	4
5	·0375	·0361	·0371	·0369	·0355	·0363	·0378	5
6	·0627	·0567	·0621	·0623	·0563	·0615	·0631	6
7	·0900	·0804	·0895	·0901	·0805	·0893	·0901	7
8	·1128	·1033	·1127	·1135	·1040	·1132	·1126	8
9	·1256	·1201	·1258	·1268	·1212	·1269	·1251	9
10	·1257	·1263	·1260	·1270	·1276	·1274	·1251	10
11	·1143	·1201	·1145	·1154	·1212	·1157	·1137	11
12	·0952	·1033	·0951	·0957	·1040	·0959	·0948	12
13	·0731	·0804	·0729	·0731	·0805	·0732	·0729	13
14	·0520	·0567	·0518	·0517	·0563	·0517	·0521	14
15	·0345	·0361	·0344	·0340	·0355	·0340	·0347	15
16	·0215	·0208	·0214	·0209	·0202	·0210	·0217	16
17	·0126	·0108	·0126	·0121	·0104	·0122	·0128	17
18	·0069	·0051	·0070	·0065	·0048	·0067	·0071	18
19	·0036	·0022	·0037	·0034	·0020	·0035	·0037	19
20	·0018	·0009	·0020	·0016	·0008	·0017	·0019	20
21	·0008	·0003	·0008	·0008	·0003	·0008	·0009	21
22	·0004	·0001	·0004	·0003	·0001	·0004	·0004	22
23	·0002	·0000	·0002	·0001	·0000	·0002	·0002	23
24	·0001	—	·0001	·0001	—	·0001	·0001	24
25	·0000	—	·0000	·0000	—	·0000	·0000	25

TABLE 8·1 (*cont.*)

r	$q=\cdot 05$ $n=200$			$q=\cdot 1$ $n=100$			Poisson	r
	Binomial	Normal	Type III	Binomial	Normal	Type III		
−3	—	·0000	—	—	—	—	—	−3
−2	—	·0001	—	—	·0000	—	—	−2
−1	—	·0002	·0000	—	·0002	·0000	—	−1
0	·0000	·0007	·0001	·0000	·0005	·0001	·0000	0
1	·0004	·0019	·0006	·0003	·0015	·0005	·0005	1
2	·0019	·0046	·0023	·0016	·0039	·0020	·0023	2
3	·0067	·0100	·0071	·0059	·0089	·0063	·0076	3
4	·0174	·0197	·0175	·0159	·0182	·0160	·0189	4
5	·0359	·0348	·0356	·0339	·0334	·0336	·0378	5
6	·0614	·0559	·0608	·0596	·0549	·0590	·0631	6
7	·0896	·0806	·0890	·0889	·0807	·0883	·0901	7
8	·1137	·1046	·1135	·1148	·1062	·1146	·1126	8
9	·1277	·1223	·1279	·1304	·1253	·1306	·1251	9
10	·1284	·1289	·1287	·1319	·1324	·1322	·1251	10
11	·1167	·1223	·1169	·1199	·1253	·1201	·1137	11
12	·0967	·1046	·0967	·0988	·1062	·0987	·0948	12
13	·0736	·0806	·0734	·0743	·0807	·0741	·0729	13
14	·0518	·0559	·0515	·0513	·0549	·0511	·0521	14
15	·0338	·0348	·0336	·0327	·0334	·0326	·0347	15
16	·0206	·0197	·0205	·0193	·0182	·0193	·0217	16
17	·0117	·0100	·0118	·0106	·0089	·0107	·0128	17
18	·0063	·0046	·0064	·0054	·0039	·0055	·0071	18
19	·0032	·0019	·0033	·0026	·0015	·0027	·0037	19
20	·0015	·0007	·0016	·0011	·0005	·0013	·0019	20
21	·0007	·0002	·0008	·0005	·0002	·0006	·0009	21
22	·0003	·0001	·0003	·0002	·0000	·0002	·0004	22
23	·0001	·0000	·0001	·0001	—	·0001	·0002	23
24	·0000	—	·0001	·0000	—	·0001	·0001	24
25	—	—	·0000	—	—	·0000	·0000	25

8·12. The hypergeometric distribution.

The binomial distribution is a satisfactory model for many practical problems in which the populations involved are very large. It is rather unsatisfactory, however, for sampling from a small population without replacement. Suppose, for instance, that we are told that in England and Wales 51 % of babies born are boys and are required to find the probability that out of 40 babies taken at random 24 will be boys.

We may assume that the chance of each baby being a boy is ·51 and that it is independent of the chances for the other babies. On this assumption the required probability is $\binom{40}{24}(\cdot 51)^{24}(\cdot 49)^{16}$.

Now suppose that the population (in the technical sense) consists of 100 babies only, 51 of whom are boys and that the sample of 40 is chosen at random from this group of 100 babies. What is the probability that this sample includes 24 boys? It is not correct to take the binomial term $\binom{40}{24}(\cdot 51)^{24}(\cdot 49)^{16}$. Instead we argue as follows. We imagine the sample constructed by successive drawings for the first of which the probability of a boy is ·51. If the first baby chosen were a boy, we should then be left with 99 babies, 50 of whom would be boys so that the chance of a boy at the second drawing would be 50/99. If the first baby were a girl, 51 of the remaining 99 babies would be boys and the chance of a boy at the second drawing would be 51/99. Similarly the chance of a boy at the third drawing would be 49/98, 50/98 or 51/98 according as two, one, or none of the first two babies to be chosen were boys. The chance of a boy at the fourth drawing is 48/97, 49/97, 50/97 or 51/97 and so on. Allowing for the different orders in which the sample could be constructed the required probability of obtaining exactly 24 boys in a sample of 40 is:

$$\frac{40!}{24!\,16!}\,\frac{(51.50.49\ldots.28)(49.48.47\ldots.34)}{100.99.98\ldots.61}.$$

In general, suppose we are drawing a sample of n from a population of N individuals, r of which have a certain character A and the remaining $N-r$ do not possess that character. What is the probability that the sample will include a individuals with character A?

The number of different orders in which we can build up such a sample containing exactly a individuals with character A is

$$\frac{n!}{a!(n-a)!}. \tag{8·45}$$

The probability of obtaining the required sample in a given order is

$$\frac{r(r-1)(r-2)\dots(r-a+1).(N-r)(N-r-1)\dots(N-r-n-a+1)}{N(N-1)(N-2)\dots(N-n+1)}. \tag{8·46}$$

The following notation is often used to simplify this rather complicated expression.

	Number of individuals		Total
	With A	Without A	
Selected in sample	a	c	n
Remainder of population	b	d	m
Total population	r	s	N

This type of table is usually referred to as 'a 2 × 2 table with fixed marginal limits'. The totals in the last column and the bottom line are assumed to be fixed subject to the conditions $m+n=r+s=N$. It then follows that only one of the four quantities a, b, c, d can be fixed at will, the values of the other three following from the relations

$$a+c=n, \quad a+b=r, \quad b+d=m, \quad c+d=s.$$

With this notation the expression (8·45) can be written

$$\frac{n!}{a!c!}$$

and expression (8·46) can be written

$$\frac{r!}{b!}\cdot\frac{s!}{d!}\bigg/\frac{N!}{m!}.$$

Hence the probability of having a individuals with character A in the sample of n becomes

$$\frac{m!\,n!\,r!\,s!}{N!\,a!\,b!\,c!\,d!}. \qquad (8\cdot47)$$

As a takes the values, 0, 1, 2, 3, ..., in succession the values of this expression are proportional to the terms of a hypergeometric series. The properties of such a series are dealt with in books on differential equations and it will be sufficient for the purposes of this book merely to quote the following results without proof:

If

$$\text{Pr.}\{x=a\}=\frac{m!\,n!\,r!\,s!}{N!\,a!\,b!\,c!\,d!}$$

the expected value of the distribution of x is

$$nr/N \qquad (8\cdot48)$$

and the standard deviation is

$$\sqrt{\frac{mnrs}{N^2(N-1)}}. \qquad (8\cdot49)$$

It will be noticed that in our previous notation $r/N=p$, and $s/N=q$ so that the expected value is np, as it would be in a binomial distribution. The standard deviation is $\sqrt{\left(npq\frac{m}{N-1}\right)}$, and as $N\to\infty$, n remaining finite, the standard deviation tends to $\sqrt{(npq)}$, which is the binomial value, since the ratio $\frac{m}{N-1}=1-\frac{n-1}{N-1}$ tends to unity as N tends to infinity.

EXERCISES 8

8·1 Show that if x_1 and x_2 are independent Poisson variables with parameters m_1, m_2 respectively, then $y=x_1+x_2$ is a Poisson variable with parameter (m_1+m_2).

8·2 Apply the theoretical result of Exercise 8·1 to the following problem:

The number of deaths occurring each day is recorded for each of a number of towns. It is found that the distributions so built up differ markedly from the Poisson distribution in some towns but not in others.

Suggest factors which may give rise to these effects. You may assume that the population of each town remains effectively constant.

8·3 Find the expected value, standard deviation, $\sqrt{\beta_1}$ and β_2 of the *Negative Binomial Variable*, x, for which

$$\text{Pr. }\{x=k\}=\binom{n+k-1}{k}q^{-(n+k)}p^k \quad (k=0, 1, 2, \ldots),$$

where n is a positive integer and p and q are positive numbers such that

$$q-p=1.$$

8·4 In each of a succession of independent trials the probability of a certain event E is p. Trials are continued until the event E has been observed exactly r times. If b be the number of trials, show that the distribution of b is

$$\text{Pr. }\{b=t\}=\binom{t-1}{r-1}p^r q^{t-r} \quad (t=r, r+1\ldots).$$

Find the expected value and standard deviation of b.

Discuss the application of these theoretical results in the construction of sampling systems.

8·5 Consider the frequency distribution

$$p(x)=\frac{k}{1+x^2},$$

and sketch the curve. Determine k so as to make the total frequency for all values of x equal to unity and investigate the moments of the distribution.

This is known as the *Cauchy distribution*.

8·6 The *logarithmic series* distribution is defined by

$$\text{Pr. }\{x=r\}=K\alpha^r/r \quad (r=1, 2, \ldots) \quad (0<\alpha<1).$$

(i) Find an expression for the value of K in terms of α.

(ii) Find the expected value, standard deviation, $\sqrt{\beta_1}$ and β_2 of the distribution.

8·7 Show that if x is a Poisson variable with expected value m, then

$$\text{Pr. }\{x>r\}<m^r/r!.$$

Compare this with the result of applying Tchebyshev's formula. (You need consider only values of r greater than $m+m^{\frac{3}{4}}$.)

8·8 Ten mice are selected at random from a large number. These ten mice are then divided into two groups of five, A and B. Each mouse in group A is given a dose a of a certain poison, each mouse in group B is given a dose b. The dose a will kill one in ten and the dose b three in ten of the large number of mice from which the original selection was made. What is the probability that there will be fewer deaths in group B than in group A?

8·9 Find the values of $\sqrt{\beta_1}$ and β_2 of Pearson's Type III curves and show that for these curves

$$2\beta_2-3\beta_1-6=0.$$

8·10 What is the most probable distribution of the cards of a given suit among four whist players? State any assumptions which you make.

8·11 It is believed that a certain variable x can be regarded as arising from a mixture of Poisson distributions with parameter m varying as a random variable. What will the distribution of x be if

(i) m takes a finite number of values $M_1, \ldots, M_k$, with probabilities $p_1, \ldots, p_k$ respectively,

(ii) m is distributed according to the Pearson Type III form

$$p(m) = \frac{1}{\Gamma(r+1)} \frac{1}{2\sigma^2} \left(\frac{m}{2\sigma^2}\right)^r e^{-m/2\sigma^2}?$$

8·12 Show that, by a linear change of variable, the equation of a Pearson Type I curve can be put in the form:

$$y = y_0 x^{m-1} (1-x)^{n-1} \quad (0 < x < 1)$$

For what values of m and n will this curve be (*a*) U-shaped, (*b*) J-shaped?

8·13 Using the equation of Type I curves in the form given in Exercise 8·12 find the value of y_0 from the condition: $\int_0^1 y\,dx = 1$. Find also

$$\mathscr{E}(x) = \int_0^1 xy\,dx$$

and the standard deviation of x.

BIBLIOGRAPHY

C. V. L. Charlier. *Die Grundzuge der Mathematische Statistik*. Lund, Verlag. Scientia (1920).

W. P. Elderton. *Frequency Curves and Correlation*. C. and E. Layton, London, 1938.

R. Henderson. *Mathematical Theory of Graduation*. Actuarial Studies, No. 4, Actuarial Society of America, New York.

J. V. Uspensky. *An Introduction to Mathematical Probability* (Chapters 7 and 8). McGraw Hill, New York and London, 1937.

H. Levy and L. Roth. *Elements of Probability* (Chapters 3–5). Oxford, Clarendon Press, 1936.

C. E. Weatherburn. *A First Course in Mathematical Statistics* (Chapters 2 and 3). Cambridge University Press, 1946.

F. N. David. *Probability Theory for Statistical Methods* (Chapters 3–6). Cambridge University Press, 1949.

Fuller tables of the Normal distribution will be found in:

Tables for Statisticians and Biometricians, Part 1. Ed. K. Pearson, 2nd ed., 1930. University College, London.

T. L. Kelley. *The Kelley Statistical Tables*. Macmillan, New York, 1938.

Tables of the Probability Function, Vols. I and II. F.W.A., W.P.A. New York City Mathematical Tables Project (National Bureau Standards), 1942.

CHAPTER 9

STATISTICAL HYPOTHESES

9·1. Introduction.

The last three chapters have provided us with a theory which has been specially constructed to correspond, in certain circumstances, with frequencies of occurrence of observable events. Chapter 8, in particular, has been concerned with the frequencies which might be expected when certain simple assumptions are valid. In dealing with actual problems we shall often feel doubtful about just how much it is reasonable to assume without producing a theoretical model which distorts the real situation to such a degree as to render our work valueless. In order to obtain as clear an idea as possible of the relative importance of the various assumptions we have to make, we must first have a thorough grasp of the purposes for which the theoretical model is to be constructed and employed. The reasons for the use of theoretical models have already been mentioned in Chapter 5 which should now be studied again. They are dealt with in greater detail in the following pages.

9·2. Examination of the problem.

Suppose that it is desired to investigate whether the mortality experienced by a group of persons is or is not in accordance with a certain life-table. In practice the observed rates never agree exactly with those shown in the table, yet this is not in itself regarded as evidence that the life-table used is inappropriate, for it would be unreasonable to expect exactly the proportion of lives indicated by the life-table to die in each year. On the other hand, if the deviations from the life-table values are large enough, doubts are felt as to its applicability to the group of lives concerned. Thus it is not the mere occurrence of deviations which is important. The essential question which arises is 'How large, and of what type, should the deviations be, to cause doubts about the validity of the life-table?' In many practical cases this question need not be answered at all exactly or even in purely numerical terms. The investigator uses his intuition and knowledge of the circumstances to help him in coming to a decision and if he is skilful, and experienced, his decisions will generally be correct. The results are, however, certainly subjective, and different workers may find difficulty in coming to agreement on the interpretation of the same data. More objective measures of the importance of observed deviations from life-table values would, at any rate, provide a common basis of discussion and substantially aid the investigator's intuition. To obtain such objective measures we are forced to consider what deviations from the life-table values are likely to occur, in order that only those which would occur but rarely may be regarded as evidence of departure of the experience from the life-table. The calculation of the frequency with which deviations greater than a given size may be expected to occur may be carried out by application of the theory of probability developed in Chapters 6–8. The theory is applied not to the actual observations, but to a theoretical model believed to be appropriate to the situation dealt with. The construction of the theoretical model is therefore necessarily antecedent to the application of the theory.

9·3. Construction of the theoretical model.

Suppose the life-table gives a probability q_x of dying in the next year for a person aged x exactly, and, out of n_x persons aged x exactly, $\mathring{\theta}_x$ do, in fact, die before attaining age $(x+1)$. A possible theoretical model is obtained by supposing the deaths to be events each with probability q_x, there being n_x independent trials. The number dying in a year may then be taken to correspond to a binomial variable θ_x with parameters n_x and q_x. Hence, the results obtained in the previous chapter (§§ 8·1 and 8·2) may be used to calculate the probability of a given number, r, say, of the n_x persons dying in the next year. This probability is

$$\text{Pr.}\{\theta_x = r\} = \binom{n_x}{r} q_x^r p_x^{n_x - r} \quad \text{where} \quad p_x = 1 - q_x. \tag{9·1}$$

The theoretical model provides an estimate of each of the probabilities of 0, 1, 2, ..., n_x persons out of the group of n_x persons dying before reaching age $(x+1)$. The number of deaths actually observed, $\mathring{\theta}_x$, may then be judged against the background of these theoretical probabilities.

9·4. Difficulties in the use of the theoretical model.

A very important problem arises now. Given an observed number of deaths $\mathring{\theta}_x$, the set of theoretical probabilities calculated according to (9·1) is evidently of considerable use as an aid to our judgement of the seriousness of the disagreement between observation and the life-table values. We have yet to consider, however, how best to use our information. An elementary treatment of this problem will be attempted in this section and we shall return to the same question in Vol. II. It is, however, a difficult matter which is still the subject of some controversy. While, therefore, the following statements are really only simple applications of common sense they should definitely be regarded as being incomplete. It would be a valuable mental exercise for the reader to devote some independent thought to the question. While he may not agree with others, such an exercise should certainly deepen his own appreciation of the subject and sharpen his judgement of observational data against a theoretical background.

Returning to the particular problem with which we are dealing, the essential idea here is to judge whether the observed number of deaths provides evidence that the life-table is not valid for the group of n_x persons under observation. In §A. 3·1 of the Appendix it is shown that $\binom{n}{r} p^r q^{n-r}$ may be assumed to have its maximum value when $r \doteqdot np$. Hence, Pr. $\{\theta_x = r\}$ is a maximum when r is approximately equal to the expected number of deaths $n_x q_x$ and Pr. $\{\theta_x = r\}$ decreases steadily as r moves away from that value.

A possible criterion of departure from the life-table might be the smallness of the theoretical probability of the observed number of deaths, the theoretical probability being calculated on the assumption that the life-table is valid. This has a certain intuitive appeal which is increased by the fact that smallness of probability is associated with divergence of the observed number of deaths $\mathring{\theta}_x$, from the theoretical expected number $n_x q_x$. A further problem arises immediately, however. Just how small is this probability to be before we regard it as indicative of departure from the life-table? The answer to this question must in any case be subjective. One person might require a divergence which would occur not more than once in twenty times, another a divergence which would occur not more than once in five hundred times. In fact, as we shall see later, (§9·5) we are not able to avoid this subjective element in the final use of our theory. In the present instance, however, there is the further complication that an intuitive assessment of the smallness of the probability required is extremely difficult. This may be summed up in the following statement: 'However small we require the probability to be, provided n be sufficiently large the greatest of the probabilities $\Pr.\{\theta_x = r\}$ will be less than this amount, so that the validity of the life-table would be rejected whatever the observed number of deaths.' This follows directly from Appendix 3.

9·5. Method of using the theoretical model.

This, of course, would be ridiculous and leads us to re-examine what it is that causes us to regard a difference between θ_x and $n_x q_x$ as being significant of a departure from the life-table. It is not in fact the rarity with which *exactly* that difference should occur which is important but the rarity with which a difference as large or larger should occur. In other words, denoting an observed value of θ_x by $\mathring{\theta}_x$, we are not really concerned with the smallness of the single probability $\Pr.\{\theta_x = \mathring{\theta}_x\}$ but with the smallness of $\sum_{r=\mathring{\theta}_x}^{n_x} \Pr.\{\theta_x = r\}$ (if $\mathring{\theta}_x > n_x q_x$) or $\sum_{r=0}^{\mathring{\theta}_x} \Pr.\{\theta_x = r\}$ (if $\mathring{\theta}_x < n_x q_x$). If (as will usually be the case) n is fairly large these probabilities, as we have seen in §8·6, may be evaluated with a close degree of approximation from the table in Appendix 4 as

$$1 - F\left(\frac{\mathring{\theta}_x - \frac{1}{2} - n_x q_x}{\sqrt{(n_x q_x p_x)}}\right) \quad (\text{if } \mathring{\theta}_x > n_x q_x)$$

or

$$F\left(\frac{\mathring{\theta}_x + \frac{1}{2} - n_x q_x}{\sqrt{(n_x q_x p_x)}}\right) \quad (\text{if } \mathring{\theta}_x < n_x q_x),$$

where $$F(y) = \frac{1}{\sqrt{(2\pi)}} \int_{-\infty}^{y} e^{-\frac{1}{2}t^2}\, dt.$$

By taking $\mathring{\theta}_x$ close to the expected value $n_x q_x$ the probabilities may be made to approach the value $\frac{1}{2}$, whatever be the value of n_x. The present system does not, therefore, suffer from the defect of leading to certain rejection of the life-table if n_x is large enough.

Example 9·1.

In a homogeneous group of persons 170 die in a six months' period. The expected number of deaths in this group in the same period was 143. It is required to decide how often deviations from the expected number as large as, or greater than this, are likely to occur among similar groups under similar conditions.

In this case we are not given the total number of persons in the group (the quantity represented by the symbol n_x in earlier sections) but, since q_x is small (less than ·1 say) except at advanced ages, we may assume that the random variable representing the number of deaths in our theoretical model is a Poisson variable (§8·4) with expected value $m = 143$. From §8·6 we know that if m is fairly large (e.g. greater than 10) the probability of observing 170 or more deaths is very nearly

$$1 - F\left(\frac{170 - \cdot 5 - 143}{\sqrt{(143)}}\right), \quad \text{where} \quad F(y) = \frac{1}{\sqrt{(2\pi)}} \int_{-\infty}^{y} e^{-\frac{1}{2}t^2}\, dt.$$

The required probability is therefore

$$1 - \frac{1}{\sqrt{(2\pi)}} \int_{-\infty}^{2\cdot 216} e^{-\frac{1}{2}t^2}\, dt = \cdot 0133$$

so that 170 or more deaths would be expected to occur about once in 75 times by chance.

We might possibly decide, in certain circumstances, to include deviations of equal magnitude in the opposite direction (i.e. 116 deaths or less) in which case the probability would be doubled.

9·6. Statistical hypotheses.

We now have to build up a general framework of concepts bearing in mind what we have learnt from the discussion in §§9·2–9·5.

First, the reason for the investigation was to decide whether a life-table was valid for a particular group of persons. This purpose may be expressed in more general terms as reaching a decision on the truth of the hypothesis that the life-table was valid for this group of persons. The word 'hypothesis' is used here in the sense in which it is used generally in scientific work, as a supposition about the objective properties of the things studied. In problems susceptible of statistical treatment where a theoretical model has been constructed a hypothesis about the objects studied has its conceptual counterpart in a *statistical hypothesis* about the theoretical model.

The suppositions that deaths occur independently and that the group of persons is homogeneous correspond to the statistical hypothesis that the random variable θ_x representing the number of deaths occurring is a binomial variable with parameters n_x and q, where $0 \leqslant q \leqslant 1$. The validity of the life-table requires further that, in the theoretical model, the value of the parameter q shall be q_x, the rate of mortality. A statistical hypothesis may be formally defined as follows:

'A statistical hypothesis is any statement restricting, in any way, the distribution function(s) of random variable(s).'

9·7. Tests of statistical hypotheses.

When a set of observations is examined to find whether they provide evidence that some particular hypothesis is usefully tenable it is said that this hypothesis is being *tested*. In other words, a test of a statistical hypothesis consists of the examination of data to find out whether a particular theoretical model is a useful representation of actual conditions. Thus, it might be desired to test the hypothesis that two variables are uncorrelated, i.e. that a certain theoretical model in which the two variables are uncorrelated constitutes a useful representation of the actual conditions. To make the test the coefficient of correlation r in one or more samples would be calculated and used to test whether these observed values were in accordance with the assumptions made.

The examination usually takes the form of

(i) calculation of some function of the observations (a *test function* or *criterion*).

(ii) appraisal of the calculated value of the test function against the theoretical background provided by the hypothesis being tested.

As a further example of the application of this method consider the situation of Example 9·1. Suppose the statistical hypothesis to be tested is that specifying a Poisson distribution of deaths with expected value 143. A possible test function in this case would be simply the observed number of deaths, in which case (i) above would not involve any calculations. Under (ii) we might use the information obtained in Example 9·1 that the probability of observing a number of deaths as great as, or greater than 170 (the number actually observed) would be about 1 in 75, supposing the hypothesis tested to be true. This probability is rather small and casts doubt on the validity of the hypothesis.

Although this appears quite simple and straightforward, closer examination shows that, in fact, quite an elaborate conceptual system has been built up in evaluating and using this probability. In finding the probability it has been assumed that the number of deaths may be represented with sufficient accuracy by a Poisson variable. This is a statistical hypothesis, itself based on assumptions as to homogeneity and size of the group, independence of occurrence of deaths and smallness of the probability of death for any particular individual. In using the value obtained for the probability we take into account, even though somewhat vaguely, the values which would be obtained for the probability of the same event if the expected number of deaths were not 143 but some other number. This may indeed often be done mentally but the mere fact that they are taken into consideration implies that some assumptions must be made about suitable *alternative hypotheses*. In Example 9·1, for instance, it may be assumed instinctively that if the expected number of deaths were not 143, the number of deaths might be represented by a Poisson variable with some other expected value. The test described above would be appropriate if the alternative hypotheses specified expected values *greater* than 143—as might be reasonable if it were suspected that the group of persons concerned were subject to special risks. Should it be desired, however, to take into account expected values both greater and less than 143, it would be more appropriate to find the probability of a deviation (*either positive or negative*) as great as, or greater than, that actually observed. As pointed out in Example 9·1, this probability would be about 1 in 37·5.

Sometimes the student may feel that he has no alternative hypotheses in mind when he is applying the test and even an experienced worker sometimes finds difficulty in specifying exactly what they are in a particular case. Nevertheless, the mere fact that a test is being made implies that the hypothesis may not be the correct one, i.e. that some alternative hypothesis is envisaged (even if only subconsciously). For instance, a manufacturer may wish to test the hypothesis that the proportion of defective units of a certain product is equal to or less than 1 %. He evidently contemplates that this hypothesis may not be borne out if tests are made and the alternative hypotheses with which he would be concerned would be those specifying a *larger* proportion than 1 %, i.e. a greater proportion of defective units.

As we shall see in the second volume of this book detailed consideration of the possible alternative hypotheses which may provide a suitable theoretical model is of great importance in further developments of the theory.

This brief treatment of the question should be sufficient to show that the testing of a hypothesis is a very complex operation. The calculation of a probability, itself the end product of a series of assumptions and deductions, is only a part of the test. Preceding this calculation there is the specification of a statistical hypothesis to be tested and the set of possible alternative (statistical) hypotheses. This must be somewhat subjective since it depends on human choice. Following the calculation there is an even more subjective part of the test in which the investigator uses the results provided by the theoretical background which he has constructed to reach some decision on the problem before him.

As has already been stated in Chapter 6, according to some theories of probability the investigator's final state of mind on the matter considered should be represented numerically by a probability measuring 'reasonable degree of belief'. As was pointed out, however, in that chapter, the word probability, as used in this book, has no such connotation. The probability calculated in the course of applying the test is merely an estimate of the frequency of occurrence of a certain event subject to some assumptions. This estimate is used by the investigator and may indeed produce in his mind a certain 'degree of belief'. This latter may, with some justification, be called a 'probability' but it is distinct from the concept 'probability' used in this book, as has already been pointed out in §6·10.

The student should not feel that testing a statistical hypothesis requires, in practice, detailed analysis as outlined above any more than the writing of a report involves a conscious and detailed analysis of the grammar used. A knowledge of the principles of such analysis nevertheless lies behind the construction of the report.

9·8. Significance.

The technical part of a test of a statistical hypothesis, i.e. that part of the test concerned with the calculation of a probability, may very often be described in the following way. First, some function of the observed data is calculated. In Example 9·1, for instance, the function

$$\frac{(\text{Observed number of deaths}) - (\text{Expected number of deaths})}{(\text{Expected number of deaths})^{\frac{1}{2}}}$$

was obtained. It will be remembered (§5·2) that such a function is called a *statistic*. Secondly, on the assumption that the statistical hypothesis tested is valid we calculate the probability that the random variable corresponding to this statistic should have a value in a certain range, at one extremity of which lies the observed value of the statistic. Provided the range of values has been suitably chosen, the size of this probability may then be used as an aid to judgement of the validity of the statistical hypothesis. In general the smaller the calculated probability, the more impressive is the evidence against the validity of the statistical hypothesis tested and a small probability is therefore regarded as being significant. The value of the calculated probability is called the *significance level*. As there is some chance of confusion it should be noted that the smaller the numerical value of the significance level as above defined, the greater is the evidence of departure from the statistical hypothesis tested.

The calculation of an exact significance level each time a test is applied may be unduly troublesome. To avoid the necessity of such calculations tables are constructed showing those values of the statistic which would give certain chosen significance levels (e.g. ·01, ·1, ·2, etc.). The value of the statistic which would give a significance level ϵ is called the ϵ (or 100ϵ %) *significance limit* of the random variable associated with the statistic. An observed value of the statistic, placed against the framework of values provided by such a table, will give a very useful idea of the exact significance level.

In Example 9·1, the second table of Appendix 4 could be used in this way. The significance level of the statistic

$$y = \frac{(\text{Observed number of deaths}) - (\text{Expected number of deaths})}{(\text{Expected number of deaths})^{\frac{1}{2}}}$$

as used in the test applied in the example is

$$1 - \frac{1}{\sqrt{(2\pi)}} \int_{-\infty}^{y} e^{-\frac{1}{2}t^2}\, dt = 1 - F(y).$$

From the table in Appendix 4 the 1 % significance limit of y is 2·326, the $2\frac{1}{2}$ % limit is 1·960. The observed value of 2·216 then gives quite a good indication of the actual significance level (which, as we calculated, was 1·33 %).

9·9. Use of significance limits.

When a table of significance limits is used repeatedly, the values tabulated acquire a certain critical meaning. That is to say, although the table is used primarily for the purpose of assessing the actual significance level, the first thing noted is whether the calculated value of a statistic falls above or below a few significance limits (usually not more than two). This is equivalent to noting whether the actual significance level is greater or less than a few selected values. This can be done very rapidly and often gives a sufficiently clear idea of the significance of the statistic without the necessity for more detailed and exact estimation of the actual significance level. Sometimes this procedure is standardized for a whole set of tests and it is agreed to consider a statistic to be significant if the significance level is less than some predetermined (usually small) value. Any observed value of the statistic has then only to be compared with the predetermined significance limit. This standardization of procedure is useful in practice if a large number of tests have to be carried out and also in certain theoretical comparisons of tests which we shall deal with in the second volume. Standardization may, on the other hand, lead to undue rigidity in interpretation of the tests and may obscure the importance of the actual significance level.

9·10. Choice of significance limits.

It has already been pointed out (§ 9·2) that the final use of any calculated or observed significance level is to help the formation of a subjective or personal judgement. The smallness of the significance level required to affect a decision will not only vary from person to person in any particular case, but also for any one person, according to the problem considered and the consequences of the decisions to be made. Let us suppose, for example, that we are considering the results of a (physical) test on the strength of a number of steel bars taken from a batch and the hypothesis that the strength is a certain value is under consideration. The significance level required to produce a decision to reject the batch will undoubtedly depend on the purpose for which the bars are to be used and on the size and cost of the batch. Similarly, if the observed rates of mortality of a group of lives are under examination, the amount of departure from life-table values required to justify a change in the calculation of premium rates will depend, among other things, on the importance of the class of business concerned.

Despite all these differences in the use of significance limits there are some which are used fairly generally as reference points. The most common are the 5 and 1 % significance limits while others often used are the 10, $2\frac{1}{2}$ and ·1 % significance limits. As a guide to the implication of these standard probabilities or frequencies of occurrence, the expected frequencies of certain simple events, calculated on the theoretical bases stated, are shown below.

I. *Throws of a coin assuming that the probability of throwing a head is $\frac{1}{2}$ at each throw, and that all throws are independent.*

Event	Relative frequency	
	Formula	Expressed as a percentage to 3 places of decimals
		%
Same face (either head or tail):		
in each of 4 throws	$2 \times (\frac{1}{2})^4$	12·500
,, 5 ,,	$2 \times (\frac{1}{2})^5$	6·250
,, 6 ,,	$2 \times (\frac{1}{2})^6$	3·125
,, 8 ,,	$2 \times (\frac{1}{2})^8$	·781
,, 11 ,,	$2 \times (\frac{1}{2})^{11}$	·098

II. *Throws of a six-faced die assuming that the probability of any particular face falling uppermost is $\frac{1}{6}$ at each throw, and that all throws are independent.*

Event	Relative frequency	
	Formula	Expressed as a percentage to 3 places of decimals
		%
Same face (1, 2, 3, 4, 5 or 6):		
in each of 3 throws	$(\frac{1}{6})^2$	2·778
,, 4 ,,	$(\frac{1}{6})^3$	·463
Each face once in 6 throws	$6!/6^6$	1·543

III. *Drawing playing cards (without replacement) from a normal pack of 52 cards, each card remaining in the pack being equally likely to be drawn.*

Event	Relative frequency	
	Formula	Expressed as a percentage to 3 places of decimals
		%
One card of each suit in 4 draws	$13^4 \Big/ \binom{52}{4}$	10·550
All four aces in 13 draws	$\binom{48}{9}\binom{4}{4} \Big/ \binom{52}{13}$	·264
No hearts in 13 draws	$\binom{39}{13} \Big/ \binom{52}{13}$	1·279

9·11. Recapitulation.

It is useful now to summarize the salient features of the normal procedure employed when applying statistical theory to test a hypothesis. The steps to be taken are:

(i) Construct a theoretical model.

(ii) Specify a *statistical* hypothesis, applicable to the theoretical model, which shall correspond to the hypothesis to be tested.

(iii) Specify a statistic to be calculated from the observations for the purpose of testing the statistical hypothesis.

(iv) Calculate the significance level of the observed statistic, on the assumption that the hypothesis tested is true. (As we have seen approximate assessment of the significance level, based on a table of significance limits, may be used.)

(v) Use the results so obtained as an aid to subjective judgement.

Of these steps (i), (ii) and (v) are greatly influenced by factors which are not purely statistical. Steps (i) and (ii), indeed, will make use of the general background provided by probability and statistical theory, but the conditions of the problem will determine how this theory is to be used. Steps (iii) and (iv) belong more completely to statistical theory and may be said to constitute the *statistical technique* of the test. A large proportion of the theoretical development in this book is concerned with this statistical technique, but the fact that the technique is part of a longer process should not be forgotten.

The method described above has been applied, in this chapter, to the actuarial problem described in Example 9·1. The following is a further example of the application of the general method, this time to a non-actuarial problem. It is, perhaps, inevitable in describing a process step by step in detail in this way that emphasis should be placed on difficulties rather than on advantages; this should be borne in mind in assessing the merits of the method.

Example 9·2.

From a large sack of fertilizer a small amount is removed in a scoop and chemically analysed to determine the percentage of available nitrogen. This operation is repeated six times on the same sack, the following results being obtained from the chemical analyses.

We require to test whether the fertilizer satisfies a guarantee of 6% available nitrogen.

Scoop	% available nitrogen
1	6·2
2	5·7
3	5·8
4	5·8
5	6·1
6	5·9

It may be assumed that the standard error of the percentage of available nitrogen determined by this method is ·25%.

Step (i). A useful theoretical model may be constructed as follows. We first regard the six observed percentages as observed values of six independent random variables x_1, x_2, x_3, x_4, x_5, x_6 each with standard deviation ·25. As a final assumption we suppose each x to be approximately Normally distributed with a common expected value ξ. We thus suppose each x to be a continuous variable. This is a reasonable assumption, as the percentage of available nitrogen may vary by very small amounts although the observed values are discontinuous.

We note, also, that the assumption of Normality is certainly incorrect, since x_i cannot possibly be less than zero, or greater than 100, but it may nevertheless provide a serviceable model. Evidently the probability that x_i is less than zero or greater than 100, as defined by the model chosen, should be small. This means, in turn, that ξ, which corresponds to the percentage of available nitrogen in the whole sack of fertilizer, should differ from zero or 100 by a reasonably large multiple of the standard deviation.

This leads us at once to step (ii). The particular statistical hypothesis we have to test is that $\xi=6$, the other conditions being supposed fixed. Now if $\xi=6$ we know that the arithmetic mean $\bar{x}$ of the six x's will be distributed very nearly Normally with expected value 6 and standard deviation $\cdot 25/\sqrt{6}=\cdot 102$ (see (7·30)). We use this result in step (iii). We can take as criterion the standardized arithmetic mean $\bar{x}'=(\bar{x}-6)/(\cdot 102)$ which would be distributed very nearly as a unit Normal variable if the statistical hypothesis being tested were true. We now take into consideration the alternative hypotheses which we consider likely to occur. The contingency which we desire most to avoid is that the percentage of available nitrogen should be below the guaranteed figure of 6%. In our model therefore we consider alternative statistical hypotheses defined by values of ξ less than 6, other conditions remaining fixed. In such cases

$\bar{x}'$, defined as above, will no longer be a standardized variable. It will still have unit standard deviation, but its expected value will no longer be zero. The expected value of $\bar{x}'$ will, in fact, be $(\xi - 6)/(\cdot 102)$ which is negative, since $\xi < 6$. We shall therefore compare the calculated value of

$$\frac{(\text{Mean percentage of available nitrogen}) - 6}{\cdot 102}$$

with the significance limits of the Normal curve, taking account only of the probability of falling *below* the observed value. Consequently, as step (iv) we calculate the mean percentage of available nitrogen, from the six values given. This is $\frac{1}{6}(6\cdot 2 + 5\cdot 7 + 5\cdot 8 + 5\cdot 8 + 6\cdot 1 + 5\cdot 9) = 5\cdot 917$.

The value of the criterion is therefore $\dfrac{5\cdot 917 - 6}{\cdot 102} = -\cdot 817$ and from the table in Appendix 4 we see that the significance limit $-\cdot 817$ corresponds to a significance level of just over 20 %, i.e.

$$\frac{1}{\sqrt{(2\pi)}} \int_{-\infty}^{-\cdot 817} e^{-\frac{1}{2}t^2}\, dt$$

is slightly greater than ·20.

Finally in step (v) this result has to be used as an aid to judgement. The strong subjective element makes it difficult to reach precise conclusions, although in the present case the significance level is so far removed from the conventional boundary levels that we are unlikely to consider that the percentage of available nitrogen has fallen below the level of 6 %. Obviously our conclusion may be wrong, but we do know that if the percentage were in fact 6 %, and our other assumptions were valid, then the average of six determinations of the percentage would be as low or lower than 5·917 % (the observed value) rather more frequently than once in five times.

9·12. Estimation.

When dealing with observed rates of mortality it is not always desired merely to compare them with those of some standard life-table but to obtain limits within which the theoretical rates of mortality might reasonably lie. These limits will be obtained from a consideration of a theoretical model constructed as before for testing a hypothesis but they will involve a different theoretical treatment of the model. As this is a probability model the aim will be to define limits which will include the theoretical rate of mortality at a given age with a high probability, i.e. very frequently. The probability found by such a method is called the *confidence coefficient* and the limits are called *confidence limits* enclosing a *confidence interval.* Just as the significance limits in general use correspond to small significant levels so confidence limits are constructed in such a way that the corresponding confidence coefficient is high, common values being ·95 and ·99 (i.e. the method of construction is such that the calculated limits 'straddle' the fixed, but unknown, value of the parameter which is being estimated in about 95% or 99% of cases respectively). An example should help to make the principles of interval estimation clear.

Example 9·3.

Given that 151 persons in a large homogeneous group die in a certain year, find 95% confidence limits (i.e. corresponding to a confidence coefficient ·95) for the expected number of deaths in that year.

Assuming that the number of deaths may be represented by a Poisson variable, y, with parameter m, m being the expected number of deaths, then, to a fairly close degree of approximation

$$\Pr.\{\alpha<(y-m)\,m^{-\frac{1}{2}}<\beta\}=\frac{1}{\sqrt{(2\pi)}}\int_{\alpha}^{\beta} e^{-\frac{1}{2}t^2}\,dt$$

(omitting the continuity correction).
In particular therefore

$$\Pr.\{-1{\cdot}96<(y-m)\,m^{-\frac{1}{2}}<1{\cdot}96\}=\frac{1}{\sqrt{(2\pi)}}\int_{-1\cdot96}^{1\cdot96} e^{-\frac{1}{2}t^2}\,dt=\cdot95,$$

the values of α and β being found with the help of the second table in Appendix 4.

(*Note.* It is usual for α and β to be numerically equal but of opposite sign but this is not essential. The student will find it instructive to consider the position when $\alpha \neq \beta$, and how he would deal with such practical problems as a guarantee of performance of a particular product where failure to reach a certain standard is much more important than exceeding the standard.)

The inequalities

$$-1{\cdot}96<(y-m)\,m^{-\frac{1}{2}}<1{\cdot}96$$

are equivalent to the inequalities $m_1(y)<m<m_2(y)$, where $m_1(y)$ and $m_2(y)$ are roots of the equation

$$(y-m)^2=(1{\cdot}96)^2\,m.$$

i.e.

$$(151-m)^2=(1{\cdot}96)^2 m.$$

The solutions of this equation are:

$$m_1(y) = 128{\cdot}8,$$
$$m_2(y) = 177{\cdot}1.$$

It must be emphasized that m is a constant while $m_1(y)$ and $m_2(y)$ are random variables.

9·13. Conclusion.

The reader may now feel that so many assumptions have to be made in applying the methods of analytical statistics that the value of the results is doubtful and their use largely a matter of faith. There is indeed considerable weight in these arguments but they could be made equally well about the application of other types of scientific method. They appear to be more important here simply because statistical method instead of ignoring the difficulties involved in making fundamental assumptions emphasizes them and tries to allow for them. As in other branches of science, statistical method, in spite of any doubts attaching to particular conclusions, is justified by its long-term usefulness. The theoretical backgrounds used, which are based on no more than certain beliefs as to the nature of variation, have neither more nor less justification than other beliefs which we all use in our daily work and which are finally based on induction from the experience of our whole lives.

EXERCISES 9

9·1 In a random sample of n, r objects are observed to have a character A. Using the binomial distribution show how to form approximate confidence limits for the proportion of individuals with character A in the population.

In 100 throws of a penny 'heads' is thrown 55 times. Obtain approximate 90, 95 and 99% confidence limits for the probability of throwing 'heads' at any particular throw. Attempt an interpretation of your results.

9·2 In a book of mathematical tables there are 600 pages. Each page contains a large number of entries, there being the same number on each page. 322 errors are found in the book, 385 pages being free from error. Using these data test the hypothesis that the distribution of errors in the book is random.

9·3 It is desired to test whether temperance affects longevity. Data from the experience of the total abstainers' and non-abstainers' sections of an assurance company are available. Describe in a general way the steps to be taken, relating them to the standard methods of § 9·11.

9·4 Construct charts from which can be read off approximate confidence limits for the parameter p in a binomial population. Take the cases $n=50$, 100 and 200 and use confidence coefficients ·95 and ·99.

9·5 Why is it impossible to obtain exact 95% confidence intervals in Exercise 9·4? How would you deal with the cases where n is not large enough for your approximations to be used with confidence? Illustrate your answer for the cases $n=5$ and $n=10$.

9·6 From the *a posteriori* distribution (6·14) values ϖ_1 and ϖ_2 can be determined such that

$$\text{Pr.}\,\{\varpi_1<\varpi<\varpi_2 \mid E_i\}=\int_{\varpi_1}^{\varpi_2} p_2(\varpi \mid E_i)\,d\varpi=\cdot 99 \text{ say.}$$

In what way do ϖ_1, ϖ_2 differ from the 99% confidence limits determined as described in this chapter?

9·7 What difference would it make in the analysis of the data of Example 9·2 if it were known that the guarantee of 6% of available nitrogen was to be tested against the following specification:

'Two scoops are to be taken from each sack and the available nitrogen content in each scoop determined. In each case the percentage of available nitrogen content must not be less than 6%.'

If the manufacturer desires that at least 95% of his output should pass this specification, what standards should he require in his own tests?

9·8 It has been suggested that it is misleading to speak of probability in connexion with confidence intervals because if a fresh set of data were used, new, and in general distinct, confidence intervals will be obtained. Put forward arguments against this point of view, indicating in what way the concept of probability enters into the construction of confidence intervals.

9·9 The theory underlying the calculation of significance levels involves certain assumptions (of randomness, etc.) which are often not fully justified by the circumstances. Explain, with illustrations, why the theory may nevertheless usefully be employed in many cases.

*9·10 If T_1 and T_2 are statistics (not depending on θ) such that

$$\text{Pr.}\,\{T_1<\theta<T_2 \mid \theta\}=\alpha,$$

whatever is the value of the parameter θ, then (T_1-T_2) is a 100α% confidence interval for θ. Show how T_1 and T_2 may be used in the construction of a criterion to test the hypothesis $\theta=\theta_0$.

Give special consideration to the following cases:

(i) $T_1=T-\lambda_1$, $T_2=T+\lambda_2$, where T is a statistic and λ_1 and λ_2 are numbers.

(ii) $T_1=T\lambda_1$, $T_2=T\lambda_2$.

(iii) $T_1=T-\lambda_1 U$, $T_2=T+\lambda_2 U$, where U is a statistic.

9·11 How would you use a table of random numbers to construct samples from a Normal population?

Describe a sampling experiment designed to check the adequacy of the formula $\bar{x} \pm 1{\cdot}96\,\sigma/\sqrt{n}$ for 95% confidence limits for the population expected value ξ.

Would you expect this formula to be reasonably useful for non-Normal populations?

BIBLIOGRAPHY

P. G. Hoel. *An Introduction to Mathematical Statistics* (Chapter 3). New York, J. Wiley and Son. London, Chapman and Hall.

C. H. Goulden. *Methods of Statistical Analysis* (Chapters 1–4). J. Wiley and Son, New York. London, Chapman and Hall, 1939.

R. A. Fisher. *Statistical Methods for Research Workers* (Chapter 3). London, Oliver and Boyd, 10th ed., 1948.

L. H. C. Tippett. *Methods of Statistics* (Chapters 1, 2). London, Williams and Norgate, 2nd ed., 1938.

CHAPTER 10

SIMPLE STATISTICAL TESTS

10·1. Time-series.

Certain types of statistical data are characterized by the fact that the observations are in a well-defined order which is of great importance in the analysis of the data.

A common form of this type of data is composed of the observed values of some economic variable for successive (usually approximately equal) periods of time. For example, in any analysis of the imports of cocoa beans year by year the order of the observed values is clearly of great importance.

Since the order is frequently defined by the time of the observation, as in the case described above, data of this type are called *time-series*. As will be seen in § 10·3 the order is not always determined by time, but whether it is or not, the methods of dealing with ordered data are very much the same. The problems associated with ordered data of any kind may be considered to be covered by the subject of time-series in connexion with which these methods were first developed.

10·2. Pictorial representation.

The theory of time-series is beyond the scope of this book.* We shall, however, show how the methods of descriptive statistics may be applied in this connexion. The Z-chart, which has already been referred to (§ 2·8) may be used if the character observed is cumulative. Another kind of pictorial representation is obtained by constructing a 'scatter diagram' with the observed values of the character, and time (or other ordering factor) as co-ordinates. Diagrams of this type may be constructed for ordered data whether cumulative or not.

* Moving averages and graduation formulae, which are useful in dealing with time-series, are treated in considerable detail in *Mortality and Other Investigations*.

Example 10·1.

TABLE 10·1

Numbers of Fellows and Associates of the Institute of Actuaries for the twenty years 1920–39

On 31st March	Fellows	Associates	On 31st March	Fellows	Associates	On 31st March	Fellows	Associates
1920	305	345	1927	371	325	1934	444	296
1921	324	345	1928	381	315	1935	456	296
1922	319	344	1929	381	320	1936	462	304
1923	336	350	1930	396	318	1937	475	316
1924	353	353	1931	413	315	1938	505	310
1925	360	345	1932	427	304	1939	510	335
1926	366	333	1933	440	295			

These data are clearly not cumulative and are represented in Fig. 10·1 by dots for the numbers of Fellows and by small crosses for the numbers of Associates

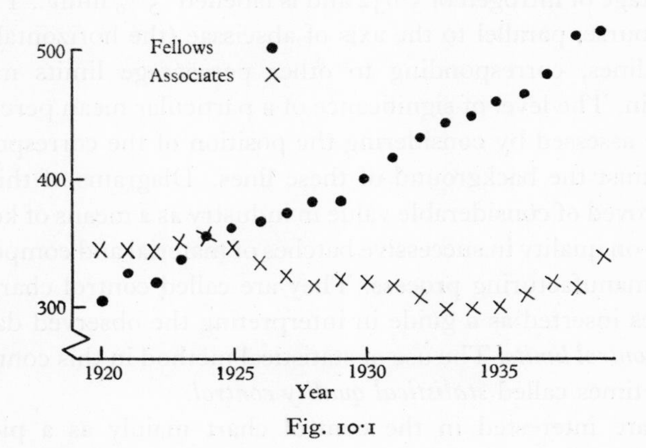

Fig. 10·1

10·3. Control charts.

We shall now return to Example 9·2. Suppose that six estimates of the percentage of nitrogen are available in respect of every third sack in a series of sacks ordered according to time of packing. We are interested in fluctuations of this percentage and particularly interested in testing whether the nitrogen content is at least 6 %. The available data are more complicated than in Example 9·2 when only one sack was considered. As a first step we try to obtain a clearer appreciation of the position by some form of pictorial representation.

We note that the series of means of the six estimates of percentage of nitrogen for each sack sampled form a time series in the sense of § 10·1. (The ordering factor here is not time explicitly, but the number of the sack.) We can therefore form a diagram like Fig. 10·1, with mean percentage of nitrogen as ordinate, and number of sack as abscissa.

Such a diagram is a valuable aid to judgement of the data. It may be made even more useful by indicating in some way the results of applying the test described in Example 9·2 to the observations for each sack. This is done by drawing lines on the diagram corresponding to various chosen significance levels of the test. Thus the 5 % significance limit for observed mean percentage of nitrogen is 5·832. A line is drawn on the diagram corresponding to a mean percentage of nitrogen of 5·832 and is labelled '5 % limit'. The line is, of course, parallel to the axis of abscissae (the horizontal axis). Other lines, corresponding to other percentage limits may be drawn in. The level of significance of a particular mean percentage may be assessed by considering the position of the corresponding dot against the background of these lines. Diagrams of this type have proved of considerable value in industry as a means of keeping a check on quality in successive batches of material and components in the manufacturing process. They are called control charts and the lines inserted as a guide in interpreting the observed data are called *control limits*. The use of statistical method in this connexion is sometimes called *statistical quality control*.

We are interested in the control chart mainly as a pictorial illustration of a statistical test, and the following examples should be regarded in that light.

Example 10·2.

Under the conditions of Example 9·2 suppose that the means of six estimates of percentage of nitrogen for a number of sacks were shown in Table 10·2.

Following the method of § 10·3 we obtain the control chart shown in Fig. 10·2. The 1 and 5 % control limits are shown in the diagram.

TABLE 10·2

Sack no.	Mean percentage of nitrogen	Sack no.	Mean percentage of nitrogen
123	6·1	144	5·8
6	6·2	7	5·85
9	6·35	150	6·0
132	6·05	3	5·75
5	5·95	6	6·05
8	5·95	9	6·0
141	6·1	162	6·2

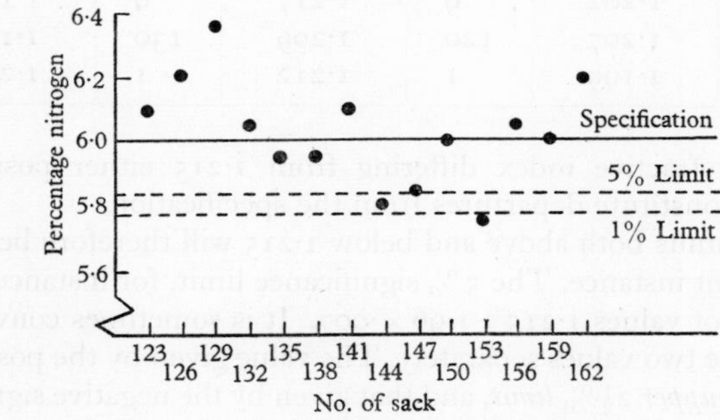

Fig. 10·2. Means of samples of 6.

Example 10·3.

The specification for a certain type of glass requires it to have a refractive index of 1·215. Samples of four pieces of glass are taken from each batch manufactured and the refractive index of each piece is measured. The means of the four measurements of refractive index for thirty successive batches are shown in Table 10·3. It is required to form a control chart for these data.

It may be assumed that sampling deviations and errors of measurement combine to give a standard deviation of ·014 for a single measurement of refractive index. The standard deviation of a mean of four such measurements is $\frac{\cdot 014}{\sqrt{4}} = \cdot 007$.

The hypothesis to be tested is that the population refractive index is 1·215.

In this problem it is reasonable to include values of refractive index both greater than 1·215 and less than 1·215 in the alternative hypotheses.

TABLE 10·3

Mean refractive index in samples of 4

Batch no.	Mean ref. index	Batch no.	Mean ref. index	Batch no.	Mean ref. index
102	1·211	112	1·198	122	1·216
3	1·211	3	1·195	3	1·221
4	1·227	4	1·203	4	1·215
5	1·222	5	1·210	5	1·213
6	1·229	6	1·203	6	1·213
7	1·204	7	1·218	7	1·204
8	1·216	8	1·214	8	1·210
9	1·202	9	1·217	9	1·199
110	1·207	120	1·209	130	1·197
1	1·199	1	1·212	1	1·205

Values of refractive index differing from 1·215 either positively or negatively constitute departures from the specification.

Control limits both above and below 1·215 will therefore be required in the present instance. The 5 % significance limit, for instance, is given by the pair of values $1{\cdot}215 \pm 1{\cdot}96 \times {\cdot}007$. It is sometimes convenient to refer to these two values separately. The value given by the positive sign is called the *upper* $2\frac{1}{2}$ % *limit*, and that given by the negative sign is called the *lower* $2\frac{1}{2}$ % *limit*. We note that the upper $2\frac{1}{2}$ % limit in the present case would be simply the $2\frac{1}{2}$ % limit if the alternative hypotheses included only values of the population refractive index greater than 1·215.

Numerical values for control limits which may be used in the present instance are:

Lower $2\frac{1}{2}$ % limit 1·201 Upper $2\frac{1}{2}$ % limit 1·229.

Lower ·1 % limit 1·193 Upper ·1 % limit 1·237.

The latter two combine to give a significance level of ·2 %.

The control chart obtained using these limits is shown in Fig. 10·3.

The chart shows that the refractive index has a tendency to fall below the specification value. There is evidence of a bad period between batches 110 and 115, and also of the commencement of a bad period at the end of the series.

It should be noted that the statement of the hypothesis to be tested is in fact a convenient simplication of the position. What is really required is a population refractive index value falling within a small interval containing 1·215 but not *exactly* equal to 1·215.

As a matter of convenience control limits are often taken at distances twice and three times the standard deviation from the population mean on the hypothesis tested. These limits are the upper and lower 2·275 and ·135% limits respectively. (See Appendix 4.)

The dependence of the control limits on the assumption of Normality should be always borne in mind.

It may be noted, however, that, provided the conditions for Gauss' inequality are satisfied (§7·16), the probability of a deviation

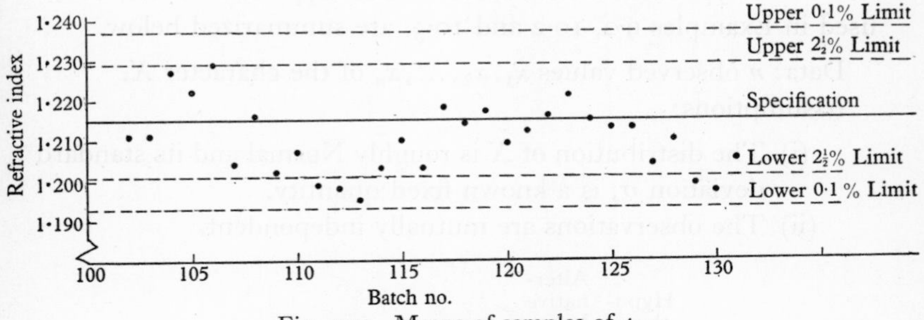

Fig. 10·3. Means of samples of 4.

from the expected value greater in absolute magnitude than twice the standard deviation is certainly less than 11·11% while the probability of a deviation greater in absolute magnitude than three times the standard deviation is certainly less than 4·94%.

10·4. Test of population mean.

(*a*) *Population standard deviation known.*

The technical part of statistical tests—steps (iii) and (iv) of §9·11—may be conveniently summarized by formulae for the criterion to be used and for the significance level of an observed value of the criterion. We shall now proceed to such a summary of the technical part of the statistical test which has been developed in Examples 9·2, 10·2 and 10·3. This is essentially a test of whether the population mean of a certain character has some particular value, given the value of the population standard deviation of that character.

Using symbols, we may denote the character in question by X, its expected value (the population mean) by ξ and its standard deviation (in the population) by σ. Then the hypothesis tested is that $\xi = \xi_0$, given the value of σ. The hypothesis will usually also include some assumption about the shape of the distribution of X in the population. Strictly speaking the alternative hypotheses considered allow only of variation in the value of ξ. In Examples 9·2 and 10·2 the alternative hypotheses are defined by values of ξ less than ξ_0. In Example 10·3 values of ξ either greater than ξ_0 or less than ξ_0 are contemplated. Actually some types of variation in the shape of the distribution of X may not have a grave effect on the test used. The hypothesis tested, the alternative hypotheses and the tests used in Examples 9·2, 10·2 and 10·3, are summarized below.

Data: n observed values $x_1, x_2, \ldots, x_n$ of the character X.

Assumptions:

(i) The distribution of X is roughly Normal and its standard deviation σ, is a known fixed quantity.

(ii) The observations are mutually independent.

	Hypothesis tested	Alternative hypotheses	Criterion	Significance level
(Examples 9·2 and 10·2)	$\xi=\xi_0$	$\xi<\xi_0$	$\sqrt{n}(\bar{x}-\xi_0)\,\sigma^{-1}=u$	$\frac{1}{\sqrt{(2\pi)}}\int_{-\infty}^{u} e^{-\frac{1}{2}v^2}\,dy$
(Example 10·3)	$\xi=\xi_0$	$\xi\neq\xi_0$	$\lvert u \rvert$	$\sqrt{\left(\frac{2}{\pi}\right)}\int_{\lvert u \rvert}^{\infty} e^{-\frac{1}{2}v^2}\,dy$

10·5. Test of population mean.

(b) Population standard deviation unknown.

Knowledge of the magnitude of the population standard deviation (σ) has been of great value in constructing the tests summarized in § 10·4. This knowledge must be obtained from previous experience of variation occurring in similar measurements, possibly combined with theoretical considerations. For instance, the figure of ·25 % for the standard deviation of percentage nitrogen content determined by chemical analysis would be based on previous experience of such analyses.

In many cases the experience necessary to enable an estimate of the standard deviation to be made is lacking. The same problem of checking the average value of X in the population has still to be faced. The criteria $u=\sqrt{n}(\bar{x}-\xi_0)\,\sigma^{-1}$ or $\lvert u \rvert$ cannot be used as the value of σ is not definitely known and we are led to replace it in the formula for u by a statistic (i.e. a quantity which may be calculated from the observed values) which will be an estimate of σ. From §7·11 we know that if

$$s^2 = \frac{1}{n} \sum_{i=1}^{n} (x_i - \bar{x})^2$$

then $$\mathscr{E}(s^2) = \frac{n-1}{n} \sigma^2, \quad \text{i.e.} \quad \mathscr{E}\left(\frac{n}{n-1} s^2\right) = \sigma^2.$$

Hence it seems reasonable to use the statistic $s\sqrt{[n/(n-1)]}$ as an estimate of σ. This leads to the replacement of u by

$$t = \sqrt{(n-1)}\,(\bar{x} - \xi_0)\, s^{-1}.$$

It will be noted that both the numerator and denominator of the expression for t correspond to random variables in the theoretical model. This fact affects our concept of the distribution of the values of t. We cannot assume t to correspond to a unit Normal variable without preliminary theoretical investigation. This will be carried out in the second volume (Chapter 11).

We can, however, see that if n be sufficiently large $s\sqrt{[n/(n-1)]}$ will be a very good estimate of σ, and hence t and u will differ very little. For sufficiently large values of n, therefore, t may be taken to correspond to a unit Normal variable, and may therefore be treated in the same way as u. Theoretical investigation shows that values of n greater than 20 may be regarded as sufficiently large for most practical purposes. The technical part of the tests developed in this section may be summarized as below.

Data: $n\,(>20)$ observed values $x_1, x_2, \ldots, x_n$ of the character X.

Assumptions:

(i) The distribution of X is roughly Normal.

(ii) The observations are mutually independent.

	Hypothesis tested	Alternative hypotheses	Criterion	Significance level
(Examples 9·2 and 10·2)	$\xi = \xi_0$	$\xi < \xi_0$	$\sqrt{(n-1)}\,(\bar{x} - \xi_0)\, s^{-1} = t$	$\frac{1}{\sqrt{(2\pi)}} \int_{-\infty}^{t} e^{-\frac{1}{2}y^2}\, dy$
(Example 10·3)	$\xi = \xi_0$	$\xi \neq \xi_0$	$\lvert t \rvert$	$\sqrt{\left(\frac{2}{\pi}\right)} \int_{\lvert t \rvert}^{\infty} e^{-\frac{1}{2}y^2}\, dy$

The significance levels are approximate and tend to underestimate the theoretical significance levels to an increasing extent as n decreases.

Example 10·4.

The intelligence quotients of a group of 400 children were measured. The average intelligence quotient was found to be 101·3 and the standard deviation of the distribution of 400 observed values of the intelligence quotient was 17·6. It is desired to test whether the observed values may be regarded as occurring as a result of sampling from a population in which the average intelligence quotient is 100.

Here it is reasonable to assume that alternative hypotheses may specify values of the population mean intelligence quotient either greater than or less than 100. Hence the appropriate criterion is

$$|t| = \left|\frac{(101{\cdot}3 - 100)\sqrt{(399)}}{17{\cdot}6}\right| = 1{\cdot}475$$

and the approximate significance level is

$$\sqrt{\left(\frac{2}{\pi}\right)}\int_{1\cdot475}^{\infty} e^{-\frac{1}{2}y^2}\,dy = {\cdot}1402.$$

This would probably not be regarded as evidence that the hypothesis tested was untrue.

It may be noted that with n (the sample size) as big as 400 it makes little difference if $(n-1)$ be replaced by n in the formula for t. This would give

$$|t| = \left|\frac{(101{\cdot}3 - 100)\sqrt{(400)}}{17{\cdot}6}\right| = 1{\cdot}477$$

with an approximate significance level of

$$\sqrt{\left(\frac{2}{\pi}\right)}\int_{1\cdot477}^{\infty} e^{-\frac{1}{2}y^2}\,dy = {\cdot}1397.$$

There is no practical difference in using one formula instead of the other with n as big as this.

In the present problem it is as easy to use $(n-1)$ as n but later we shall see that replacement of $(n-1)$ by n may facilitate the calculation of certain criteria.

It is not usually necessary to work out exact significance levels. Thus in the present case the observed values of $|t|$ could be compared with the 5% significance limit (1·960) and the 10% significance limit (1·645).

10·6. Difference between population means.

(*a*) *Population standard deviations known.*

This section and the next deal with the hypothesis that the average values of a certain character X in two populations differ by a certain amount, δ_0 say. In the case most commonly met with, δ_0 is zero. That is to say the hypothesis states that the two populations do not differ from each other in respect of the average value of character X. For example, we may wish to test whether the percentage nitrogen content is the same in each of two sacks. The two sacks then correspond to two populations in our theoretical model and the statistical hypothesis to be tested is the hypothesis that the difference between the two population means of X is zero.

If the standard deviations of X in each of the two populations are known a test criterion analogous to u is easily formed. The resultant tests are summarized below. The population mean and standard deviation of the character X in the population Π_i are denoted by ξ_i, σ_i respectively ($i=1, 2$).

Data:

n_1 observed values $x_{11}, x_{12}, \ldots, x_{1n_1}$ of the character X in population Π_1.

n_2 observed values $x_{21}, x_{22}, \ldots, x_{2n_2}$ of the character X in population Π_2.

Assumptions:

(i) The distributions of X in each population are roughly Normal.

(ii) The population standard deviations σ_1 and σ_2 are known fixed quantities.

(iii) The observations are mutually independent.

Hypothesis tested	$\xi_1 - \xi_2 = \delta_0$	$\xi_1 - \xi_2 = \delta_0$
Alternative hypotheses	$\xi_1 - \xi_2 > \delta_0$	$\xi_1 - \xi_2 \neq \delta_0$
Criterion	$(\bar{x}_1 - \bar{x}_2 - \delta_0)(n_1^{-1}\sigma_1^2 + n_2^{-1}\sigma_2^2)^{-\frac{1}{2}} = u$	$\lvert u \rvert$
Significance level	$\dfrac{1}{\sqrt{(2\pi)}}\displaystyle\int_u^\infty e^{-\frac{1}{2}y^2}\,dy$	$\sqrt{\left(\dfrac{2}{\pi}\right)}\displaystyle\int_{\lvert u \rvert}^\infty e^{-\frac{1}{2}y^2}\,dy$

$$\left(\bar{x}_1 = \frac{1}{n_1}\sum_{i=1}^{n_1} x_{1i};\ \bar{x}_2 = \frac{1}{n_2}\sum_{i=1}^{n_2} x_{2i}\right).$$

We note that u is a standardized variable since:

$$\text{(i)}\quad \mathscr{E}(\bar{x}_1-\bar{x}_2-\delta_0)=\xi_1-\xi_2-\delta_0=0$$

provided the statistical hypothesis $\xi_1-\xi_2=\delta_0$ is valid, and (ii) the standard deviation of the random variable $\bar{x}_1-\bar{x}_2$ is

$$(n_1^{-1}\sigma_1^2+n_2^{-1}\sigma_2^2)^{\frac{1}{2}}.$$

If n_1 and n_2 are not very small (in this case not less than 10) then u will be distributed very nearly as a unit Normal variable.

It will be noted that we use the same symbols $x_{11}, x_{12}, \bar{x}_1, \ldots$, etc., for observed values and for the corresponding random variables in the theoretical model. This should not cause confusion, but the reader should continually keep in mind the distinction between the two meanings of the symbols. Where it is necessary to emphasize the distinction observed values may be denoted by $\mathring{x}_{11}$, $\mathring{x}_{12}$ etc. (see § 9·3–9·5).

Example 10·5.

It is known that in repeated experiments the standard deviation of an estimate of viscosity of a certain liquid by a standard method—method *A* as we shall call it—is ·13 unit. An alternative method, method *B*, gives rise to a standard deviation of ·32 unit. This greater variability is offset by the greater ease of application of method *B*. While it may be assumed that method *A* is unbiased, it is possible that estimates by method *B* may be biased. An experiment has been carried out to test this point. The mean of ten observations by method *A* was 16·18, the mean of fifty observations by method *B* was 16·44. The hypothesis to be tested is that the difference between population mean estimates of viscosity is zero (i.e. $\delta_0=0$).

Unless there is reason to expect bias in some particular direction the alternative hypotheses must allow for bias in either direction. The criterion used is therefore

$$|u|=\left|\frac{16{\cdot}44-16{\cdot}18}{\sqrt{\left(\frac{(\cdot 13)^2}{10}+\frac{(\cdot 32)^2}{50}\right)}}\right|=\frac{\cdot 26}{\sqrt{(\cdot 003738)}}=4{\cdot}253$$

and the significance level is $\sqrt{\left(\frac{2}{\pi}\right)}\int_{4\cdot 253}^{\infty} e^{-\frac{1}{2}y^2}\,dy=\cdot 00003.$

This would probably be regarded as substantial evidence that method *B* was biased. The question then arises of estimating the amount of the bias. The reader should attempt to obtain confidence limits for the bias, using methods analogous to those of Example 9·3.

10·7. Difference between population means.

(*b*) *Population standard deviations not known.*

Previous experience of the variation to be expected may be lacking when we compare the means of two populations as it was assumed to be when we tested the value of a single population mean (see § 10·5). Just as the lack of experience forced us to replace σ by an estimate of σ in the case of a single population mean, so it forces us to replace σ_1 and σ_2 by estimates when comparing two population means. The estimates used are, naturally,

$$\sqrt{\left(\frac{n_1}{n_1-1}\right)}\, s_1 = \sqrt{\left(\frac{1}{n_1-1}\sum_{i=1}^{n_1}(x_{1i}-\bar{x}_1)^2\right)} \quad \text{as an estimate of } \sigma_1$$

and

$$\sqrt{\left(\frac{n_2}{n_2-1}\right)}\, s_2 = \sqrt{\left(\frac{1}{n_2-1}\sum_{i=1}^{n_2}(x_{2i}-\bar{x}_2)^2\right)} \quad \text{as an estimate of } \sigma_2.$$

We thus obtain the statistical tests summarized below.

Data:

$n_1\,(>20)$ observed values $x_{11}, x_{12}, \ldots, x_{1n_1}$ of the character X in population Π_1.

$n_2\,(>20)$ observed values $x_{21}, x_{22}, \ldots, x_{2n_2}$ of the character X in population Π_2.

Assumptions:

(i) The distributions of X in each population are roughly Normal.

(ii) The observations are mutually independent.

Hypothesis tested	$\xi_1-\xi_2=\delta_0$	$\xi_1-\xi_2=\delta_0$
Alternative hypotheses	$\xi_1-\xi_2>\delta_0$	$\xi_1-\xi_2\neq\delta_0$
Criterion	$(\bar{x}_1-\bar{x}_2-\delta_0)\{(n_1-1)^{-1}s_1^2+(n_2-1)^{-1}s_2^2\}^{-\frac{1}{2}}=t$	$\lvert t \rvert$
Significance level	$\dfrac{1}{\sqrt{(2\pi)}}\displaystyle\int_t^\infty e^{-\frac{1}{2}y^2}\,dy$	$\sqrt{\left(\dfrac{2}{\pi}\right)}\displaystyle\int_{\lvert t\rvert}^\infty e^{-\frac{1}{2}y^2}\,dy$

As in § 10·5 the significance levels shown above are only approximations to the theoretical values. In this case the degree of approximation depends not only on the two sample sizes n_1 and n_2 but also, to a slight extent, on the ratio σ_1/σ_2 of the population standard deviations. If n_1 and n_2 are reasonably large (greater than 20) the significance levels given above may be used with a fair degree of confidence.

Example 10·6.

An assurance office examined its data for whole-life assurances (with profits) effected in 1946 and found that in a sample of 106 the average age at entry was 39·11 years while the standard deviation of this age in the sample was 11·24 years. The corresponding values in a sample of 100 policies effected in 1906 were: mean 45·50 years and standard deviation 10·69 years. What evidence do these figures give of a change in the mean age at entry?

The criterion is

$$|t| = \frac{6{\cdot}39}{\sqrt{\left(\frac{(11{\cdot}24)^2}{105} + \frac{(10{\cdot}69)^2}{99}\right)}} = 2{\cdot}710$$

and the significance level is

$$\sqrt{\left(\frac{2}{\pi}\right)} \int_{2{\cdot}710}^{\infty} e^{-\frac{1}{2}y^2}\, dy = {\cdot}0068.$$

This would be regarded as substantial evidence that the mean age had in fact altered. In this connexion it should be borne in mind that during the forty years 1906–46, the popularity of whole-life assurances has diminished and endowment assurances have largely replaced them, more especially at the young ages where the rate of premium is not so heavy.

10·8. Test of population standard deviation.

It is sometimes desired to keep a check on the variability of a character X. This variability may be represented in the theoretical model by the standard deviation of the random variable corresponding to an observed value of X. If it is desired to test whether the variability is at a certain level, the statistical hypothesis to be tested is the hypothesis that σ has a particular value σ_0.

The statistic

$$\sqrt{\left(\frac{n}{n-1}\right)}\, s = \sqrt{\left(\frac{1}{n-1}\sum_{i=1}^{n}(x_i - \bar{x})^2\right)}$$

has an intuitive appeal as a criterion for this test. Remembering the approximate formula for the standard deviation of s (Exercises 7·10–11) we deduce that

$$\left[\sqrt{\left(\frac{n}{n-1}\right)}s-\sigma\right]\Big/\sigma\sqrt{\left[\frac{1}{4n}\left(\beta_2-\frac{n-3}{n-1}\right)\right]}$$

is approximately a standardized variable.

If n be sufficiently large and the distribution of X fairly close to Normality, then the variable $(\sqrt{[n/(n-1)]}.s-\sigma)/\sigma\{2(n-1)\}^{-\frac{1}{2}}$ is approximately standardized. Assuming, further, that this variable is Normally distributed we obtain the tests summarized below.

Data:

$n\,(>20)$ observed values $x_1, x_2, \ldots, x_n$ of the character X.

Assumptions:

(i) The distribution of X is roughly Normal.

(ii) The observations are mutually independent.

Hypothesis tested	$\sigma=\sigma_0$	$\sigma=\sigma_0$
Alternative hypotheses	$\sigma>\sigma_0$	$\sigma\neq\sigma_0$
Criterion	$(\sqrt{[n/(n-1)]}\,s-\sigma_0)/\sigma_0\{2(n-1)\}^{-\frac{1}{2}}=u$	$\lvert u\rvert$
Significance level	$\frac{1}{\sqrt{(2\pi)}}\int_u^\infty e^{-\frac{1}{2}y^2}\,dy$	$\sqrt{\left(\frac{2}{\pi}\right)}\int_{\lvert u\rvert}^\infty e^{-\frac{1}{2}y^2}\,dy$

The formulae for significance levels are again approximations to theoretical values, the approximation improving with increasing sample size n. It will be noted that the hypothesis tested $(\sigma=\sigma_0)$ involves no assumption about the value of the population mean ξ and that no such assumption is needed in the construction of the criteria. This is because theory enables a value for the standard deviation of the random variable s to be obtained which is independent of ξ. The standard deviation of s is in fact determined (approximately) by the hypothesis $\sigma=\sigma_0$.

For this reason we shall not at present develop separate tests for the cases ξ known, and ξ unknown, as was done for the cases σ known, and σ unknown, in earlier sections. It is, indeed, possible to construct separate tests for the two cases but the difference between them is slight for the values of n with which we are dealing.

Example 10·7.

It is desired to keep a check on the variability of batches of electric lamp bulbs as regards the character 'length of life'. A standard deviation of not more than 110 hr. is aimed at. The length of life is determined for each of a sample of 25 bulbs from each batch manufactured and the sample standard deviation is worked out for each batch. The results are shown in Table 10·4. Analyse the data using a control chart.

TABLE 10·4

Standard Deviation of length of life of Electric Lamp Bulbs. (Samples of 25)

Batch no.	Standard deviation (hr.)	Batch no.	Standard deviation (hr.)
70	104	78	81
71	97	79	103
72	90	80	115
73	61	81	126
74	82	82	93
75	111	83	112
76	140	84	124
77	97	85	107

In this case the only alternative hypotheses which we need consider are those specifying values of the population standard deviation (σ) greater than 110. The hypothesis tested specifies '$\sigma = 110$'. If s be the standard deviation observed in a sample of 25 the appropriate criterion is then

$$u = \frac{\sqrt{\left(\frac{25}{24}\right)}s - 110}{110\sqrt{\left(\frac{1}{2\times 24}\right)}} = \frac{1{\cdot}021s - 110}{15{\cdot}88}$$

and the approximate significance level is

$$\frac{1}{\sqrt{(2\pi)}}\int_u^\infty e^{-\frac{1}{2}y^2}dy.$$

We could carry out sixteen separate tests, one for each batch, but it is more convenient to construct a control chart giving a single concise picture of the results of applying each of these sixteen tests.

Such a control chart might be constructed by plotting the sixteen values of u against the corresponding batch numbers and putting in an approximate $2\frac{1}{2}$ % control limit at $u = 2$, an approximate ·1 % limit at

$u=3$ and so on. If, however, the statistic used is s instead of u the chart will be more readily understood by a non-statistician and the labour of calculating u for each batch will be avoided. If u_α, s_α be the 100α % control limits of u and s respectively then

$$u_\alpha=(1{\cdot}021s_\alpha-110)/15{\cdot}88$$

so that $$s_\alpha=(110+15{\cdot}88u_\alpha)/1{\cdot}021=107{\cdot}7+15{\cdot}55u_\alpha.$$

This gives the approximate $2\frac{1}{2}$ % control limit

$$s_{\cdot025}=107{\cdot}7+2\times15{\cdot}55=138{\cdot}8$$

and the approximate $\cdot1$ % control limit

$$s_{\cdot001}=107{\cdot}7+3\times15{\cdot}55=154{\cdot}3.$$

We note that if the simpler formula

$$u=(s-110)/110(2\times25)^{-\frac{1}{2}}=(s-110)/15{\cdot}56$$

were used the corresponding control limits for s would be 141·1 and 156·7. These differ but little from the more exact values in this case. The control chart is shown in Fig. 10·4.

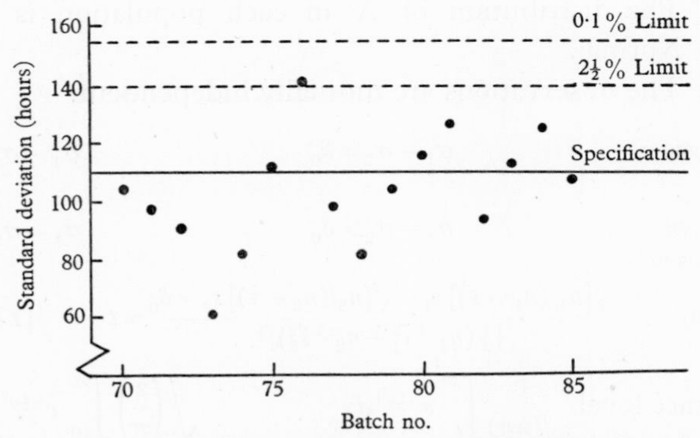

Fig. 10·4. Length of life of electric lamp bulbs. Samples of 25.

The data would probably not be considered to indicate excess variability. The value 140 for batch no. 76 is indeed above the approximate $2\frac{1}{2}$ % limit, but it must be remembered that values exceeding this limit are expected to occur in about one in forty cases even when the hypothesis tested holds good.

10·9. Comparison of standard deviations in two populations.

The comparison of standard deviations in two populations is a problem which occurs frequently. Its importance arises, not only from the necessity of keeping a check on the changes in factors affecting variability, but because consideration of relative variability must arise whenever the accuracy of estimates of population means is in question.

Proceeding in a manner similar to that of § 10·7 (not 10·6) we obtain tests, the technical portions of which are summarized below. It will be noted that in contradistinction to § 10·8 sample estimates of the standard deviations have to be inserted in the denominators of the criteria because the hypothesis tested does not specify the actual values of the σ's but only the difference between them.

Data:

$n_1\,(>20)$ observed values $x_{11} \dots x_{1n_1}$ of the character X in population Π_1.

$n_2\,(>20)$ observed values $x_{21} \dots x_{2n_2}$ of the character X in population Π_2.

Assumptions:

(i) The distribution of X in each population is roughly Normal.

(ii) The observations are mutually independent.

Hypothesis tested	$\sigma_1 - \sigma_2 = \delta_0$	$\sigma_1 - \sigma_2 = \delta_0$
Alternative hypotheses	$\sigma_1 - \sigma_2 > \delta_0$	$\sigma_1 - \sigma_2 \neq \delta_0$
Criterion	$\dfrac{\sqrt{[n_1/(n_1-1)]}\, s_1 - \sqrt{[n_2/(n_2-1)]}\, s_2 - \delta_0}{\{\frac{1}{2}(n_1^{-1}\hat{s}_1^2 + n_2^{-1}\hat{s}_2^2)\}^{\frac{1}{2}}} = t$	$\lvert t \rvert$
Significance level	$\dfrac{1}{\sqrt{(2\pi)}}\displaystyle\int_t^\infty e^{-\frac{1}{2}y^2}\,dy$	$\sqrt{\left(\dfrac{2}{\pi}\right)}\displaystyle\int_{\lvert t \rvert}^\infty e^{-\frac{1}{2}y^2}\,dy$

where $\hat{s}_1$ and $\hat{s}_2$ are defined by the equations $\hat{s}_1 - \hat{s}_2 = \delta_0$, and $(n_1 - 1)\,\hat{s}_1^2 + (n_2 - 1)\,\hat{s}_2^2 = n_1 s_1^2 + n_2 s_2^2$. Usually simpler formulae, obtained by replacing $n_1 - 1$ by n_1 and $n_2 - 1$ by n_2, may be used.

Again separate tests are not developed for the cases where the population means are known and where they are unknown. The case most usually occurring corresponds to $\delta_0 = 0$. The hypothesis to be tested is then that the two population standard deviations are equal.

For comparing standard deviations another criterion is more commonly employed. This is based on the ratio of the sample standard deviations, s_1/s_2. Using the results of § 7·12 we obtain the scheme summarized below. The data and assumptions are the same as before. The sample sizes n_1 and n_2 are supposed to be sufficiently large for the approximations involved to be valid.

Hypothesis tested	$\dfrac{\sigma_1}{\sigma_2}=\zeta_0$	$\dfrac{\sigma_1}{\sigma_2}=\zeta_0$
Alternative hypotheses	$\dfrac{\sigma_1}{\sigma_2}>\zeta_0$	$\dfrac{\sigma_1}{\sigma_2}\neq\zeta_0$
Criterion	$\dfrac{(s_1/s_2)-\zeta_0}{\zeta_0\{\frac{1}{2}(n_1^{-1}+n_2^{-1})\}^{\frac{1}{2}}}=u$	$\lvert u \rvert$
Significance level	$\dfrac{1}{\sqrt{(2\pi)}}\displaystyle\int_u^\infty e^{-\frac{1}{2}y^2}\,dy$	$\sqrt{\left(\dfrac{2}{\pi}\right)}\displaystyle\int_{\lvert u \rvert}^\infty e^{-\frac{1}{2}y^2}\,dy$

It will be noticed that as n_1 and n_2 are large the expression

$$(\tfrac{1}{2}n_1^{-1}+\tfrac{1}{2}n_2^{-1}+\tfrac{3}{4}n_1^{-1}n_2^{-1})$$

corresponding to (7·39) has been replaced by $\frac{1}{2}(n_1^{-1}+n_2^{-1})$ in this test.

Example 10·8.

It is desired to compare the homogeneity of iron-ore supplied from two different sources. Samples of twenty-five portions of a fixed size are taken from the ore from each source and the percentage of available iron estimated by chemical analysis for each of the fifty portions thus chosen. The sample standard deviations are 3·5 and 2·6%. Unless homogeneity or heterogeneity is particularly associated with one source (as it might be were it a question of replacing one source of supply by another), the appropriate criterion is

$$\lvert t \rvert=\frac{\left\lvert\sqrt{\left(\frac{25}{24}\right)}\times 3\cdot 5-\sqrt{\left(\frac{25}{24}\right)}\times 2\cdot 6\right\rvert}{\sqrt{\left\{\frac{1}{48}[(3\cdot 5)^2+(2\cdot 6)^2]\right\}}}=\frac{\cdot 9186}{\sqrt{\cdot 3960}}=1\cdot 46.$$

The approximate significance level is

$$\sqrt{\left(\frac{2}{\pi}\right)}\int_{1\cdot 46}^\infty e^{-\frac{1}{2}y^2}\,dy=\cdot 144.$$

which would probably not be regarded as significant of real difference between the two population standard deviations.

It may be noted that when the two sample sizes are equal, as in the present case, the simpler formula gives exactly the same value of t as the more exact formula. In this example the simpler formula gives

$$|t| = \frac{|3 \cdot 5 - 2 \cdot 6|}{\sqrt{\{\frac{1}{50}[(3 \cdot 5)^2 + (2 \cdot 6)^2]\}}} = 1 \cdot 46.$$

Instead of basing the criterion on the difference between sample standard deviations we could use their ratio as follows. The hypothesis tested is $\zeta_0 = 1$.

$$|u| = \frac{\left|\frac{3 \cdot 5}{2 \cdot 6} - 1\right|}{\sqrt{\frac{1}{25}}} = 1 \cdot 81.$$

giving a significance level $\sqrt{\left(\frac{2}{\pi}\right)} \int_{1 \cdot 81}^{\infty} e^{-\frac{1}{2}y^2}\, dy = \cdot 070.$

It is to be noted that the two tests do not give the same significance level. This is to be expected as they are distinct tests and the problem of deciding which is the better to use is evidently of importance. It will be considered in the second volume.

10·10. Tests of a population proportion.

Our data may consist of a number of observations each of which may be classed in one of two groups, X and not—X, say. We may then wish to test whether the proportion of X in the population, p say, has some specified value. If conditions permit we may assume the number of X's observed among n individuals to be represented by a binomial variable with parameters n and p. Representing the number of X's observed by the random variable x, we have

$$\text{Pr.}\{x = r\} = \binom{n}{r} p^r q^{n-r} \quad (r = 0, 1, \ldots, n).$$

We know then that x has expected value np and standard deviation $\sqrt{(npq)}$.

The setting up of the hypotheses and the criteria follow familiar lines but the significance level gives rise to new problems because we are no longer dealing with a Normal population. As we have seen in Table 8·1, however, the binomial and the Normal distributions are not very different in many cases and equations (8·35) give the limits of the Normal integral which provide an approximation for the true binomial significance level.

We thus have the following technique:

Data:

n observations x of which are regarded as 'Successes'.

Assumptions:

(i) The distribution of successes follows a binomial law with parameters n and p.

(ii) The values of n and the hypothetical proportion p_0 are such that the Normal approximation can be used for the significance levels.

Hypothesis tested	$p=p_0$	$p=p_0$
Alternative hypotheses	$p>p_0$	$p\neq p_0$
Criterion	$\dfrac{x-np_0-\frac{1}{2}}{\sqrt{(np_0q_0)}}=u$	$\dfrac{\lvert x-np_0\rvert-\frac{1}{2}}{\sqrt{(np_0q_0)}}=u'$
Significance level	$\dfrac{1}{\sqrt{(2\pi)}}\displaystyle\int_u^\infty e^{-\frac{1}{2}y^2}\,dy$	$\sqrt{\left(\dfrac{2}{\pi}\right)}\displaystyle\int_{u'}^\infty e^{-\frac{1}{2}y^2}\,dy$

where $q_0=1-p_0$.

Similar considerations apply for a Poisson population for which

$$\text{Pr.}\{x=r\}=e^{-m}\frac{m^r}{r!} \quad (r=0, 1, 2, \dots)$$

except that the expected value and standard deviation of x are now m and $\sqrt{m}$ instead of np and $\sqrt{(npq)}$ respectively. Generally speaking, however, the Normal approximation for the significance level will be less satisfactory than for the binomial population. The point is rather important in actuarial theory because tests implicitly based on a Poisson distribution are commonly used in dealing with mortality data.

Example 10·9.

An assurance company investigating the mortality experienced by the policyholders of a certain class finds that in a given year out of 754 people aged 63, ten died within 12 months. According to a table of mortality used for calculating premiums and in valuation the rate of mortality at age 63 is ·02631.

In the notation of the previous section $p=\cdot 02631$. The expected number of deaths

$$np=754\times\cdot 02631$$
$$=19\cdot 84.$$

The number actually observed $=10$.

As we are interested in values above as well as below the expected number we take as the criterion

$$u' = \frac{|19{\cdot}84 - 10| - \frac{1}{2}}{\sqrt{(19{\cdot}84 \times {\cdot}97369)}} = 2{\cdot}04.$$

The approximate significance level is

$$\sqrt{\left(\frac{2}{\pi}\right)} \int_{2{\cdot}04}^{\infty} e^{-\frac{1}{2}y^2}\, dy = {\cdot}0416.$$

This would probably not be regarded as convincing evidence that the experience differed from the mortality rate specified.

The test based on the Poisson distribution is left as an exercise for the reader. The conclusion is virtually the same as in the above.

10·11. Equality of proportions.

A rate of mortality is of the nature of a proportion, viz. the proportion of lives who do not survive one year from the age to which the rate applies. Comparison of mortality rates is therefore a comparison of proportions in two or more populations.

In the previous section the population proportion was specified by the hypothesis tested. In the present type of problem the population proportions are not usually specified in this way and they must therefore be estimated from the sample data.

The technical procedure may be summarized as follows:

Data:

n_1 observations of which x_1 have the character X, from population Π_1.

n_2 observations of which x_2 have the character X, from population Π_2.

Assumptions:

(i) The distributions of x_1, x_2 are each binomial with parameters n_1 and p_1, n_2 and p_2 respectively.

(ii) The samples are mutually independent.

(iii) The values of n_1, n_2, p_1 and p_2 are such that the Normal approximation may be used without the continuity correction. (This implies, *inter alia*, that both n_1 and n_2 must be fairly large (> 30, say).)

Hypothesis tested	$p_1 - p_2 = \delta_0$	$p_1 - p_2 = \delta_0$
Alternative hypotheses	$p_1 - p_2 > \delta_0$	$p_1 - p_2 \neq \delta_0$
Criterion	$\dfrac{\dfrac{x_1}{n_1} - \dfrac{x_2}{n_2} - \delta_0}{\left\{\dfrac{\hat{p}_1(1-\hat{p}_1)}{n_1} + \dfrac{\hat{p}_2(1-\hat{p}_2)}{n_2}\right\}^{\frac{1}{2}}} = t$	$\lvert t \rvert$
Significance level	$\dfrac{1}{\sqrt{(2\pi)}}\displaystyle\int^{\infty} e^{-\frac{1}{2}y^2}\,dy$	$\sqrt{\left(\dfrac{2}{\pi}\right)}\displaystyle\int_{\lvert t\rvert}^{\infty} e^{-\frac{1}{2}y^2}\,dy$

$$\text{where}\quad \hat{p}_1 = \frac{x_1 + x_2}{n_1 + n_2} + \frac{n_2}{n_1 + n_2}\delta_0; \quad \hat{p}_2 = \frac{x_1 + x_2}{n_1 + n_2} - \frac{n_1}{n_1 + n_2}\delta_0$$

(satisfying the conditions $\hat{p}_1 - \hat{p}_2 = \delta_0$; $n_1\hat{p}_1 + n_2\hat{p}_2 = x_1 + x_2$).

Usually $\delta_0 = 0$ and we test to find if the two proportions in the populations are equal. For Poisson variables the denominator of the criterion is

$$(n_1^{-1}\hat{p}_1 + n_2^{-1}\hat{p}_2)^{\frac{1}{2}}$$

but otherwise the technique is the same.

Example 10·10.

An assurance company wishes to know whether the ratio of with-profit to non-profit policies is the same for whole-life as for endowment assurances. The following data have been obtained:

	With profits	Without profits	Total	Proportion of with-profit policies
Whole-life assurances	112	38	150	·747
Endowment assurances	209	41	250	·836

The hypothesis we wish to test is that the proportions are equal in the populations and we shall examine the alternative hypothesis that $p_1 < p_2$, where p_1 refers to whole life and p_2 to endowment assurances. In this case $\delta_0 = 0$; and $\hat{p}_1 = \hat{p}_2 = \frac{321}{400} = \cdot 8025$. The criterion is

$$\frac{\cdot 747 - \cdot 836}{\{\cdot 8025 \times \cdot 1975\,(\frac{1}{150} + \frac{1}{250})\}^{\frac{1}{2}}} = \frac{-\cdot 089}{\cdot 041} = -2\cdot 17.$$

The significance level is

$$\frac{1}{\sqrt{(2\pi)}}\int_{-\infty}^{-2\cdot 17} e^{-\frac{1}{2}y^2}\,dy = \cdot 015.$$

This would probably be regarded as substantial evidence that the proportion of with-profit policies was in fact less among whole-life than among endowment assurances.

It should, perhaps, be emphasized that these figures relate to one particular office and have no general application. The experience of offices in this respect differs widely.

10·12. General remarks.

The statements of tests of a variety of hypotheses summarized in the previous sections provide easily followed instructions for carrying out the technical portions of the tests. It should be remembered that this technical process is preceded by the specification of the appropriate theoretical model and statistical hypothesis and is followed by the interpretation of the results so obtained. A certain vagueness and uncertainty cannot be avoided in these two latter operations. If this is kept in mind the approximations made in the formulae for the significance levels of many of the tests are seen in truer perspective. As long as the inaccuracies introduced by these approximations are small compared with the inherent uncertainties involved in other parts of the test there can be no objections to using them.

A consideration of the limitations of the methods used in this chapter is instructive in pointing to the lines on which the second volume will be developed. There are two main points to be noted. The first is the desirability of finding more exact expressions for the theoretical significance levels. This entails further developments of probability theory which will be dealt with in Chapter 11. The second point is concerned with the choice of criteria. We have already seen in § 10·9, for example, that the hypothesis that two population standard deviations are equal may be tested by two different criteria (for each of the sets of alternative hypotheses considered). The question naturally arises, which of the two is the better. More generally, we have the question of what technical properties of a test are desirable and of how to construct tests having properties which we have decided to be desirable. These questions are very important and very difficult, and final solutions cannot be said to be available in every case. Chapter 14 contains a simple presentation of the subject and should be studied especially thoroughly by readers proceeding thus far.

EXERCISES 10

Note. In the numerical kind of question the student may find it helpful to construct a diagrammatic representation of the data before proceeding to a detailed analysis.

10·1. A number of householders were asked whether they owned certain kinds of electrical appliances. The results of the inquiry are summarized below. The households are classified according to area and income group and may be assumed to form comparatively small random samples in each subgroup.

Area ...	I			II		
Income group ...	Low	Middle	High	Low	Middle	High
Possessing appliance						
A	362	321	82	465	314	67
B	77	80	51	90	78	40
C	203	158	51	258	147	33
D	89	210	83	133	199	66
No. of households in sample	500	400	100	560	360	80

Write a report based on the figures in this table, giving interval estimates of such population proportions as may be of interest.

10·2 Construct a test of the hypothesis that an experience follows a certain mortality table using only the signs of the deviations from expected deaths in each age-group. It may be assumed that if the table is followed, positive and negative deviations are equally likely.

Calculate tables of approximate 5 % significance limits for your criteria for numbers of age-groups between 10 and 30 inclusive.

10·3 Assuming that the mean deviation in large samples of n from a Normal population with standard deviation σ, is approximately Normally distributed, has expected value $\frac{4}{5}\sigma$ and standard deviation $\frac{3}{5}\sigma/\sqrt{n}$, construct approximate tests of the following hypotheses using sample means and mean deviations only.

(i) The population mean is equal to ξ_0, σ being unknown.

(ii) $\sigma = \sigma_0$.

(iii) The means of two Normal populations are equal, their standard deviations being unknown.

(iv) The standard deviations of two Normal populations are equal.

10·4 A large hospital has, in the course of the last 5 years, compiled statistics of cases treated for two special diseases. The following is an extract:

	Disease '*A*'		Disease '*B*'	
	Medical	Surgical	Medical	Surgical
Completely cured	387	218	156	275
Died	83	52	104	310
Total cases in sample	1000	500	500	1000

The words 'Medical' and 'Surgical' relate to the type of treatment adopted. What differences in the results do you regard as statistically significant, and what conclusions do you feel justified in drawing? It may be assumed that none of the cases observed suffered from both diseases or had both forms of treatment.

10·5 An examination is held in several different centres and the following data have been extracted from the results:

	No. of candidates	Mean percentage of marks obtained	Standard deviation of mean percentage of marks
All centres combined	2346	47·3	6·5
Centre *A*	127	44·8	8·3

Do you consider these data significant of any difference between the candidates at centre *A* and all the candidates and, if so, why? (Institute of Actuaries Examinations, May 1930.)

10·6 The following data relate to the distribution of body length of two types of earwig collected by Djakanov:

Body length central value in mm.	Low type	High type
10	5	—
11	38	2
12	139	21
13	219	144
14	216	265
15	69	257
16	15	114
17	—	15
Total	701	818

Test whether the standard deviations of body length are the same for the two types of earwig and obtain confidence intervals for the difference between the average body length of the two types.

10·7 'The general standard of physical efficiency of the nation was reflected by the percentages in the various grades of physical fitness found during medical examination of 3,750,000 men for the services in the war: grade I, 65·7; grade II, 15·2; grade III, 8·8; grade IV, 10·3. Percentages for more than 1,250,000 volunteers were 85·1, 9·1, 3·1 and 2·7 respectively.' (Report in *The Times*, 10th October 1947, of a speech by Field-Marshal Montgomery.)

Do these figures indicate any significant difference between volunteers and others?

10·8 Obtain approximate formulae for confidence limits for a population standard deviation based on a random sample of n individuals from a Normal population. Find the (approximate) expected value of the width of confidence intervals based on these limits.

How large a sample should be taken if the expected width of the 99% confidence interval is not to exceed 5% of the value estimated?

10·9 Using the information given in Exercise 10·8 construct a fresh control chart for the data of Example 10·2. Discuss the interpretation of this control chart.

10·10 In place of the criterion t (or $|t|$) of § 10·5 the criterion t' (or $|t'|$), obtained by replacing s by $\frac{5}{4}$ (sample mean deviation) in the expression for t might be used. Do you consider this would be justifiable? Can you suggest any practical reasons why t' might be preferable to t?

10·11 Show how Gauss' inequality may be used in the assessment of significance levels, pointing out the particular merits and disadvantages of your methods.

Make a detailed numerical study of the case when the criterion is s (or s^2).

10·12 Describe the construction of approximate confidence limits for the ratio of two population standard deviations. Give a numerical illustration of your results.

10·13 Examine the data in the following table relating to the results of four different methods of treatment of a certain illness. Make any tests of significance which you consider appropriate and summarize your conclusions briefly in a report.

Immediate results of treatment

Series	Sulpha-pyridine	Sulphathiazole (a)	Sulphathiazole (b)	Penicillin
Dosage	4·5 g. for 5 days	6 g. for 3 days	8 g. for 6 days	100,000 units
Group *A*	72	94	38	24
Group *B*	3	12	4	2
Group *C*	2	4	2	—
Total cases	77	110	44	26

Group *A*: patients requiring no further treatment after the initial course.

Group *B*: patients requiring a second course of treatment which resulted in a successful outcome.

Group *C*: patients requiring further treatment after the second course.

(Drs A. J. King and E. Gallagher, *Lancet*, 22nd June 1946.)

BIBLIOGRAPHY

E. S. PEARSON. *British Standards* 600 (Industrial Standardization and Quality Control). British Standards Institute, 1935. Reprinted 1948.

YULE AND KENDALL. *An Introduction to the Theory of Statistics* (Chapters 20 and 21). London, Griffin and Co., 14th ed., 1948.

W. B. RICE. *Control Charts in Factory Management*. New York, J. Wiley and Son; London, Chapman and Hall, 1947.

PAUL PEACH. *Industrial Statistics and Quality Control*. Edwards and Broughton, Raleigh, N.C., 1947.

C. E. WEATHERBURN. *A First Course in Mathematical Statistics* (Chapters 6 and 7). Cambridge University Press, 1946.

Appendix I

Corrections for Grouping

A. 1·1. Sheppard's adjustments.

We shall assume that the variable x is continuous over the range a to b and that the frequency for values between x and $x+\Delta x$ (Δx small) is $f(x)\,\Delta x$, where $f(x)$ is finite and continuous, although there is no need for a or b to be finite. We shall also assume that $f(x)$ and its first n derivatives vanish at both limits.

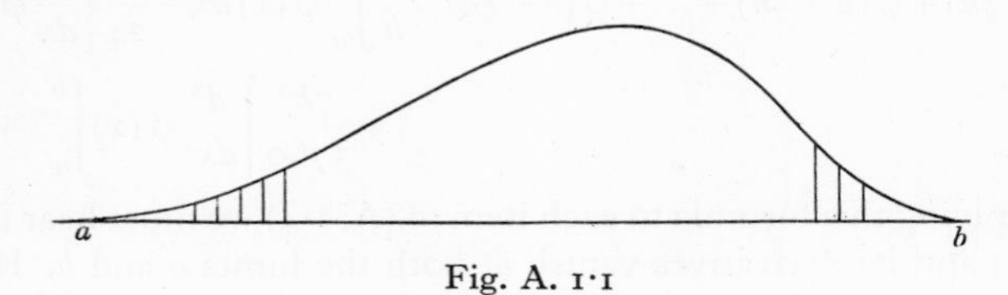

Fig. A. 1·1

The total frequency $=\int_a^b f(x)\,dx = N$ say.

The true rth moment $m'_r = \frac{1}{N}\int_a^b x^r f(x)\,dx.$ (A. 1·1)

If h is the class interval and we assume the frequency in each group to be concentrated at the mid-point of that group we obtain the expression

$$m'_r\,(\text{approx.}) = \frac{1}{N}\Sigma x_i^r \int_{-\frac{1}{2}h}^{\frac{1}{2}h} f(x_i+y)\,dy, \qquad \text{(A. 1·2)}$$

where the summation embraces all groups.

Expanding $f(x_i+y)$ by Taylor's theorem we obtain

$$\int_{-\frac{1}{2}h}^{\frac{1}{2}h} f(x_i+y)\,dy = \int_{-\frac{1}{2}h}^{\frac{1}{2}h} \left\{ f(x_i) + y f^{\text{i}}(x_i) + \frac{y^2}{2!} f^{\text{ii}}(x_i) + \dots \right\} dy$$

$$= h f(x_i) + \frac{h^3}{24} f^{\text{ii}}(x_i) + \frac{h^5}{1920} f^{\text{iv}}(x_i) + \dots. \qquad \text{(A. 1·3)}$$

Hence expression (A. 1·2) becomes

$$\frac{1}{N}\left[h\Sigma x_i^r f(x_i) + \frac{h^3}{24}\Sigma x_i^r f^{\text{ii}}(x_i) + \frac{h^5}{1920}\Sigma x_i^r f^{\text{iv}}(x_i) + \dots \right], \qquad \text{(A. 1·4)}$$

where each of the summations is taken from $i = a+\frac{1}{2}h$ to $i = b-\frac{1}{2}h$ at intervals of h.

We now need a slight modification of the Euler-Maclaurin expansion (see *Mathematics for Actuarial Students*, Part II, pp. 188–9).

If h is the unit of differencing

$$E \equiv 1 + \Delta \equiv e^{hD}, \quad \text{where} \quad D \equiv d/dx.$$

Therefore

$$\Delta^{-1} E^{\frac{1}{2}} \phi(x) = (e^{hD} - 1)^{-1} e^{\frac{1}{2}hD} \phi(x)$$
$$= (hD)^{-1} [1 - \tfrac{1}{2}hD + \tfrac{1}{12}h^2D^2 - \dots][1 + \tfrac{1}{2}hD + \tfrac{1}{8}h^2D^2 + \dots] \phi(x)$$

which reduces to $[(hD)^{-1} - \frac{1}{24}hD + \frac{7}{5760}h^3D^3 + \dots] \phi(x)$.

Between limits a and b we have therefore

$$\phi(a + \tfrac{1}{2}h) + \phi(a + \tfrac{3}{2}h) + \dots + \phi(b - \tfrac{1}{2}h) = \frac{1}{h} \int_a^b \phi(x)\,dx - \frac{h}{24}\left[\frac{d}{dx}\phi(x)\right]_a^b + \frac{7h^3}{5760}\left[\frac{d^3}{dx^3}\phi(x)\right]_a^b + \dots.$$

In applying this formula to each item of (A. 1·4) we must bear in mind that $f(x)$ and its derivatives vanish at both the limits a and b. Hence

$$\int_a^b x^r f(x)\,dx \doteq h \sum_{i=a+\frac{1}{2}h}^{b-\frac{1}{2}h} x_i^r f(x_i).$$

Similarly $\int_a^b x^r f^{ii}(x)\,dx \doteq h \Sigma x_i^r f^{ii}(x_i)$ and so on.

When we make these substitutions the expression (A. 1·4) becomes approximately

$$\frac{1}{N} \int_a^b \left\{ x^r f(x) + \frac{h^2}{24} x^r f^{ii}(x) + \frac{h^4}{1920} x^r f^{iv}(x) + \dots \right\} dx. \qquad \text{(A. 1·5)}$$

Integrating the second term by parts we have

$$\int_a^b x^r f^{ii}(x)\,dx = [x^r f^i(x)]_a^b - r \int_a^b x^{r-1} f^i(x)\,dx.$$
$$= [x^r f^i(x) - r x^{r-1} f(x)]_a^b + r(r-1) \int_a^b x^{r-2} f(x)\,dx.$$

Since $f(x)$ and its first n derivatives vanish at both limits this expression reduces to its last term.

Similarly $\int_a^b x^r f^{iv}(x)\,dx$ can be transformed into the term

$$r(r-1)(r-2)(r-3) \int_a^b x^{r-4} f(x)\,dx.$$

Substituting in (A. 1·5) we obtain the expression

$$\frac{1}{N}\int_a^b \left\{x^r + \frac{h^2}{24} r(r-1)x^{r-2} + \frac{h^4}{1920} r(r-1)(r-2)(r-3)x^{r-4} + \dots\right\} f(x)\,dx,$$

i.e.

$$m'_r(\text{approx.}) = m'_r + \frac{h^2 r(r-1)}{24} m'_{r-2} + \frac{h^4}{1920} r(r-1)(r-2)(r-3)\,m'_{r-4} + \dots$$

in view of (A. 1·1).

Putting $r=1, 2, \dots$, successively we obtain

$$\left.\begin{aligned} m'_1(\text{approx.}) &= m'_1, \\ m'_2(\text{approx.}) &= m'_2 + \frac{h^2}{12}, \\ m'_3(\text{approx.}) &= m'_3 + \frac{h^2}{4} m'_1, \\ m'_4(\text{approx.}) &= m'_4 + \frac{h^2}{2} m'_2 + \frac{h^4}{80}. \end{aligned}\right\}$$

From these we obtain

$$\left.\begin{aligned} m'_2 &= m'_2(\text{approx.}) - \frac{h^2}{12}, \\ m'_3 &= m'_3(\text{approx.}) - \frac{h^2}{4} m'_1(\text{approx.}), \\ m'_4 &= m'_4(\text{approx.}) - \frac{h^2}{2} m'_2(\text{approx.}) + \frac{7h^4}{240}. \end{aligned}\right\} \qquad (\text{A. } 1\cdot 6)$$

For moments about the mean

$$m'_1 = m'_1(\text{approx.}) = 0,$$

and we see that m_3 (approx.) needs no correction.

The other relations are of the same form as before.

In the above m'_r (approx.) means the rth moment calculated on the assumption that class frequencies are concentrated at the mid-points of the group.

The assumption made above that $f(x)$ and its first n derivatives vanish at a and b means that in practice Sheppard's adjustments should not be made unless the frequency dwindles to nothing at each end of the range considered and has negligible first and second differences as the ends are approached. (It should be borne in mind that we can often only *estimate* the form of $f(x)$ from the given data.)

The most common adjustment is the deduction of $h^2/12$ to adjust m_2 but it is doubtful whether this correction is worth making unless the data are fairly extensive (say a total frequency of about 1000).

A. 1·2. Mean deviation.

The expressions (3·21) and (3·22) for the mean deviation m were obtained for a discrete variable but they may be applied to grouped data on the usual assumption about frequencies being concentrated at the mid-points of the groups with n_G or n_L and $\sum_G x_i$ or $\sum_L x_i$ determined on this assumption.

The value thus obtained needs correction for two reasons. First consider the group containing the mean $\bar{x}$ and assume its limits to be $X-\frac{1}{2}h$ and $X+\frac{1}{2}h$, the group frequency being F. In the approximate measure this group has contributed to $\Sigma\,|\,x_i-\bar{x}\,|$ a term

$$F\,|\,X-\bar{x}\,|. \tag{A. 1·7}$$

A range $X+\frac{1}{2}h-\bar{x}$ lies above the mean and $\bar{x}-X+\frac{1}{2}h$ below the mean. We may assume that the frequencies lying above and below the mean are in the same ratio and are concentrated at the points A and B (Fig. A. 1·2) lying midway between the mean and the ends of the range of the group.

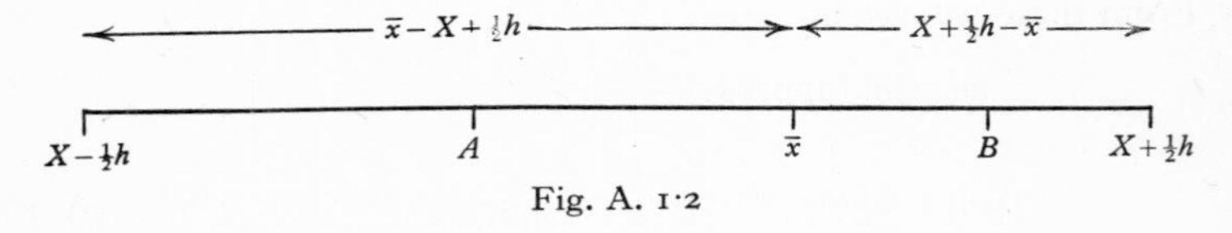

Fig. A. 1·2

The contribution of the group on this assumption is then

$$F\left\{\frac{X+\frac{1}{2}h-\bar{x}}{h}\cdot\tfrac{1}{2}(X+\tfrac{1}{2}h-\bar{x})+\frac{\bar{x}-X+\frac{1}{2}h}{h}\cdot\tfrac{1}{2}(\bar{x}-X+\tfrac{1}{2}h)\right\}.$$

The correction is therefore

$$F\left[\frac{1}{2h}\{(X+\tfrac{1}{2}h-\bar{x})^2+(\bar{x}-X+\tfrac{1}{2}h)^2\}-|\,X-\bar{x}\,|\right]$$
$$=F\left[\frac{(X-\bar{x})^2}{h}+\frac{h}{4}-|\,X-\bar{x}\,|\right]. \tag{A. 1·8}$$

It will be noted that if $\bar{x}$ happens to coincide with X the approximate expression (A. 1·7) vanishes although the group clearly contributes to $\Sigma\,|\,x_i-\bar{x}\,|$ and the student may wonder why the even moments m_2, m_4, etc., do not receive a similar correction. Clearly if the mean happens to coincide with the mid-point of a group, that group will in effect be left out of account in calculating any even moment, whereas if the actual spread of values over the class interval be allowed for, an appreciable term would arise from the group.

Such a correction is never made and although the frequency in the group containing the mean is usually great the adjustment would be small particularly for m_4 and higher moments. This is because the distances from the mean must be small for all observations in the same group as the mean and when distances are squared as in m_2 or raised to the fourth power as in m_4 the effect of the observations near the mean is made less important.

If in Example 3·2, for instance, we assume the frequency of 396 in the group 61–65 to be evenly spread instead of concentrated at the mid-point we obtain a correction of about 20 in a total of 27,657 for $\Sigma x^2 f_x$. With coarser grouping the effect might be appreciable.

The second type of correction corresponds to Sheppard's adjustments of the moments.

Assume that $f(x)$ is approximately of the form $a+bx$ over any given class interval (a and b will, of course, vary from one interval to the next).

A group with mid-point X_k will contribute to $\Sigma\,|\,x_i-\bar{x}\,|$ a term

$$\int_{X_k-\frac{1}{2}h}^{X_k+\frac{1}{2}h}(a+bx)(x-\bar{x})\,dx=-a\bar{x}h+(a-b\bar{x})hX_k+\frac{b}{3}\left(3X_k^2h+\frac{h^3}{4}\right),$$

$$=(X_k-\bar{x})(ah+bhX_k)+\frac{bh^3}{12} \qquad \text{(A. 1·9)}$$

provided that
$$X_k-\frac{h}{2}>\bar{x}.$$

The corresponding term in the approximate method is

$$(X_k-\bar{x})(ah+bhX_k).$$

To deduce the 'true' value (A. 1·9) we must therefore add

$$\frac{bh^3}{12}=\frac{h^2}{12}\{f(X_k+\tfrac{1}{2}h)-f(X_k-\tfrac{1}{2}h)\}. \qquad \text{(A. 1·10)}$$

If we sum this expression for all groups to the right of the mean we have a total of

$$-\frac{h^2}{12}\{f(x)\text{ at the upper limit of the group containing the mean}\}$$

$$\doteqdot -\frac{h}{12}F.$$

Similarly the correction for all groups below the mean is $-\frac{h}{12}F$, making the total correction $-\frac{h}{6}F$.

This correction does not apply unless $f(x)$ is zero at both ends of the range but an obvious modification can be made to it in other cases.

Incorporating the above correction with (A. 1·9) we finally obtain

$$F\left\{\frac{(X-\bar{x})^2}{h}+\frac{h}{12}-|X-\bar{x}|\right\}.$$

Dividing by the total frequency we obtain the correction to the mean deviation

$$\frac{\text{Frequency in group containing the mean}}{\text{Total frequency}}\left\{\frac{(X-\bar{x})^2}{h}+\frac{h}{12}-|X-\bar{x}|\right\}. \quad \text{(A. 1·11)}$$

APPENDIX 2

Stirling's approximation to n!

A. 2·1. Wallis's theorem.

In demonstrating Stirling's approximation to $n!$ we shall make use of Wallis's theorem which can be proved as follows:

Let
$$I_t=\int_0^{\frac{1}{2}\pi}\sin^t\theta\,d\theta.$$

Integrate by parts taking $\sin^{t-1}\theta$ as the first part and $\sin\theta$ as the second.

$$I_t=\Big[-\sin^{t-1}\theta\cos\theta\Big]_0^{\frac{1}{2}\pi}+(t-1)\int_0^{\frac{1}{2}\pi}\sin^{t-2}\theta\cos^2\theta\,d\theta.$$

The first term on the right vanishes at both limits and if we replace $\cos^2\theta$ by $1-\sin^2\theta$ in the second term we have

$$I_t=(t-1)(I_{t-2}-I_t),$$

i.e.
$$I_t=\frac{t-1}{t}I_{t-2} \quad \text{(A. 2·1)}$$

$$=\frac{t-1}{t}\frac{t-3}{t-2}I_{t-4} \quad \text{similarly}$$

$$=\frac{t-1}{t}\frac{t-3}{t-2}\frac{t-5}{t-4}I_{t-6}$$

and so on.

Proceeding in this way we eventually reduce the integral to a multiple of

$$I_3=\tfrac{2}{3}\int_0^{\frac{1}{2}\pi}\sin\theta\,d\theta=\tfrac{2}{3} \quad \text{if } t \text{ is an odd integer} \quad \text{(A. 2·2)}$$

or $$I_4=\frac{3}{4}\int_0^{\frac{1}{2}\pi}\sin^2\theta\,d\theta=\frac{3}{4}.\frac{1}{2}.\frac{\pi}{2}\quad\text{if } t \text{ is an even integer.}\qquad(\text{A. }2\cdot3)$$

If $$0\leqslant\theta\leqslant\frac{\pi}{2};\quad 0\leqslant\sin\theta\leqslant 1.$$

Hence, over that range

$$\sin^{2n-1}\theta\geqslant\sin^{2n}\theta\geqslant\sin^{2n+1}\theta$$

and $$I_{2n-1}\geqslant I_{2n}\geqslant I_{2n+1}.\qquad(\text{A. }2\cdot4)$$

But $I_{2n+1}=\dfrac{2n}{2n+1}I_{2n-1}$ and hence as n tends to infinity I_{2n-1}, I_{2n} and I_{2n+1} all tend to the same limit. Therefore if n is large we may take

$$I_{2n}\doteqdot I_{2n+1}\qquad(\text{A. }2\cdot5)$$

Replacing the integrals by products obtained as above we have (n being a positive integer)

$$\frac{(2n-1)(2n-3)\dots3.1.\pi}{2n(2n-2)\dots4.2.2}\doteqdot\frac{2n(2n-2)\dots4.2}{(2n+1)(2n-1)\dots5.3.1},$$

i.e. $$\tfrac{1}{2}\pi\doteqdot\frac{(2n)^2(2n-2)^2\dots4^2.2^2}{(2n+1)(2n-1)^2(2n-3)^2\dots3^2.1^2}.\qquad(\text{A. }2\cdot6)$$

This is Wallis's theorem.

A. 2·2. Stirling's approximation.

The Euler-Maclaurin expansion may be written in the following form (see *Mathematics for Actuarial Students*, Part II, p. 189):

$$\int_1^n f(x)\,dx=\tfrac{1}{2}f(1)+f(2)+f(3)+\dots+f(n-1)+\tfrac{1}{2}f(n)-\tfrac{1}{12}\{f^{\text{i}}(n)-f^{\text{i}}(1)\}$$
$$+\tfrac{1}{720}\{f^{\text{iii}}(n)-f^{\text{iii}}(1)\}+\dots.$$

Put $f(x)=\log x$. The left-hand side of the equation becomes on integration

$$\Big[x(\log x-1)\Big]_1^n=n\log n-n+1.\qquad(\text{A. }2\cdot7)$$

The right-hand side becomes

$$\tfrac{1}{2}\log 1+\log 2+\dots+\log(n-1)+\tfrac{1}{2}\log n-\frac{1}{12}\left(\frac{1}{n}-1\right)+\frac{1}{360}\left(\frac{1}{n^3}-1\right)+\dots$$
$$=\log n!-\tfrac{1}{2}\log n-\frac{1}{12n}+O\left(\frac{1}{n^3}\right)+\text{a term independent of } n,$$

where $O(1/n^3)$ means a sum of terms of the third and higher powers of $1/n$. We thus obtain on rearrangement

$$\log n! \doteqdot (n+\tfrac{1}{2})\log n - n + \frac{1}{12n} + R \quad \left(\text{ignoring } O\left(\frac{1}{n^3}\right)\right), \qquad \text{(A. 2·8)}$$

where R represents a term independent of n.

Replacing n by $2n$

$$\log(2n)! \doteqdot (2n+\tfrac{1}{2})\log 2n - 2n + \frac{1}{24n} + R.$$

But $$(2n)! = \{1.3.5.....(2n-1)\}\{2.4.6.....2n\}$$
$$= \{1.3.5.....(2n-1)\}\,2^n n!.$$

Therefore
$$\log(2n)! = \log\{1.3.5.....(2n-1)\} + n\log 2 + \log n!.$$

Substituting the approximate values for $\log(2n)!$ and $\log n!$ and simplifying we obtain

$$n\log n + (n+\tfrac{1}{2})\log 2 - n - \frac{1}{24n} \doteqdot \log\{1.3.5.....(2n-1)\}. \qquad \text{(A. 2·9)}$$

Hence

$$\log\frac{2.4.6.....2n}{1.3.5.....(2n-1)} = n\log 2 + \log n! - \log\{1.3.5.....(2n-1)\}$$
$$\doteqdot \tfrac{1}{2}\log n - \tfrac{1}{2}\log 2 + R \qquad \text{from (A. 2·8) and (A. 2·9)}$$
$$\doteqdot \tfrac{1}{2}\log 2n - \log 2 + R.$$

Hence $$2R - 2\log 2 \doteqdot \log\frac{2^2.4^2.....(2n)^2}{1^2.3^2.....(2n-1)^2\,2n}.$$

If the last term of the denominator of the R.H.S. is replaced by $2n+1$ we obtain from Wallis's theorem

$$2(R-\log 2) = \log\tfrac{1}{2}\pi$$
$$R = \tfrac{1}{2}\log 2\pi.$$

Substituting in (A. 2·8) we obtain Stirling's approximation

$$\log n! \doteqdot (n+\tfrac{1}{2})\log n - n + \tfrac{1}{2}\log 2\pi + \frac{1}{12n}, \qquad \text{(A. 2·10)}$$

that is $$n! \doteqdot \sqrt{(2\pi)}\,n^{n+\frac{1}{2}}\exp\left(-n+\frac{1}{12n}\right). \qquad \text{(A. 2·11)}$$

Ignoring the last term in (A. 2·11) we have

$$n! \doteqdot \sqrt{(2\pi)}\,n^{n+\frac{1}{2}}e^{-n}. \qquad \text{(A. 2·12)}$$

This is the usual form, although (A. 2·11) is more accurate.

These formulae give quite good approximations even if n is small as the following table shows:

n	Values of $n!$		
	Correct value	Formula (A. 2·11)	Formula (A. 2·12)
3	6	6·0006	5·8362
5	120	120·00	118·02
6	720	720·01	710·08

Appendix 3

A. 3·1. The Normal curve as an approximation to the binomial probabilities.

The $(r+1)$th term of the binomial expansion $(p+q)^n$ is

$$\frac{n!}{r!\,(n-r)!}\,p^r q^{n-r}$$

and this is greater than the rth term if $r<p(n+1)$.

Since n is to be assumed very large and we confine p to positive numbers less than 1 we can, without appreciable loss of precision, assume np to be an integer so that the greatest term occurs when $r=np$.

The greatest term in the expansion is therefore

$$y_0=\frac{n!}{(np)!\,(nq)!}\,p^{np}q^{nq}. \qquad \text{(A. 3·1)}$$

Taking a new origin at np we have for the general term

$$r=np+x$$

and

$$y_x=\frac{n!}{(np+x)!\,(nq-x)!}\,p^{np+x}q^{nq-x}. \qquad \text{(A. 3.2)}$$

Hence

$$\log\frac{y_x}{y_0}=\log\{(np)!\}+\log\{(nq)!\}-\log\{(np+x)!\}-\log\{(nq-x)!\}$$
$$+x\log p-x\log q. \qquad \text{(A. 3·3)}$$

Substituting the approximate expressions derived from formula (A. 2·11) we obtain on simplifying

$$\log\frac{y_x}{y_0}=-(np+x+\tfrac{1}{2})\log\left(1+\frac{x}{np}\right)-(nq-x+\tfrac{1}{2})\log\left(1-\frac{x}{nq}\right)$$
$$+\frac{x}{12np\,(np+x)}-\frac{x}{12nq\,(nq-x)}.$$

Expanding the logarithms we deduce

$$\log\frac{y_x}{y_0}=-\frac{x^2}{2npq}+x\frac{(p-q)}{2npq}+\text{terms involving the second and higher powers of } 1/n. \qquad (A.\ 3\cdot 4)$$

If $\dfrac{p-q}{npq}$ is small the second term on the right can be ignored and we have

$$y_x=y_0e^{-x^2/2npq}$$

$$=y_0e^{-x^2/2\sigma^2} \text{ since for the binomial distribution } \sigma^2=npq. \quad (A.\ 3\cdot 5)$$

*A. 3·2. Laplace's theorem.

Instead of considering the whole of a binomial distribution and the corresponding Normal curve we may be interested in the sum of a number of terms of the binomial distribution and the corresponding section of the curve. *Laplace's theorem* states that: If x be a binomial variable so that

$$\Pr.\{x=r\}=\binom{n}{r}p^r q^{n-r} \quad (r=0, 1, 2, \ldots, n) \quad 0<p<1 \quad \text{and} \quad q=1-p.$$

Then

$$\lim_{n\to\infty} \Pr.\{\alpha<x'<\beta\}=\frac{1}{\sqrt{(2\pi)}}\int_\alpha^\beta e^{-\frac{1}{2}t^2}\,dt$$

where x' is the standardized variate $\dfrac{x-np}{\sqrt{(npq)}}$.

Proof. Let $P=\Pr.\{\alpha<x'<\beta\}$.

Then $P=\Pr.\{np+\alpha\sqrt{(npq)}<x<np+\beta\sqrt{(npq)}\}$.

Hence if α_n be the smallest integer greater than $np+\alpha\sqrt{(npq)}$ and β_n the greatest integer less than $np+\beta\sqrt{(npq)}$

$$P=\sum_{r=\alpha_n}^{\beta_n}\binom{n}{r}p^r q^{n-r}.$$

When n is sufficiently large, values of r between α_n and β_n will be of the order of n and will therefore be large. Applying Stirling's approximation we have

$$\log\binom{n}{r}=\log(n!)-\log(r!)-\log[(n-r)!]$$

$$=-\tfrac{1}{2}\log 2\pi+(n+\tfrac{1}{2})\log n-(r+\tfrac{1}{2})\log r-(n-r+\tfrac{1}{2})\log(n-r)+R_{n,r} \qquad (A.\ 3\cdot 6)$$

where $R_{n,r}$ is of the order $1/n$.

Hence

$$\log\left\{\binom{n}{r}p^r q^{n-r}\right\}=-\tfrac{1}{2}\log 2\pi-(r+\tfrac{1}{2})\log\frac{r}{np}-(n-r+\tfrac{1}{2})$$

$$\times\log\frac{n-r}{nq}-\tfrac{1}{2}\log npq+R_{n,r}. \qquad (A.\ 3\cdot 7)$$

Let $r' = \dfrac{r-np}{\sqrt{(npq)}}$ so that $\Delta r' = \dfrac{1}{\sqrt{(npq)}}$

$$\log\left\{\binom{n}{r} p^r q^{n-r}\right\} = -\tfrac{1}{2}\log 2\pi - [np+\tfrac{1}{2}+r'\sqrt{(npq)}]\log\left[1+r'\sqrt{\left(\frac{q}{np}\right)}\right]$$

$$-[nq+\tfrac{1}{2}-r'\sqrt{(npq)}]\log\left[1-r'\sqrt{\left(\frac{p}{nq}\right)}\right]+\log(\Delta r')+R'_{n,r}, \quad \text{(A. 3·8)}$$

where $R'_{n,r}$ is of the order $n^{-\frac{1}{2}}$.

Therefore $\log\left\{\binom{n}{r} p^r q^{n-r}\right\} = -\tfrac{1}{2}\log 2\pi - \tfrac{1}{2}r'^2 + \log(\Delta r') + R''_{n,r}$,

where $R''_{n,r}$ is also of the order $n^{-\frac{1}{2}}$.

Therefore $\binom{n}{r} p^n q^{n-r} = \dfrac{1}{\sqrt{(2\pi)}} e^{-\frac{1}{2}r'^2}\,\Delta r'(1+R'''_{n,r})$,

where $R'''_{n,r}$ is also of the order $n^{-\frac{1}{2}}$.

Therefore
$$P = \sum_{r=\alpha_n}^{\beta_n} \frac{1}{\sqrt{(2\pi)}} e^{-\frac{1}{2}r'^2}\,\Delta r' + K_n, \quad \text{(A. 3·9)}$$

where
$$K_n = \sum_{r=\alpha_n}^{\beta_n} \frac{1}{\sqrt{(2\pi)}} e^{-\frac{1}{2}r'^2}\,\Delta r'\, R'''_{n,r}. \quad \text{(A. 3·10)}$$

Since there are approximately $(\beta-\alpha)\sqrt{(npq)}$ terms in the summation and $\Delta r' = \dfrac{1}{\sqrt{(npq)}}$, K_n is also of the order $n^{-\frac{1}{2}}$ and $\lim\limits_{n\to\infty} K_n = 0$.

Hence in (A. 3·9) we may ignore K_n and if we apply the Euler-Maclaurin theorem to the remaining term, remembering that the summation is at intervals of $\dfrac{1}{\sqrt{(npq)}}$, we have approximately

$$P = \frac{1}{\sqrt{(2\pi)}}\int_{\alpha_n}^{\beta_n} e^{-\frac{1}{2}t^2}\,dt + \frac{1}{2\sqrt{(2\pi npq)}}\{e^{-\frac{1}{2}\alpha_n^2}+e^{-\frac{1}{2}\beta_n}\} \quad \text{(A. 3·11)}$$

and
$$\lim_{n\to\infty} P = \frac{1}{\sqrt{(2\pi)}}\int_{\alpha}^{\beta} e^{-\frac{1}{2}t^2}\,dt, \quad \text{(A. 3·12)}$$

since
$$\lim_{n\to\infty}\alpha_n=\alpha, \quad \lim_{n\to\infty}\beta_n=\beta.$$

The more accurate form (A. 3·11) allows for the fact that α and β in general are not positive integers so that the limits of the range considered do not coincide with terms of the binomial expansion and a systematic error is introduced by using formula (A. 3·12).

APPENDIX 4

Values of the ordinate and the cumulative distribution function for the Normal curve

The ordinate y or $p(x) = \frac{1}{\sqrt{(2\pi)}} e^{-\frac{1}{2}x^2}$.

The area to the left of the ordinate at the point x (the cumulative distribution function) is

$$F(x) = \frac{1}{\sqrt{(2\pi)}} \int_{-\infty}^{x} e^{-\frac{1}{2}t^2}\, dt.$$

The values are tabulated for positive values of x only; a change in the sign of x does not affect y while $F(-x) = 1 - F(x)$.

For intermediate values second difference interpolation is usually sufficient although on occasions third differences should be allowed for if great accuracy is required.

x	$y=p(x)$	$F(x)$	x	$y=p(x)$	$F(x)$
·0	·39894	·50000	2·5	·01753	·99379
·1	·39695	·53983	2·6	·01358	·99534
·2	·39104	·57926	2·7	·01042	·99653
·3	·38139	·61791	2·8	·00792	·99744
·4	·36827	·65542	2·9	·00595	·99813
·5	·35207	·69146	3·0	·00443	·99865
·6	·33322	·72575	3·1	·00327	·99903
·7	·31225	·75804	3·2	·00238	·99931
·8	·28969	·78814	3·3	·00172	·99952
·9	·26609	·81594	3·4	·00123	·99966
1·0	·24197	·84134	3·5	·00087	·99977
1·1	·21785	·86433	3·6	·00061	·99984
1·2	·19419	·88493	3·7	·00042	·99989
1·3	·17137	·90320	3·8	·00029	·99993
1·4	·14973	·91924	3·9	·00020	·99995
1·5	·12952	·93319	4·0	·00013	·99997
1·6	·11092	·94520	4·1	·00009	·99998
1·7	·09405	·95543	4·2	·00006	·99999
1·8	·07895	·96407	4·3	·00004	·99999
1·9	·06562	·97128	4·4	·00002	·99999
2·0	·05399	·97725	4·5	·00002	
2·1	·04398	·98214	4·6	·00001	
2·2	·03547	·98610	4·7	·00001	
2·3	·02833	·98928	4·8	·00000	
2·4	·02239	·99180			

From the above table the following values may be obtained:

$F(x)$	x	$F(x)$	x
·001	−3·090	·999	3·090
·005	−2·576	·995	2·576
·010	−2·326	·990	2·326
·025	−1·960	·975	1·960
·050	−1·645	·950	1·645
·25	−·674	·75	·674

ANSWERS TO THE EXERCISES AND NOTES ON THE SOLUTIONS

These notes are not intended to provide complete solutions to any of the exercises. Their purpose is to aid the student by indicating promising lines of treatment for certain of the more difficult problems and to provide numerical answers by which the work can be checked. It should be clearly appreciated that, if the maximum benefit is to be obtained from working through the exercises, reference to these notes should not be made until a serious attempt has been made to solve the problems unaided.

In many cases there are alternatives to the methods suggested; it is always desirable to consider what alternative methods of treatment might be used.

EXERCISES 1

1·4 Total 180; *A*, 135; *B*, 120.

1·5 Attacking bombers, 12; defending bombers, 8; attacking fighters, 8; defending fighters, 36.

EXERCISES 2

In Exercises 2·1 and 2·8 care should be taken to distinguish between those characters which are of the cumulative type and those which are not.

EXERCISES 3

Exercise no.	Arithmetic mean	Mean deviation		Standard deviation		$\sqrt{b_1}$	b_2
		Crude	Corrected	Crude	Corrected		
(1)	(2)	(3)	(4)	(5)	(6)	(7)	(8)
3·1	101·55	12·93	12·93	16·59	16·53	·228	3·199
3·2	49·04	12·37	12·29	14·72	14·65	·327	2·217
3·3	156·14	34·98	34·72	44·42	44·28	·523	3·639
3·4 (1881 data)	43·95	7·97	7·85	9·53	9·42	·202	2·130
(1902 data)	48·02	10·27	10·26	12·41	12·33	·394	2·279

N.B. (*a*) The figures in columns (2)–(6) should be expressed in appropriate units.

(*b*) Sheppard's adjustments have been applied in obtaining the figures in columns (7) and (8).

3·7 Consider the possibility of using the coefficient of variation or some modification thereof.

3·8 The correction is $-h^2m(m+1)/3(2m+1)^2$.

3·9 q_{32}, ·00700; q_{37}, ·00798; q_{42}, ·00902; q_{47}, ·01095;

$\mu_{32\frac{1}{2}}$, ·00702; $\mu_{37\frac{1}{2}}$, ·00801; $\mu_{42\frac{1}{2}}$, ·00906; $\mu_{47\frac{1}{2}}$, ·01102.

Deduce μ for ages 32, 37, etc., by interpolation.

3·10 Mean 52·40 years. Standard deviation 26·50 years. $\sqrt{b_1} - {\cdot}7623$. (Sheppard's adjustments are not applicable.)

3·12 It can be shown that $d\{\log f(r)\}/dr$ is not negative. The proof of this result depends on the inequality

$$\prod_{i=1}^{n} X_i^{X_i} \geqslant \bar{X}^{n\bar{X}},$$

where the X_i's are any positive numbers.

It can also be shown that $f(0)$ is equal to the geometric mean of the distribution. It is of interest to note that:

$\lim_{r\to+\infty} f(r)$ equals the greatest value in the distribution,

$\lim_{r\to-\infty} f(r)$ equals the least value in the distribution.

EXERCISES 4

4·1 Regression line of ratio of percentage of old (y) on pauperism ratio (x) is

$$y = {\cdot}1103x + 96{\cdot}348.$$

Regression line of x on y is

$$x = {\cdot}3612y + 27{\cdot}976.$$

4·4 Consider the function

$$\sum_{j=1}^{n} \left\{\frac{x_{1j}-\bar{x}_1}{s_1} + \frac{x_{2j}-\bar{x}_2}{s_2} + \frac{x_{3j}-\bar{x}_3}{s_3}\right\}^2,$$

where x_{ij} is the value of the character X_i for the jth individual and

$$\bar{x}_i = n^{-1}\sum_{j=1}^{n} x_{ij}, \quad s_i = \left\{n^{-1}\sum_{j=1}^{n}(x_{ij}-\bar{x}_i)^2\right\}^{\frac{1}{2}}.$$

4·5 Graphical methods will be found of use in this problem.

4·7 Regression line of maximum stress at 600° C. (y) on maximum stress at 15° C. (x) is

$$y = {\cdot}90x - 14{\cdot}5.$$

4·9 Regression line of y on x is

$$y = 1{\cdot}868x - 69{\cdot}930.$$

Note that the last column of the table is not needed unless the regression line of x on y is to be calculated. This last column is then used to calculate s_y as follows.

Since $\bar{y} = 34{\cdot}5557$ we have

$$1653 s_y^2 = 22[(3{\cdot}61)^2 + (17{\cdot}21)^2] + 57[(4{\cdot}22)^2 + (22{\cdot}09)^2] + \ldots$$
$$+ 19[(4{\cdot}01)^2 + (55{\cdot}97)^2] - 1653(34{\cdot}5557)^2 = 105658{\cdot}6,$$

whence $s_y = 7{\cdot}995$. The regression line of x on y is

$$x = {\cdot}437y + 40{\cdot}83.$$

4·10 We require to find $\bar{x}$, $\bar{y}$, s_x, s_y and p for the combined data. Using the method given in the notes on Exercise 4·9 we proceed as follows:

$$\bar{x} = 24{\cdot}11533, \quad \bar{y} = 30{\cdot}82267.$$

Take arbitrary origins for x and y at 24 and 30 respectively:

$$375 s_x^2 = 75[({\cdot}311)^2 + (-1{\cdot}29)^2] + 100[({\cdot}420)^2 + ({\cdot}98)^2]$$
$$+ 200[({\cdot}271)^2 + ({\cdot}21)^2] - 375({\cdot}11533)^2,$$

whence $375 s_x^2$ equals $264{\cdot}262$.

Also $375 s_y^2$ equals $44{\cdot}358$.

By an obvious extension of this method

$$375p = 75[({\cdot}761)({\cdot}311)({\cdot}277) + (-1{\cdot}29)(1{\cdot}02)]$$
$$+ 100[({\cdot}811)({\cdot}420)({\cdot}351) + ({\cdot}98)({\cdot}52)]$$
$$+ 200[({\cdot}833)({\cdot}271)({\cdot}255) + ({\cdot}21)({\cdot}90)]$$
$$- 375({\cdot}11533)({\cdot}82267) = -17{\cdot}199.$$

Hence the overall correlation coefficient is

$$\frac{-17{\cdot}119}{\sqrt{(264{\cdot}262 \times 44{\cdot}258)}} = -{\cdot}158.$$

EXERCISES 5

5·4 (*a*) Average age of group is at least 6·5 years.
(*b*) Average age lies between 6·5 and 108·5 years.
(*c*) Average age lies between 27·0 and 59·6 years.

5·6 Consider each method from the following points of view:
(i) Amount of labour involved.
(ii) Possible systematic bias introduced.
(iii) Amount of non-biased variation likely to be present.

EXERCISES 6

6·2 Consider the definitions of 'probability' mentioned in this chapter.

6·3 Examine the statement in the light of §§ 6·2 and 6·9.

6·4 (*b*) It may be noted that $\left(1-\frac{1}{2^2}\right)$ might be considered the proportion of numbers not divisible by $2^2, 4^2, 6^2$, etc.; $\left(1-\frac{1}{2^2}\right)\left(1-\frac{1}{3^2}\right)$ the proportion not divisible by $2^2, 3^2, 4^2, 6^2, 8^2, 9^2$, etc.; and so on.

6·5 63/67. 6·6 2/3. 6·7 ·3343.

6·8 $q_x p_y p_z/(q_x p_y p_z + q_y p_z p_x + q_z p_x p_y)$. 6·11 5/24.

EXERCISES 7

7·1 (i) $F(x)=(l_0-l_y)/l_0$, where y is the least integer greater than x.
(ii) $F(x)=(l_0-l_x)/l_0$.
(iii) $F(n)=0 \quad (n<Nl_0/T_0)$
$=1 \quad (n\geqslant Nl_0/T_0)$.

n is, in fact, a constant.

7·2 Expected value $\frac{1}{2}$; standard deviation $(\frac{1}{12}+\frac{1}{6}n^{-1})^{\frac{1}{2}}$.

7·3 Expected value $\gamma+\theta$; standard deviation θ; $\sqrt{\beta_1}=2$; $\beta_2=9$;
$F(x)=1-e^{-(x-\gamma)/\theta}\ (x\geqslant\gamma)$.

7·4 $-1/(n-1)$.

7·5 First prove

$$\mathscr{E}(x_i x_j)=\mathscr{E}\{x_i\mathscr{E}(x_j\mid x_i)\}=\mathscr{E}\{x_i(N\bar{u}-x_i)/(N-1)\}=\bar{u}^2-\sigma^2/(N-1).$$

7·6 $\sum_{j=1}^{n} a_{1j}a_{2j}=0$. This is known as a condition of *orthogonality*.

7·7 Use the method of § 7·12. Consider the application of the results of this exercise to index numbers (see chapter 3).

7·8 Use the method of § 7·12, noting also the result quoted in Exercise 7·12.

7·9, 7·11 and 7·12 Assume that x is a standardized variable. (This does not imply any loss of generality provided, of course, that β_1 and β_2 exist.)

7·10 Assume $\mathscr{E}(x)=0$.

7·12 Find a and b so as to make the integral a minimum. The result follows for this (the least favourable) case.

7·13 It is not essential to carry out detailed mathematical analysis in this problem, as the result required can be obtained by general arguments.

7·14 It is necessary to study the amount of correlation likely to be introduced by common factors such as the total number of births. The approximate methods of § 7·12 will probably be found useful.

7·17 Probability that all four aces appear in the last $(52-n)$ cards is $\binom{52-n}{4}\Big/\binom{52}{4}$.

7·18 Consider the probability of the following events:

(*a*) One ace appears in the first r cards.
(*b*) Three aces appear in the last $(52-r)$ cards.
(*c*) An ace appears as the $(r+1)$th card.

EXERCISES 8

8·3 $\mathscr{E}(x)=np$; $\sigma_x{}^2=npq$; $\sqrt{\beta_1}=(q+p)/(npq)^{\frac{1}{2}}$; $\beta_2=3+(1+6pq)/(npq)$.

8·4 $\mathscr{E}(b)=r/p$; $\sigma_b{}^2=rp^{-2}(1-p)$.

8·5 $k=1/\pi$ (assuming $-\infty<x<\infty$).
Second and higher absolute moments are infinite.

8·6 $K=-1/\log_e(1-\alpha)$;
$\mu_1'=K\alpha(1-\alpha)^{-1}$; $\mu_2=K\alpha(1-K\alpha)(1-\alpha)^{-2}$;
$\sqrt{\beta_1}=(1+\alpha-3K\alpha+2K^2\alpha^2)(K\alpha)^{-\frac{1}{2}}(1-K\alpha)^{-\frac{3}{2}}$;
$\beta_2=\{1+4\alpha+\alpha^2-4K\alpha(1+\alpha)+6K^2\alpha^2-3K^3\alpha^3\}(K\alpha)^{-1}(1-K\alpha)^{-2}$.

8·8 ·10087. 8·10 4, 4, 3, 2. (Trial and error.)

8·11 (i) Pr. $\{x=X\}=\left(\sum_{j=1}^{k} p_j m_j^X e^{-m_j}\right)\Big/X!$; $(X=0, 1, 2, \ldots)$

(ii) Pr. $\{x=X\}=\left(\int_0^\infty m^X e^{-m}\, p(m)\, dm\right)\Big/X!$;

$=\binom{X+r}{r}(2\sigma^2)^X(2\sigma^2+1)^{-(X+r+1)}$ if r is an integer.

8·13 $y=\Gamma(m+n)/\Gamma(m)\Gamma(n)$; $\mathscr{E}(x)=m/(m+n)$;
$\sigma_x{}^2=mn/(m+n)^2(m+n+1)$.

See *Mathematics for Actuarial Students*, Vol. 1, p. 148.)

EXERCISES 9

9·1 Solve the equation $(x-np)^2=k^2npq$,
where $n=100$, $x=55$, and $k=1{\cdot}645$, $1{\cdot}960$ or $2{\cdot}576$.

Approximate 90% limits: ·468, ·629.
Approximate 95% limits: ·452, ·644.
Approximate 99% limits: ·423, ·671.
(continuity correction not used).

9·2 Assuming a Poisson distribution, an estimate of the parameter m is 322/600 and the probability that a page is free from error would then be $e^{-m} = \cdot 58469$. Hence the expected number of pages free from error is 350·8 and the distribution of the random variable corresponding to the number of such pages would be binomial.

The data show considerable departure from what would be expected were the hypothesis (of random distribution of errors) valid. Suitable alternative hypotheses might correspond to a tendency for errors to occur in groups.

9·7 The actual percentage of available nitrogen in the fertilizer must exceed the value $6 + \cdot 25 \times 1\cdot 955 = 6\cdot 5$. The manufacturer's tests should aim at maintaining this standard at least.

9·10 The object in all cases is to rearrange the inequalities $T_1 < \theta < T_2$ in a suitable manner:

(i) The inequalities $T - \lambda_1 < \theta < T + \lambda_2$ reduce to $-\lambda_1 < \theta - T < \lambda_2$.

(ii) $T\lambda_1 < \theta < T\lambda_2$ reduce to $\lambda_1 \lesseqgtr \theta T^{-1} \lesseqgtr \lambda_2$ according as $T \lesseqgtr 0$.

(iii) $T - \lambda_1 U < \theta < T + \lambda_2 U$ reduce to $-\lambda_1 < U^{-1}(\theta - T) < \lambda_2$.

Note that the alternative hypotheses will probably be specified as $\theta \neq \theta_0$.

EXERCISES 10

10·4 Owing to absence of a random element in selection no valid comparison can be made between 'Medical' and 'Surgical'. Compare disease A with disease B in each category.

10·5 For a comparison of independent values consider A and all centres *except* A.

10·6 99% confidence limits are 1·029 and 1·315 mm.

10·8 (See Exercise 7·11.) 5300 approx.

10·13 As there are small numbers in some of the categories approximations should be used with caution if at all.

INDEX